The Boeing 737 used at NASA Langley on the ramp at Orlando, Florida.

On the cover:
"The Wind Shear
Flight Tests" (1993)
by John Clark, depicting
research by the
Boeing 737 aircraft
operated by NASA's
Langley Research Center.
Courtesy NASA
Art Program.

AIRBORNE TRAILBLAZER

by Lane E. Wallace

Two Decades With NASA Langley's 737 Flying Laboratory

The NASA History Series

NASA SP-4216

National Aeronautics and
Space Administration

NASA History Office
Washington, D.C. 1994

Library of Congress Cataloging-in-Publication Data

Wallace, Lane E., 1961–
Airborne Trailblazer/by Lane E. Wallace.
p. cm.—(The NASA history series) (NASA SP: 4216)
"Two decades with NASA Langley's 737 flying laboratory."
Includes bibliographical references and index.
1. Langley Research Center.
2. Aeronautics, Commercial—Research—United States—History.
3. Boeing 737 (Jet transport) 4. Research aircraft—United States.
I. Title. II. Series. III. Series: NASA SP: 4216.
TL521.312.W35 1994
629.1'072073—dc20 94-5874
CIP

For sale by the U.S. Government Printing Office
Superintendent of Documents, Mail Stop: SSOP, Washington, DC 20402-9328

Contents

Introduction vii

Chapter 1: NASA, Industry, and Technology: The Complex Nature of Progress 1

Chapter 2: Addressing the New Challenges of Air Transportation: The TCV/ATOPS Program 9

Chapter 3: Revolution in the Cockpit: Computerization and Electronic Flight Displays 25

Chapter 4: A Technology Eclipsed: The Microwave Landing System and the Dawn of GPS 41

Chapter 5: "The Best That We Can Do": Taming the Microburst Windshear 55

Chapter 6: Improving Aircraft Systems 75

Chapter 7: Improving Aircraft Operations 89

Chapter 8: A National Facility 105

Conclusion 119

Chapter Notes 125

Bibliographic Essay 141

Illustration Credits 143

Glossary of Acronyms 145

737 TSRV Specifications 147

737 TSRV Flight Log 149

Acknowledgements 177

Index 179

Fabric tufts affixed to the wing of the Boeing 737 testbed aircraft at Langley Research Center to illustrate airflow behavior for high-lift research.

BOEING 737
EXPERIMENTAL

Introduction

This book is the story of a very unique airplane and the contributions it has made to the air transportation industry. NASA's Boeing 737-100 Transport Systems Research Vehicle was the prototype 737, acquired by the Langley Research Center in 1974 to conduct research into advanced transport aircraft technologies. In the twenty years that followed, the airplane participated in more than twenty different research projects, evolving from a research tool for a specific NASA program into a national airborne research facility. It played a critical role in developing and gaining acceptance for numerous significant transport technologies, including "glass cockpits," airborne windshear detection systems, data link for air traffic control communications, the microwave landing system, and the satellite-based global positioning system (GPS). Because of its unique research equipment, which included a complete second cockpit in the cabin, the airplane also served as a magnet for joint NASA-industry research efforts as well as joint projects with other government agencies.

The chapters that follow offer more than a simple, biographical history of a single research plane, however. Since the airplane played a role in such a wide variety of research programs, its story also provides an enlightening study of the many factors that influence the selection, development, and application of new technologies. Contrary to popular myth, technology neither drives nor sells itself. Successfully transferring government-sponsored research into operational systems or commercial products can be difficult, but NASA's use of the 737 showed that strategies such as cooperative research efforts and flight demonstration can have a significant impact on the acceptance of new procedures or technology.

Ever since 1915, the United States government has supported aeronautical research and technology because it was considered important to the welfare of the nation. Although the initial focus was on building and maintaining a strong air commerce system and national defense, increasing international competition in the aerospace market has added a new concern. Innovation, research and technological advancement are considered critical elements to the competitiveness of the U.S. aeronautics industry, which has become one

Left—Christening of the first Boeing 737 at the Boeing corporate headquarters in Seattle, Washington. Right—The first flight of this airplane took place on April 9, 1967, shown here in flight test at Seattle, Washington.

of the few remaining fields in which the U.S. still has a positive balance of trade. As a result, maximizing the effectiveness of government-sponsored research and the transfer of that information to users has become the topic of much discussion in recent years. The history of NASA's Boeing 737 Transport Systems Research Vehicle offers some valuable insights that can make future aeronautical research efforts more effective, which, in turn, can help the United States maintain that critical competitive edge.

The first two chapters of this book contain background information on the 737 airplane and the technology research and transfer process. Chapter One provides an overview of the role the U.S. government has played in researching aeronautical technology and the complex process involved in transferring that knowledge to industry or other users. Chapter Two covers the history of NASA's Boeing 737 airplane and the Langley Research Center program it was purchased to support. While these chapters do not focus on particular research projects that involved the airplane, they provide a historical and theoretical context that helps explain the challenges the Terminal Configured Vehicle (TCV)/Advanced Transport Operating Systems (ATOPS) program researchers faced and the significance of their accomplishments.

The next three chapters describe three of the most significant research efforts conducted with the airplane: electronic flight display technology, the microwave landing system/global positioning system (GPS) research, and the development of an airborne windshear detection system. The remainder of the research projects that involved the 737 are grouped thematically in the following three chapters. Chapter Six discusses technology research that was geared toward improving systems in individual aircraft; Chapter Seven covers research efforts designed to improve the operation of aircraft within the air traffic control system; and Chapter Eight looks at a variety of research projects that used the 737 research aircraft because of its special capabilities.

Although the chapters focus on the research the 737 conducted, the story of this unusual research vehicle has a human element, as well.

Twenty years after the aircraft was purchased, quite a few of the people who helped bring the airplane home to Langley and conducted its first research projects are still involved with the airplane. The NASA researchers, technicians and office personnel who have worked with the airplane also possess a fierce sense of loyalty to the airplane and pride in what it has done that is echoed in the offices of industry engineers who worked with the airplane in its early days at NASA. One executive at the Boeing Commercial Airplane Company even keeps two large prints of the airplane and its unique aft research cockpit on the wall above his desk.

It would be easy to lose sight of these engineers, technicians, and office workers in assessing the airplane's accomplishments. Indeed, this book focuses much more on the technology the airplane helped to research and why those

The Boeing 737 at Langley Research Center in 1980 with the staff working on the Advanced Transport Operating Systems (ATOPS) Program.

technologies were, or in some cases were not, developed into commercial applications. Yet without the efforts of those individual people, the airplane could not have achieved what it did. The TCV/ATOPS program was both technically and organizationally challenging, and it was not always popular. It involved political pressure and deadlines foreign to many NASA researchers. The engineers who worked with the TCV/ ATOPS program were trying to research and transfer aeronautical technology in a new and more complex industrial climate, where published research papers were no longer sufficient to win the support of airlines or manufacturers. With hindsight, it is easy to see how the program's cooperative research efforts, personal connections and flight demonstrations helped gain acceptance for many research concepts, but the researchers at the time were breaking new ground. They had no manuals or guidelines on how to successfully transfer complex, systems-oriented transport technology to its many users. They had only their own experience of what seemed to work, a collective creativity and resourcefulness, and a conviction that the technology they were researching needed to be put to use. These researchers, technicians, and office workers may not be as visible as the 737 airplane or its accomplishments, but the program never would have succeeded without them. Their names are too numerous to list, but in recognition of their years of loyalty, dedication, late nights, early mornings, patient efforts, and perseverance, this book is respectfully dedicated to the NASA professionals who made the contributions of the 737 and the TCV/ATOPS program possible.

Chapter I

NASA, Industry, and Technology: The Complex Nature of Progress

United States government support of aeronautical research dates back almost to the beginning of flight itself. In 1914, as the world found itself on the brink of war, only 23 of the 3,700 airplanes in the world were U.S. owned.[1] Recognizing the disadvantage at which this imbalance put the United States, a rider to the Naval Appropriations Act of 1915 established the National Advisory Committee for Aeronautics "to supervise and direct the scientific study of the problems of flight, with a view to their practical solution."[2]

This was not the first time the United States government had cooperated with industry to further technology. The successful development of the railroads and modern agricultural methods, for example, evolved from government-industry cooperation.[3] Government-supported research was to play a particularly important role in the progress of aviation, however, from the creation of the N.A.C.A. engine cowling in the late 1920s and the wide variety of N.A.C.A. airfoil designs, to the development of jet aircraft.[4]

In the early 1980s, a proposal to reduce or even eliminate government support for aeronautical research led the White House Office of Science and Technology Policy (OSTP) to re-examine the government's role in aeronautical research and development (R&D). After a year-long study, its final report concluded that government support of aeronautics was not only still appropriate, but was a critical element to the continued economic health of the country.[5]

There were numerous compelling arguments for continued government support of technology development.[6] A 1983 report of the White House Science Council stated that "The ultimate purpose of Federal support for R&D is to develop the science and technology base needed for a strong national defense, for the health and well-being of U.S. Citizens, and for a healthy economy."[7] Certainly, national defense had been a leading reason for government support of aeronautics research since N.A.C.A. was formed in 1915. But President Ronald Reagan's science advisor also noted in 1982 that "aircraft are now the dominant common carrier for inter-city travel, and the safety and control of that travel are a federal responsibiliaty."[8]

As aeronautical technology became more complex and expensive, it was also more difficult for individual companies to shoulder the entire

Left—Langley metal workers installing NACA cowling on a Curtiss XF7C-1 Seahawk aircraft for test in 1928. For this work, the NACA received the 1929 Collier Trophy awarded annually for achievement in aeronautics in America. Right—Model of a Boeing 737 in wind tunnel test in 1976.

financial burden for researching and developing new technology and its products. The capital investment required to develop a dramatically new aircraft could exceed the net worth of the sponsoring company. For a manufacturer to be willing to invest the money into a new technology, it had to have short-term, concrete payoffs. Industry did not have the capability or incentive to pursue long term or high-risk projects, or research areas with uncertain benefits.

Furthermore, firms made decisions on what research to pursue based on its value to the company, not its value to society. Technologies that benefitted society but had less certain financial returns for a specific company, therefore, needed government support or involvement in order to be developed. Safety, for example, may be a desirable goal for society, but it is a difficult commodity for manufacturers to sell.[9]

By the mid-1980s, there was yet another argument for continued government support of aeronautical research: the diminishing level of U.S. industrial competitiveness in the global market. In 1986, United States high-technology imports exceeded exports for the first time. The aerospace industry was one of the only remaining fields with a trade surplus, 90 percent of which was attributable to the sale of aircraft and aircraft parts. Compared to an overall U.S. trade deficit in manufactured goods of $136 billion in 1986, the aerospace industry had a surplus of $11.8 billion.[10] But the U.S. lead in aeronautics was shrinking, as well. In 1980, the U.S. market share of large civil transport sales was 90 percent. By 1992, that percentage had dropped to 70 percent and was in danger of falling even further. The lead in the commuter aircraft market had already been lost.[11] Leaders in government, industry, academia and the media all began to stress that to preserve the U.S. lead in aeronautics and, indeed, the U.S. balance of trade, the country had to accord a much higher priority to aeronautical research and development.[12]

All of these arguments build a persuasive case for continued government support of aeronautical research and development. But they also illustrate an important point about technological progress. From the material presented in many traditional textbooks and scientific histories, it would be easy to view progress as a pure, scientific process that drives itself in a cumulative, linear manner. Science and technology have often been presented as outside the realm of social and political pressures; sometimes abused by leaders, but not overtly directed by external forces. In recent years, however, our view of technological progress has begun to change.[13]

As research and development efforts become more expensive and complex, research institutions have to make choices about what technologies to pursue. Those decisions are based not only on the scientific promise of a specific technology, but on factors such as what the government or industry is willing to fund, what concepts have the highest probability of

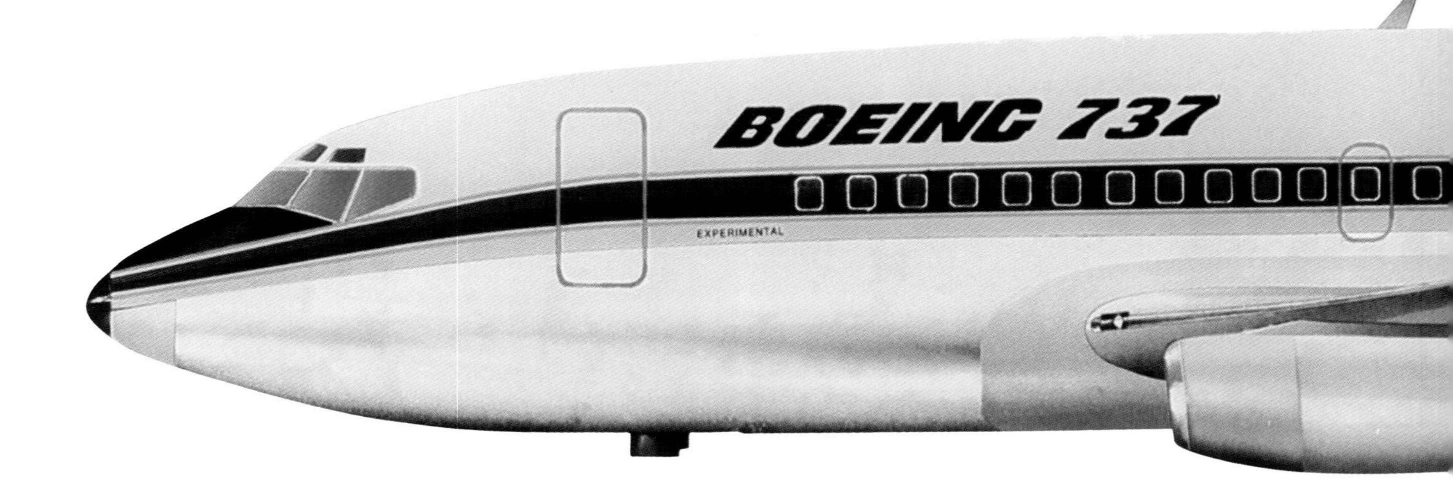

leading to a marketable product, and what kind of consumer or political pressure exists for progress in a particular area.[14] The windshear research conducted by the Federal Aviation Administration (FAA), NASA, and industry throughout the late 1980s, for example, would probably not have occurred if it were not for the political and public pressure that followed the 1985 crash of a Delta Airlines L-1011 in Dallas, Texas. Industry manufacturers cannot afford to research many kinds of technologies themselves, and when NASA funding for aeronautical research is cut back, many promising ideas may be abandoned for no other reason than the absence of money to pursue them.

Progress also does not occur through a simple, linear advancement of knowledge and capability. As one NASA publication noted, "Technological development ... will have second and third order consequences, often unintended, beyond the main objective."[15] This notion that advancements may be accompanied by new and unforeseen consequences or difficulties is what scholar Thomas P. Hughes called "reverse salients."[16] A breakthrough may solve one difficult problem, but it may also open the door on a whole new set of research problems that did not exist before the new technology was developed. The computerization of many airline cockpit functions, for example, greatly expanded the capabilities of transport airplanes. But it also created an entirely new set of problems that its proponents had not anticipated. Computerization altered the pilot's role in the airplane and created enough significant human-machine interface problems that NASA eventually created an entirely new research program to help develop more human-centered automation.[17]

Furthermore, not all concepts that are researched are applied to commercial products, regardless of their intrinsic technological worth. Like progress itself, technology transfer is a complex process, affected by numerous external factors and decisions.

The 1958 National Aeronautics and Space Act that created the National Aeronautics and Space Administration (NASA) specifically mandated the agency to "provide for the widest practicable and appropriate dissemination of information concerning its activities and the results thereof."[18] But as the director of NASA's Technology Utilization office noted in 1963, "In this age of automation, there is nothing automatic about the transfer of knowledge or the application of an idea or invention to practical use."[19]

Artist's conception of prototype Boeing 737 in original colors from factory.

More recently, one industry publication listed some of what it called the "technology transfer myths," which included the idea that industry automatically "gobbles up" new technology as soon as it is revealed; that a "better mousetrap" is self-evident and doesn't need selling; and that "exciting and valid" technology will "automatically" be transferred.[20]

The reality is that there are many factors that complicate and influence the transfer of technology from government research institutions like NASA to industry. Technologies that represent a significant change in equipment or procedures, for example, may face opposition simply because of an inherent tendency on the part of people and organizations to resist change.

Theorists argue that radical new methods, technology, or scientific theories require a shift in "paradigms," or accepted truths, in order to be adopted, which is a difficult task for people or organizations.[21] Pilots accustomed to mechanical controls may not trust electronic flight computers, for example, because their use involves a departure from the control principles the pilots were taught and have used successfully for years. If a revolutionary new approach or technology becomes the norm, it also makes individuals' and companies' past experience, success, and expertise in the outdated method irrelevant. Consequently, individuals or companies who have achieved significant prestige through the use of an existing technology may resist replacing it with a new one, no matter how good the replacement is.[22]

Large, established companies also have a lot at risk, and they are often reluctant to bet the company on an untried technology. Not surprisingly, therefore, new ideas or designs are often incorporated first by small companies, or companies at the fringe of industries, who have to take greater risks to gain the necessary market share to survive.[23] Airbus Industries, for example, has incorporated more advanced technology into its aircraft, including full fly-by-wire controls, than the U.S. transport aircraft manufacturers have. But the European consortium had more motivation to innovate and less to lose than its U.S. counterparts. Boeing and McDonnell Douglas held such a commanding market position that unless Airbus distinguished itself significantly in some manner, it would be lost in Boeing's shadow.[24]

In addition, there are a number of concrete, business reasons why some technologies are not adopted by industry. The cost-effectiveness of a new concept, for example, plays a critical role in whether or not it is ever incorporated into a commercial product. To a research engineer at the Langley Research Center, success is usually measured in terms of technical objectives met. Industry, on the other hand, measures innovative success in terms of profit gained within a specific period of time. A new transport technology developed at NASA may work flawlessly and may greatly expand an airplane's capabilities, but if it is not going to translate into a profitable

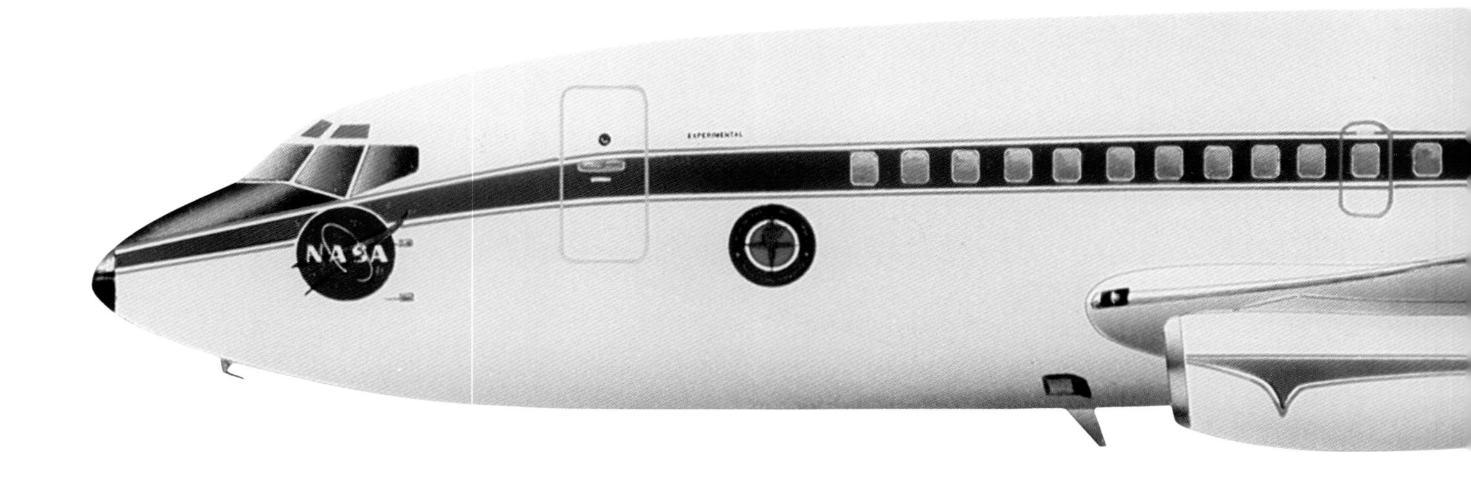

investment for a manufacturer or an airline, it is not likely to be applied by industry.[25]

External factors that affect the overall economic situation of an industry can make cost an even greater concern. For example, the deregulation of the airline industry in 1978 made the business much more competitive. As a result, accountants became more powerful players in purchase decisions, and airlines and airframe manufacturers became much more likely to reject new technology unless it was going to show a concrete, short-term profit.[26]

The cost of a new piece of technology is also not limited solely to its development or purchase price. If too dramatic a change is made in any area of a commercial airplane, the design may have to be re-certified by the FAA, which can be a very expensive process. New cockpit equipment may require an airline to retrain all of its pilots, causing the carrier to incur substantial additional costs. Consequently, a revolutionary new design usually has to offer some significant savings in order for a manufacturer to consider it a worthwhile investment.

Of course, in order to debate the cost-effectiveness of a new technology, industry first has to know about and understand what it is and what its benefits might be. The information has to be communicated effectively not only from NASA to industry engineers, but also from those engineers to all the decision makers in a particular company. If any part of that communication fails, the technology may not even be considered for a new product.

As technology has become more complex, transferring information about new concepts to the key people in industry has become more of a challenge. For years, the bulk of information about NASA research results was transferred through written documentation, such as technical memoranda, technical papers, articles in professional journals, tech briefs, and through professional conferences. In fact, a 1992 study of NASA's technology transfer activities found that researchers still often viewed successful transfer as writing a report on research results after the work was completed.[27]

Yet there is a growing consensus that technology transfer efforts stand a much greater chance of success if they occur as part of the technology development process, through personal contact between NASA and industry engineers, instead of through a passive, sterile document issued after the research is completed.

Artist's conception of Boeing 737 painted in NASA colors upon delivery in 1974.

By involving industry earlier in the development process, researchers can help insure that the effort is relevant to industry's needs, and the potential users get to observe and contribute to the development and progress of a new technology. By the time the research is completed, the users already understand it and are in a much better position to sell it to the rest of the company decision-makers.[28]

One method of involving industry researchers in technology development projects is through cooperative research efforts between NASA and one or more private companies. This approach not only shares the cost burden of the research, it also creates a group of professionals within the company that thoroughly understand the technology and can advocate its incorporation into a new product. In addition, these arrangements virtually guarantee that the research will be seriously considered by at least one company. Even if a research project is not a joint effort, however, bringing in industry representatives for input, evaluation, and demonstrations of new technology can be invaluable in gaining industry interest and support of its use in a commercial application.

Demonstrations actually can be extremely effective in convincing industry to pursue a commercial application of a technology . Old adages like "A picture is worth a thousand words," and "Seeing is believing," emphasize the power of visual demonstration. Although it might take many pages in a technical paper to explain exactly how a concept works, a demonstration can show, very clearly and persuasively, what the technology can do. A demonstration can also give a piece of technology a critical measure of credibility, because it proves the concept will work, at least in a test setting. This, in turn, can give industry enough confidence to commit to a commercial development program.[29]

The importance of this credibility was underscored by H. W. Withington, the former Vice President of Engineering at the Boeing Commercial Airplane Company, in a letter to a manager at the NASA Langley Research Center. He emphasized that "laboratory development has great appeal and usually gets substantial government support. However, ...the attainment of credibility...is (also) an important national issue. It is during this second phase that a technical concept achieves a state of readiness, validation and credibility such that private industry and financing can assume the attendant risks."[30]

Giving industry information about and confidence in a new concept is still only one step, and one factor, in the technology application process, however. Even if industry representatives are included at an early stage in the research, there is continual contact and communication between government and industry representatives, and the technology is persuasively demonstrated, a concept still may not be incorporated into a commercial application. By the same token, some research transferred less perfectly may be adopted

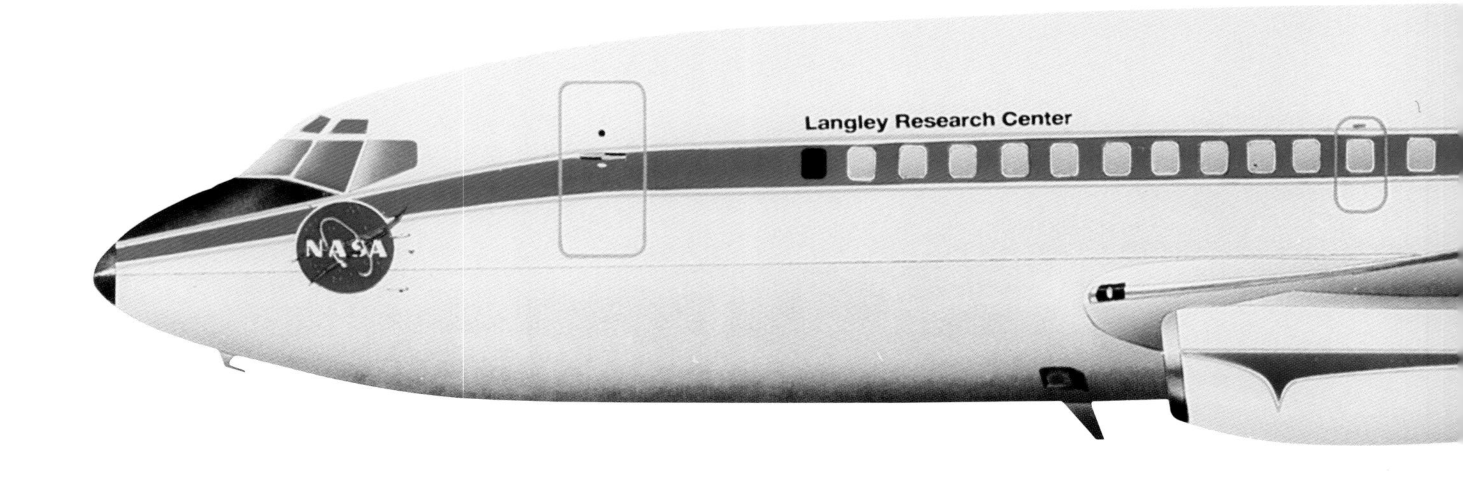

immediately by industry if, for example, federal regulations mandate that it be incorporated into forthcoming products.

Yet although it can be a complex and often frustrating process, successful technology transfer is a critical step in advancing America's aeronautical industry. In early 1993, NASA Administrator Daniel S. Goldin stated that "the transfer of our valuable technology ... must be proactively sought and given the highest priority."[31]

Goldin's words marked a renewed emphasis on technology transfer within the aeronautics and space agency. But for the engineers, pilots, researchers and staff who worked with the Terminal Configured Vehicle/Advanced Transport Operating Systems program at the Langley Research Center in Virginia, Goldin was simply restating a philosophy they had lived with for the past 20 years.

In 1973, a group of engineers at the Langley Research Center created the Terminal Configured Vehicle research program and successfully argued for the purchase of a Boeing 737 research aircraft in which to develop, test, and demonstrate advanced technologies for use by the commercial air transport industry. Over the course of the next two decades, the airplane was involved in more than 20 different research projects, most of which were focused on improving the efficiency, capacity, and safety of the air transportation system. Some of the technologies were developed into commercial applications and have had a significant impact on air transport operations. Others, equally worthy from a technical point of view, have yet to be applied.

Because it played a role in so many different projects, with widely differing results and applications, the story of NASA's 737 airplane offers a unique opportunity to examine the forces and factors that influence the development and application of new technology. Furthermore, although the Langley engineers did not set out to explore creative methods of technology transfer, their experience with the airplane and its numerous research projects contains some important lessons about how technology transfer can be accomplished, and the difference a facility like the 737 research airplane can make.

Artist's conception of Boeing 737 in present NASA colors. The yellow tail stripe and the FAA logo were removed and new NASA lettering was used.

Chapter 2

Addressing the New Challenges of Air Transportation: The TCV/ATOPS Program

When Neil Armstrong landed on the moon in July 1969, it capped off a tremendous national effort that had absorbed most of NASA's attention and resources throughout the 1960s. As the Apollo program wound down, however, it created both an opportunity and a need for NASA to re-evaluate its activities and direction. A number of people within the agency, including acting administrator Thomas O. Paine and Deputy Administrator George M. Low, felt that aeronautics should now receive greater attention and support.[1]

Congress also had begun to feel that the government needed to focus more on furthering aeronautical technology. A report issued by the Senate Committee on Aeronautical and Space Sciences in January 1968 emphasized the need for a national policy on aeronautics research and development. The report also recommended that NASA and the newly formed Department of Transportation undertake a joint study to evaluate the problems facing civil aviation and the potential benefits that might accrue from government support of Research and Development (R&D) in those areas.[2]

Left—Airliners waiting in line for take-off illustrate the airport congestion that prompted the formation of the Terminal Configured Vehicle (TCV) research program.
Right—The 737 simulator at Langley Research Center.

One of the members of the DOT-NASA study team was Barry Graves, the head of the Flight Instrumentation Division (FID) at NASA's Langley Research Center. In addition to his NASA duties, Graves was also a private pilot and had a keen interest in the problems facing civil aviation. As work progressed on the DOT-NASA Civil Aviation Research and Development (CARD) Policy Study, Graves also had a small group of people within his division evaluating ways Langley might be able to contribute to air transportation research. At the same time, John P. "Jack" Reeder, a famous NASA test pilot at Langley who was another staunch supporter of civil aviation, was formulating his own proposals for research to improve air transport operations.[3]

When the results of the CARD study were released in March 1971, the report concluded that a healthy civil aviation industry and transportation system provided a variety of significant benefits to the nation. Consequently, the study recommended, the federal government should take an active role in developing a national aviation policy and conducting R&D

to benefit civil aviation. The report also outlined priorities for these R&D efforts. The top two concerns were aircraft noise and congestion in the terminal, or airport, area.[4]

These problems had actually been developing for some time. By the late 1960s, air travel was no longer the privilege of the elite. As it became an accepted and highly popular form of transportation, however, delays were becoming commonplace. An example often used by the researchers at Langley was that in 1959, a propeller-driven Lockheed Electra took 40 minutes to fly from Norfolk, Virginia to Washington, D.C. In 1973, a Boeing 727 jet capable of flying twice as fast took 45-55 minutes to make that same trip because of increased air traffic and terminal congestion problems.[5]

Early supporters of the TCV/Advanced Transport Operating Systems (ATOPS) Program. Left to right: Edgar M. Cortright, Langley Research Center Director 1968-1975; John Reeder, research program director; and Oran W. Nicks, Langley deputy director, during arrival of the 737 in 1974.

The advent of jets also increased the noise level around commercial airports, resulting in community opposition to additional air traffic or the building of new airports. In addition to driving research on quieter engines, this meant that there was an even greater need to make the most efficient and noise-sensitive use of the country's existing airports.[6]

A couple of months after the CARD study was released, President Richard M. Nixon's Office of Science and Technology (OST) asked NASA to submit proposals on how NASA could contribute to research and development in the civil aeronautical sector. One of the six internal task groups that were formed to develop proposals looked specifically at air transportation research and development. In less than two months, the proposals were submitted and the OST asked NASA to develop its air transportation proposal into a detailed program and prepare to begin research. The task was given to the Langley Research Center.[7] Langley was the agency's oldest field organization, founded in 1918 specifically to conduct aeronautical R&D.

Although his proposals had been turned down by the Aeronautics Steering Committee in the past, Jack Reeder presented his ideas on improving airspace utilization to the group working with Barry Graves to develop the detailed air transportation research program. Reeder's ideas fit extremely well with the plans being formulated by the FID team, and the two were incorporated into a program plan that became the Terminal Configured Vehicle (TCV) program. The original name was actually the Terminal Configured Vehicle & Avionics program, but the "avionics" was soon dropped.[8]

The TCV program was an unusual research project for Langley. Instead of just looking at a single airfoil or aircraft component, the TCV program also included research into the pilot/airplane interface and the airplane's interface with the air traffic control system. This was a much broader scope of work, involving more branches, divisions, disciplines and directorates than the typical Langley research effort. But as the example of the Lockheed Electra and the B-727 illustrated, the problems facing civil air transport had grown much more complex. In the 1920s, the development of a NACA engine cowling alone was able to make a significant impact on the efficiency of air travel. By 1970, even the most aerodynamically efficient airplane could not overcome the delays imposed by traffic congestion in the terminal area. The challenge had become a systems problem, and it required a system-oriented solution.

The broad goals of the TCV program were to conduct research into advanced technology for Conventional Take-Off and Landing (CTOL) aircraft,

> *...to provide improvements in the airborne systems (avionics and air vehicle) and operational flight procedures for reducing approach and landing accidents, reducing weather minima, increasing air traffic controller productivity and airport and airway capacity, saving fuel by more efficient terminal area operations, and reducing noise by operational procedures.*[9]

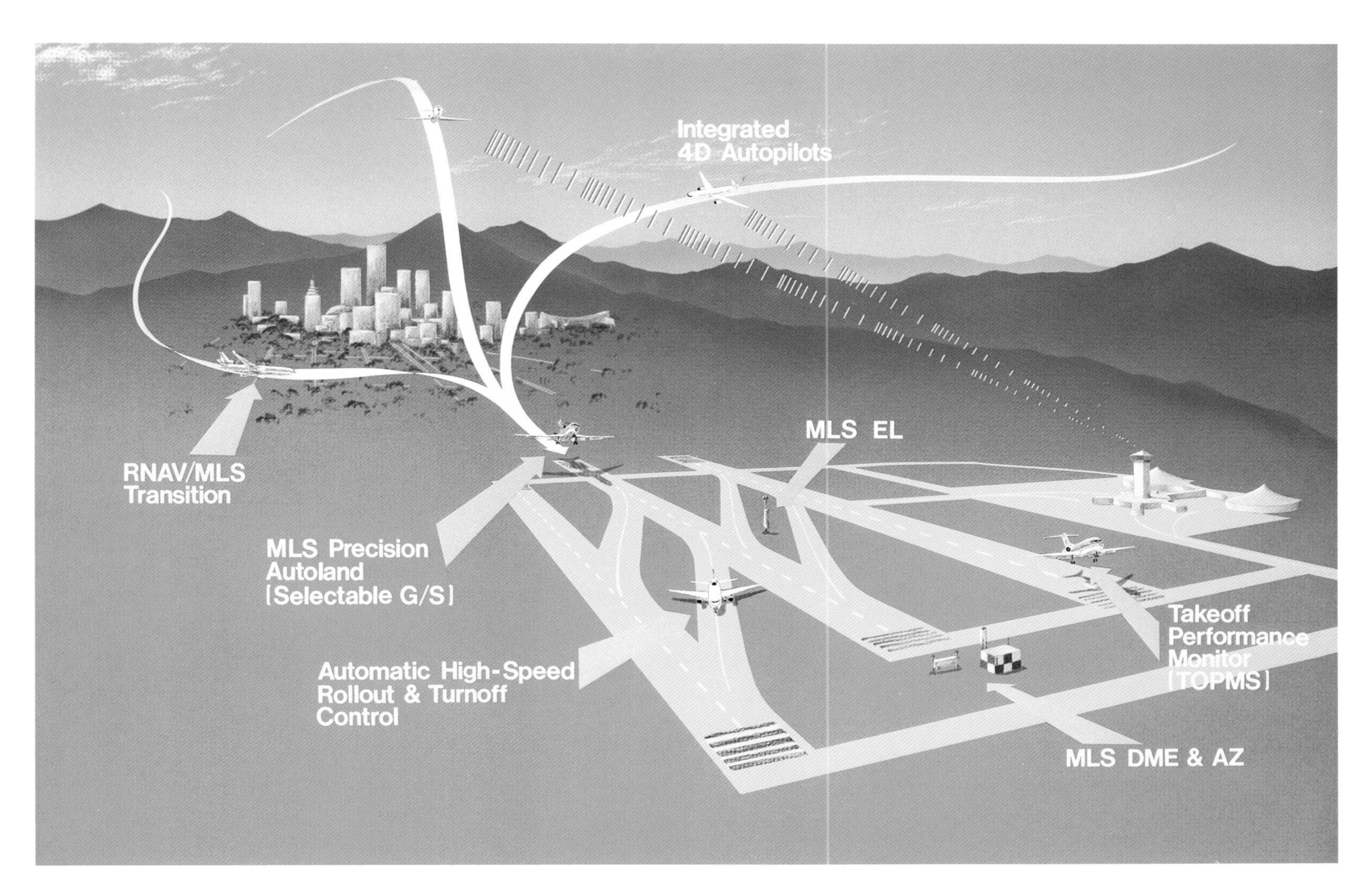

The NASA 737 research program was built on improving aircraft systems such as these used around airports.

Specifically, the TCV program wanted to look at items such as curved or non-standard approach paths for noise abatement and improved airport acceptance rates; cockpit displays of traffic information; profile and time-based navigation, which would use a computer to calculate an optimum fuel-efficient flight plan that would deliver an airplane to its touchdown spot +/- five seconds to allow closer spacing of aircraft. Other planned experiments would look at data links, high-speed runway turnoffs, and optimum uses of the new Microwave Landing System (MLS) that the Federal Aviation Administration (FAA) was developing.[10]

Aquiring a Research Aircraft

Since the focus of the work was to improve operations for commercial transport airplanes, the researchers at Langley argued that the program needed to include flight tests with a transport-size CTOL aircraft. The only large aircraft owned by NASA were a C-141A and a Convair 990 located at the Ames Research Center in California. The cost of using one of these four-engine airplanes for a 6-8 year research program was too high, however, and all the other NASA-owned airplanes were too small, or lacked the capabilities necessary to carry out the TCV research. Langley personnel working on the project also believed that in order for the results of their research to be accepted and used by the air transport industry, the technology had to be tested and developed on a commercial transport class airplane.

The best candidate for a test airplane appeared to be either a DC-9 or a Boeing 737, since both had adequate room and capability as well as manageable operating costs. The Boeing 737 was Langley's number one choice, however, since it had a slightly wider fuselage and an advanced, high-lift flap system. Money, however, was extremely tight. The market value of a used 737 in 1972 was about $3.5 million, but the Boeing Company had one particular 737 that its sales people said they might be willing to sell for substantially less.[11]

The Boeing aircraft was the original prototype 737-100, used for FAA certification tests on the model. The Dash 100 model, which had a length only one foot longer than its wingspan, was nicknamed "Fat Albert" because its shape was so stubby compared to most airliners. The prototype flew for the first time on April 9, 1967, and had only 978 flight hours on its airframe. Since the first order for 737-100s was from Lufthansa Airlines, Boeing had designated the prototype as PA-099: PA for Lufthansa, and 099 as the last one in a block of 100 aircraft numbers Boeing had reserved for the airline. The prototype was never sold, however, because it was only certified for experimental use. With all the holes, wiring and other modifications that were made to the airplane for certification tests, bringing it up to the standards of a commercial transport airplane would have been too expensive. Boeing used the airplane for a few additional flight tests and then simply set it aside.[12]

In fact, when the Langley engineers first travelled to Seattle to look at the plane, it was a dismal sight. The engines had been removed, and the airplane was sitting at the end of the ramp at Boeing's facility in Renton, Washington, with cement blocks hanging off the engine pylons to keep the airplane from falling on its tail. The interior had been stripped out, and where the cockpit instruments should have been, there were only bundles of wire dangling from the remains of a panel. Nevertheless, the plane had several characteristics that appealed to NASA. First, Boeing was willing to bring it back to flightworthy status, complete with overhauled engines, and sell it to NASA for only $2.2 million. Second, while the modifications and special instrumentation wiring and plumbing in the airplane were useless for an airline, they made PA-099 more suitable as a research airplane.[13]

The Boeing plane also had one other significant advantage. Boeing had been awarded the contract to build the U.S. Supersonic Transport (SST) aircraft, which included advanced avionics, displays and flight control systems. The program had become very controversial, however, with substantial opposition from communities and groups who were concerned about the environmental impact the plane would have. Finally, on March 24, 1971, Congress voted to cancel the SST.[14] But in

an effort to keep all the technology development efforts for the plane from being wasted, Congress authorized Boeing to do a small amount of follow-on research in a number of technology areas. Two of these areas were advanced electronic displays and digital flight controls.

Boeing had contracted with the Department of Transportation (DOT) to develop the SST Advanced Digital Electronic Displays (ADEDS) and the Automatic Guidance and Control (AGCS) digital flight control system to a point where they could be flight tested. The Boeing plans called for very limited flight testing of the experimental equipment, after which the equipment would be returned to the DOT.[15]

When the Langley engineers approached Boeing about a 737, however, they and Boeing both realized the potential benefits of integrating this advanced equipment into the prototype 737 as a research airplane for NASA. NASA would get the opportunity to experiment with the most advanced display and flight control technology available, and Boeing would get a chance to test the equipment in a specially equipped research airplane with an extensive data-gathering capability.

Flight deck of the future NASA Langley 737 testbed aircraft as it appeared after completion of Boeing prototype tests and before refurbishment for NASA. Its engines had been removed and the interior, including the instrument panel, had been stripped.

The DOT, in the fall of 1971, had asked NASA to support the Boeing follow-on tests of the SST electronic displays.[16] To put the DOT-owned display and flight control equipment in a NASA airplane on a permanent basis, however, would require a cooperative agreement between NASA and the FAA.

While cooperative efforts between the two government agencies were not unheard of, the separate roles and responsibilities of the two organizations with regard to national problems in aeronautics and civil aviation were not clearly defined. The agencies also had different mandates. NASA was a research agency, charged with furthering new technology. It did not have to worry about certifying production equipment, or regulating its operation. The FAA's primary responsibility, on the other hand, was to keep the national air traffic system operating smoothly and safely on a day to day basis. Consequently, the two agencies' research priorities and approaches often differed.

There were some people in the FAA who thought that NASA should concern itself only with airplane technology and should leave issues such as more efficient operating procedures for the terminal area to the FAA. The problem was that the FAA had fewer resources to devote to such research. NASA's aeronautics research budget and personnel typically exceeded that of the FAA's R&D department by a magnitude of at least 10. At the same time, NASA research in

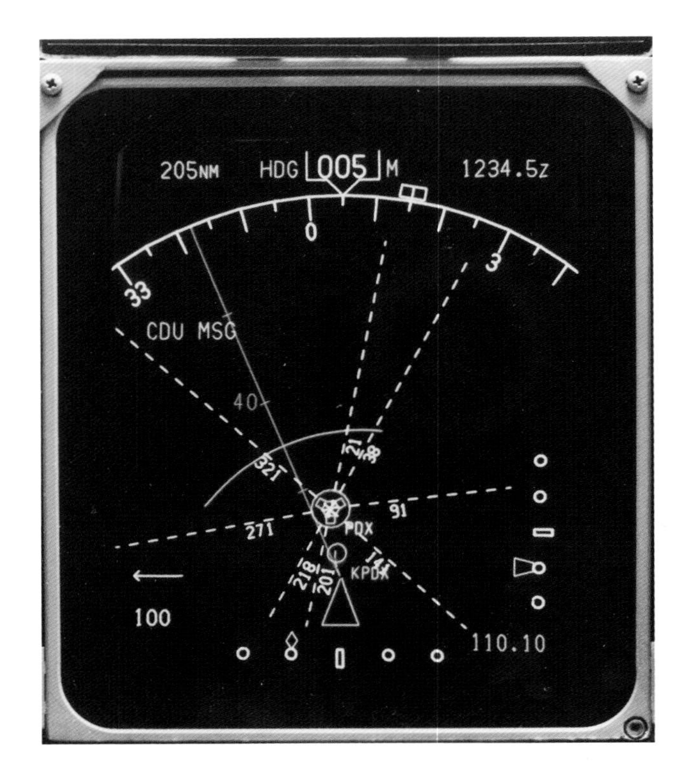

A typical map display using Cathode Ray Tube technology.

new air transportation technology and procedures would not have any practical impact without the FAA's involvement on some level, since the FAA had to approve any changes in air transport equipment or operations. But while it may have made sense for the agencies to work together on the problems, there were still areas of tension over turf, priorities, and working relationships that persisted long after a cooperative working agreement was signed.[17]

In May 1973, a cooperative agreement between NASA and the FAA was reached. In exchange for putting the SST technology in the new NASA airplane, NASA agreed to allow Boeing to use the plane first to conduct the DOT flight tests of the SST equipment. After that, the FAA would be entitled to up to 25 percent of the aircraft's flying time for its own research projects. [18]

On July 26, 1973, NASA officially purchased Boeing's prototype 737-100 aircraft. Boeing spent most of the next 10 months outfitting the aircraft to NASA's specifications and completing the DOT flight tests.[19] Wearing its new tail number of N515NA, the airplane finally arrived at Langley to begin its remarkable career as NASA's Transport Systems Research Vehicle (TSRV) on May 17, 1974.[20]

Aircraft Equipment and Research Systems

Without a doubt, NASA's new 737 was a one-of-a-kind airplane. In addition to a conventional forward flight deck, Boeing modified the airplane with a second, experimental cockpit in the forward part of the main cabin that contained the advanced SST avionics. The aft flight deck (AFD) was enclosed in a full-size fiberglass duplicate of the 737's front cockpit exterior that left just enough room for a small passageway to one side. A second fiberglass cab was used to build a high-fidelity fixed-base ground simulator that replicated the aft flight deck. The simulator, run by a high-speed Control Data Corporation CDC-6400 mainframe computer, allowed experiments to be tested and developed through real-time simulation on the ground before they were put on the airplane.

NASA flight test programs usually divided an aircraft's cockpit into two parts and installed any experimental equipment on one side, leaving a safety pilot on the other. The TCV researchers wanted the ability to evaluate new transport technology in a realistic, two-crew environment, however, so the 737 was outfitted with the complete second cockpit. For the NASA research flights, the aft cockpit was equipped with four monochrome cathode ray tube (CRT) displays. The pilot and copilot positions had both a primary flight display (PFD), and a navigation, or map, CRT display in front of them, installed above a Control and Display Unit (CDU), which was the pilot's interface with the navigation computer.[21]

In order for the pilots to be able to see the full displays, the aft flight deck was equipped with two individual handles that came out of the instrument panel instead of conventional center control yokes. Sidestick controllers, like those eventually installed in the Airbus A-320 airliner, were ruled out because they were a more dramatic departure from conventional yokes, and the researchers wanted to keep the 737's cockpit at least somewhat familiar to airline pilots. Although they were referred to in technical papers as "Panel Mounted

Controllers," the dual handles were dubbed "Brolly Handles" by a British engineer who worked on the project, because their shape reminded him of an umbrella handle, or "brolly," as it is sometimes called in England. The instrument panel of the aft flight deck also included electromechanical engine instruments and a Boeing Advanced Guidance and Control Panel (AGCS), which was used to select different levels of automatic or manual flight control.

Because the focus of the TCV research was flight operations under Instrument Flight Rules (IFR), the complete lack of visibility from the aft flight deck was not considered a problem. The FAA, on the other hand, wanted its pilots to be able to try the experimental SST equipment in a less severe environment, where they could still use outside visual cues. So the 737 was also wired to allow one set of the displays, one CDU and the AGCS Panel to be installed on the right side of the forward flight deck. Instead of brolly handles, however, the right-hand control column of the 737 was simply shortened to keep the yoke from obscuring the displays, since the FAA wanted to keep the configuration as conventional as possible. This "FAA" configuration, however, was only used once, for baseline testing of the SST equipment at the FAA's technical center in Atlantic City, New Jersey, in the fall of 1974.[22]

The airplane was also equipped to use the SST equipment in a third, "split" configuration, which would have put one set of just the displays in the right-hand side of the forward flight deck for monitoring by a safety pilot. This configuration was never actually used, however.

In all the configurations, control inputs from the experimental systems were processed through the SST program's digital flight control computer, which then interfaced with the airplane's autopilot. Because the computer relied on the autopilot system to actually drive the control surfaces, the aft flight deck was restricted to half the control authority of the forward cockpit, which used a conventional 737 powered control system.

This arrangement allowed experiments to be conducted in the aft cockpit while safety pilots monitored all the operations from the forward flight deck. This was an extremely valuable capability, as it allowed new and unproven technologies to be tested in an actual flight environment while maintaining an acceptable level of safety. It would probably have been far too risky, for example, to include autolands in the testing of the MLS curved path approaches if the plane did not have safety pilots up front who could see outside, monitor the progress of the approach, and take over if necessary. And yet the actual completion of those autolands was one of the things that made the MLS demonstrations so effective.

The safety pilots could take over control of the airplane simply by pushing one of two buttons or operating a trim system switch, and the pilots in the aft flight deck could give control back to the forward flight deck by pushing a disconnect button. Annunciation lights in both cockpits would light up with any change in command, and the pilots would also verbally notify each other of the switch over the airplane's intercom system. Status messages and requests from the aft flight deck were monitored by the safety pilots on a "Control and Command" panel on the top of the front instrument panel. Gear and speed brakes, for

Tightly packed electronics racks required to conduct research on the Boeing 737 aircraft. Each pallet had a row of three seats for researchers. Note the aft flight deck partially shown in the center background.

example, could not actually be controlled by the aft flight deck. When a pilot in the back put his gear handle down, a "Gear" light on the Control and Command panel would light up, telling the safety pilot to extend the gear. The Control and Command panel also had an emergency disconnect knob that would physically disconnect the aft flight deck interface with the aircraft controls, in case the electrical disconnect system failed.

Behind the aft flight deck were rows of pallets that housed all the computers that ran the experimental systems, as well as data gathering equipment. Behind each row of pallets was a row of seats, so researchers could monitor the data and operation of each element of the system as well as any experiment that was being conducted.

There were three major experimental subsystems installed in the plane in addition to the data and video collection equipment. One subsystem operated the actual flight controls of the airplane (aileron, elevator, rudder), controlling the airplane's physical movement. A second sub-

system provided computerized navigation functions, which controlled the airplane's flight path. The third sub-system operated the electronic flight displays in the aft cockpit.

The original experimental equipment for the three systems consisted of triply redundant General Electric (GE) ICP 723 flight control computers, a General Electric 701 digital display computer, and a Litton C-4000 navigation computer. The aircraft also incorporated a triply redundant Litton LTN51 Inertial Navigation System (INS). The General Electric computers were all prototypes, developed specifically for the SST program. The ICP 723 computers were actually not fully digital but something called "incremental word" computers; an intermediate step between analog and digital systems. [23]

The NASA 737 on the ramp during flight tests in 1992 as lightning strikes in the background.

The biggest problem with the GE equipment was that it was never intended to be operational in an airplane for a long period of time. It had been designed to operate for only one ninety-day test. Yet NASA ended up flying the display computers, for example, for 12 years. The maintenance headaches this caused were complicated further by the fact that the equipment was what the NASA technicians termed "brassboard," or only one step better than the crudely connected systems electronics researchers would initially test in a lab. There were no maintenance manuals and no replacement systems. If a problem developed, it sometimes took phone calls to six or more GE engineers who had helped design the system as well as scanning pages of blueprint drafts to figure out how it could be fixed. Then the problem had to be troubleshot down to the level of individual parts on the circuit cards, because there were not even any spare circuit cards.

Since there were no spares in a lab to use to troubleshoot problems, the crew in charge of the experimental systems had to use the airplane as their lab. During flight test periods, this meant that repairs generally had to be made at night, so the next day's experiments could still be flown. Amazingly, although some flights had to be cancelled, the late hours and the resourcefulness of the Langley personnel who worked on the equipment kept the airplane from ever missing a major research program.

Fortunately, the equipment was upgraded substantially over the years. The first change was made in 1976, when the GE ICP 723 computers were replaced with triply redundant GE 703 whole-word computers, which were full digital systems. In 1983 the GE 703 computers were replaced with a single Norden 1170 flight control computer. The single string flight control system was considered acceptable because of the back-up provided by the conventional controls in the forward flight deck. The

Norden 1170 also replaced the Litton C4000, giving the airplane its first complete flight management computer.

The system architecture of the experimental system was also changed in 1983 to a Digital Autonomous Terminal Access Communications (DATAC) data bus, invented by Boeing engineer Hans Herzog. Instead of requiring dedicated buses and connections for each item researchers wanted to get into or out of the computer, the DATAC system was a "broadcast" bus. All the information was broadcast in sequence down a single twisted pair of wires, and any station that needed information could simply connect to the bus and collect whatever data it required. The DATAC system also used magnetic coupling instead of hard connections, which made adding or changing experimental equipment vastly easier.

In 1986, the original GE 701 display computer was finally replaced with a second Norden 1170, and new Sperry/Honeywell color displays were installed. There was some debate among Langley engineers as to what size display to buy, because the only "off the shelf" displays available were small, 5" x 7" "B-size" CRTs. Sperry/Honeywell was in the process of developing bigger 8" diameter "D-size" displays, but they were not fully tested yet. However, the Langley managers decided that since the bigger displays were going to be the wave of the future in transport airplanes, they would take the risk of ordering them for the 737. Eventually, the aft flight deck was equipped with eight of the color monitors.[24]

Two years later, the Norden 1170 flight management computer was replaced with a Digital Equipment Corporation (DEC) MicroVax II computer, which was faster, smaller, cheaper, easier to cool, and took less power to operate. At the same time, the brolly handles on the left side of the aft flight deck were replaced with a McFadden side stick controller.

In 1990, a second DEC MicroVax II computer took the place of the Norden 1170 display computer, and second side stick controller was installed. The most recent upgrade to the system was the installation of new computer cards in the MicroVaxes that equipped the computers with a new processor. The upgrade changed the computers into MicroVax IVs and doubled their speed.[25]

The almost continuous upgrades in experimental equipment were necessary to keep pace with the rapid developments in computer technology over the last 20 years. The equipment has not been the only aspect of the program to change, however. The organizational structure and the level of support the program has enjoyed have both varied widely over the years.

Program Organization

By its very nature, the TCV program was destined to be an organizational challenge. Because its goal was to look at an entire system, instead of a single aerodynamic or electronic component, it required the expertise and cooperation of a wide variety of people, both inside and outside of Langley. At first, the Langley management was not even sure under which directorate the program should go.[26] For a very brief time during its initial formulation, the program was under the supervision of both the Aeronautics and the Electronics directorates. The problems inherent in that divided structure, however, led the center management to put it under the sole control of Electronics in May 1973.[27] The program was put on the same level as a division office, reporting directly to the head of the Electronics directorate, and Jack Reeder was made the program chief.

Even then, the organization was far from simple. Langley leadership had traditionally tried to avoid separating researchers from colleagues in their discipline, because it was felt that such a move would cause the researchers to fall behind in their field and would hurt the strength of the different research disciplines.[28] Consequently, all the people involved in the TCV program except a small core of program office personnel stayed administratively attached to their different branches, divisions and directorates. Their work priorities were decided by the program office, but their performance evaluations and pay raises

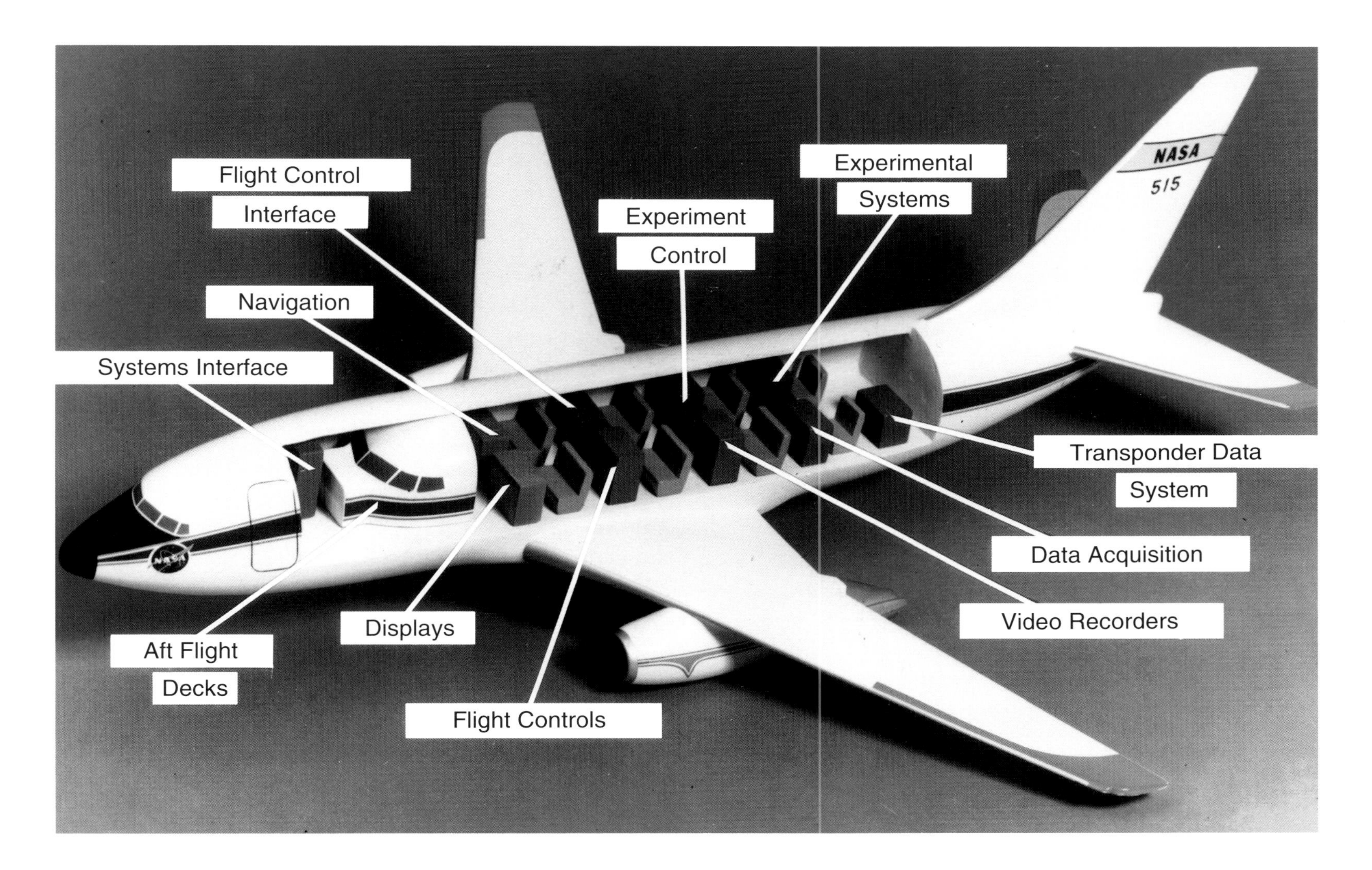

Cutaway model of the Boeing 737 used for flight research showing its aft cockpit and the location of various research pallets.

were given to them by their administrative supervisors. This kind of "matrix" organization offered a number of advantages and had been used often throughout Langley's history. It also had some inherent drawbacks, however.

A matrix arrangement allowed research programs to benefit from the contributions of highly skilled specialists that the center could not afford to assign exclusively to one particular project. When the TCV program started, for example, Langley had two or three world-renowned specialists in microwave antenna design. Antenna design was critical for a number of aircraft experiments, including the use of the microwave landing system. But it was a highly specialized field, and the center could not support a large number of researchers with that concentration. Consequently, if each one of the design researchers had been assigned full-time to a different project, the antenna design discipline at Langley would have ceased to exist. Without the benefit of a central discipline and daily contact with their colleagues, the individual researchers would have had a difficult time staying up with new developments in the antenna design field, and their work itself would undoubtedly have suffered, because it would have been more difficult for their peers to review and contribute to their research as it progressed. A matrix structure, on the other hand, left the disciplines intact and allowed them to support a number of different research projects and programs.

While a matrix organization had a lot of advantages from a research perspective, however, it was extremely difficult to manage or work within from an administrative standpoint. The program managers had no direct line authority to enforce anything, and if a researcher's administrative supervisor had different ideas or priorities than the program managers, the researcher could be caught in a very uncomfortable position. Program work deadlines and priorities had to be enforced primarily by persuasion, which meant the success of a research program depended partly on the personalities of its managers. Accomplishing tasks in this kind of environment took a lot more effort and finesse than a straight vertical organization would have required. The Monday morning TCV program coordinating meetings were legendary at the center for the heated arguments that erupted among project personnel, and many people involved in the early days of the program still believe that a matrix structure is an organizational nightmare.[29]

The problem was that nobody could figure out a better way to make a broad-based effort like the TCV program work. Managers in the Flight Systems directorate, under which the program operated after 1985, once studied what it would take to put all the researchers who supported the program in one administrative organization. They discovered they would have to remove so many researchers from other directorates and research disciplines that it would severely handicap the center's other research efforts. The TCV program simply drew from too many different areas for it to operate as a straight, vertical organization.[30]

In addition to this challenging matrix organization, the TCV program initially had to interface with a Flight Experiments Working Group, as well. The group was made up of representatives from different NASA centers and the FAA and was supposed to help select appropriate experiments for the TCV office to conduct.[31] This structure was soon changed, however, to give responsibility for approving experiments to the program and directorate management.

The TCV program also included a contingent from the Boeing Commercial Airplane Company from 1974 until 1979. The

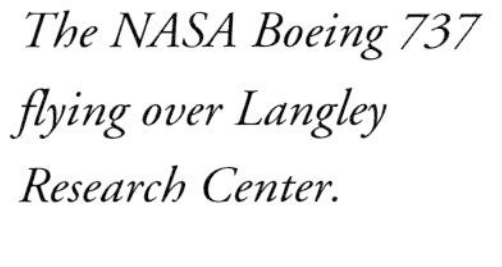
The NASA Boeing 737 flying over Langley Research Center.

initial plan was for a team of technicians and engineers to spend a year at Langley, orienting the NASA personnel to the 737 airplane and its advanced equipment. At the end of the year, however, NASA extended its contract with Boeing to keep its office at Langley open for what turned out to be another four years. At one point, Boeing had 70 employees working on the TCV program at Langley. Although this kind of long-term, side-by-side working relationship with industry was unusual for NASA, the arrangement proved to have a tremendous payoff. In addition to the support the Boeing engineers provided for the TCV program in its early years, several of the young engineers who cut their teeth on the TCV program returned to Boeing to head up various departments working to design the 757/767 airplanes. The Boeing engineers not only knew about the new technology NASA was researching; they had worked with it themselves, watched its progress, and thoroughly understood the potential benefits it could offer. As a result, they were able to help convince others within the company that the technology was worth considering. In addition, the personal relationships the Langley researchers formed with the Boeing engineers improved communication channels and gave NASA easier access to key decision-makers within Boeing. Both of these factors played an important role in Boeing's decision to incorporate some of the technologies in its new aircraft designs.[32]

At the end of 1981, the TCV program was shifted from a division level to a branch level, and put under the Control Theory and Flight Management division of the Electronics directorate. By June 1982, the name had been shortened to the Flight Control Systems division and put under the management of Dr. Jeremiah F. Creedon. The TCV name was changed, as well, to the Advanced Transport Operating Systems (ATOPS) program. The new name was chosen to reflect the program's renewed emphasis on air transportation system issues, rather than individual airplane technologies.

In July 1985, Langley split the Electronics directorate into two separate organizations. The new directorate was called Flight Systems, and the ATOPS office was moved to a division level within that directorate. The creation of the Flight Systems directorate also helped the matrix operations of the ATOPS program somewhat, because it concentrated more of the people involved with the program in a single administrative structure. In an effort to simplify the matrix operations even further and to encourage greater involvement in the ATOPS program on the division level, the ATOPS office was moved back to a branch level under the Flight Management division in 1991, although it remained in the Flight Systems directorate.[33]

The financial, institutional, and industry support the program received over its 20 year lifespan also varied greatly. At times, such as during the U.S. MLS demonstrations in 1976-78, and in the recent wind shear detection flight tests, the program was well funded and had the open support of NASA headquarters, the FAA, and industry. Funding was usually a struggle, however, and on several different occasions, the program came very close to being cancelled altogether.

In the early 1980s, for example, as the program began to refocus on broader air transportation system problems rather than individual aircraft technology, the tensions over turf and areas of responsibility between NASA and the FAA flared up once again. To save a measure of funding for the program and make it less controversial, William D. Mace, head of the Electronics directorate at Langley, agreed to take on a program to simply gather data on MLS operations using the conventional, electromechanical instruments in the forward flight deck. That MLS Service Test and Evaluation Program (STEP) was the only flight test work conducted by the 737 from July 1982 to March 1983, but it kept the airplane flying.[34]

In the mid-1980s, the program was endangered once again. This time, the funds were being pulled by NASA headquarters from various aeronautics programs to permit greater emphasis on high speed research. The Langley Research Center management was very supportive of the ATOPS program, however, and fought successfully for its survival. Soon after that, the ATOPS program almost became a victim of the Gramm-Rudman amendment, when NASA found itself facing severe budget cuts across the board. The program elements were cut to the bare bones, but the airplane was kept flying.

Recently, the program has begun to enjoy a period of renewed support. The new NASA Administrator, Daniel S. Goldin, and President Bill Clinton are both strong advocates of government support for the aviation industry, and the ATOPS program has been given approval to embark on a huge new initiative called Terminal Area Productivity (TAP). Interestingly enough, the goals of TAP are almost identical to the goals of the original TCV program.[35]

The TCV/ATOPS program has already made a number of highly significant contributions to air transportation technology. Many of the challenges that NASA and the DOT identified in the early 1970s still exist,

Aerial view of Langley Research Center in 1976. Langley became the home of the Boeing 737 testbed aircraft when it first went into service with NASA in 1974.

however. In addition, advances in technology have created new opportunities for research that did not exist 20 years ago. The demands on the national airspace system have grown and changed, and the U.S. civil aviation industry now faces more foreign competition than it did in the early 1970s.

In retrospect, perhaps the most surprising aspect of the TCV/ATOPS/TAP program is not that the work is still continuing, or that the goals have remained the same, but that the original program plan only called for the research to last five or six years. The contributions made by the TCV/ATOPS program have certainly been important steps forward. But unlike the challenge of putting an American on the moon, the goal of improving air operations in crowded airport areas is not a finite, achievable target. It is a continuing, dynamic process that will always have room for new research and ideas.

Chapter 3

Revolution in the Cockpit: Computerization and Electronic Flight Displays

When the Terminal Configured Vehicle (TCV) program began in 1973, the air transport industry was facing some dramatic changes in aircraft design and operation. The development of the computer driven cathode ray tube (CRT) made a whole new kind of aircraft display possible, and the advancement of digital technology was preparing to revolutionize aircraft operations.

By the early 1970s, digital technology was beginning to be considered reliable enough to be incorporated into commercial transport aircraft. Wide body airliners had already begun to use digital equipment for numerous subsystems, and the next generation transport airplanes were expected to incorporate digital techniques in many more areas, including automatic flight control and guidance systems. The technology was attractive because it promised potentially significant savings in fuel consumption and cost of equipment ownership for the airlines. These savings were possible because digital equipment was lighter and generally required fewer components than analog systems. It was also proving to be highly reliable, easy to troubleshoot, and could often incorporate updates in capability through simple computer software changes. As a result, digital systems were predicted to reduce maintenance costs and equipment weight and volume as much as 25-40%. Digital technology also offered the opportunity to control many aircraft guidance and navigation functions by computer, allowing much more precise and fuel-efficient flight profiles.[1] This capability became increasingly important to the airlines as jet fuel prices soared throughout the 1970s.[2]

Left—The flight deck of a 757/767, incorporating systems that the NASA 737 aided in research and development.
Right— The control tower at Wallops Flight Facility. Many of the NASA 737 aircraft research activities have taken place at this installation.

Computer driven CRTs, like those used for the displays in the aft cockpit of NASA's 737 airplane, had not been incorporated into any commercial transport airplanes when the TCV program began, but they were not an entirely new concept. Electronic displays had been used extensively in military aircraft since 1960, and they were considered important components not only for the SST design, but for the new NASA Space Shuttle, as well. Electronic displays could help reduce a pilot's workload by integrating separate instrument readings and pieces of information into a comprehensive picture of the flight situation. They were also considered vastly superior to conventional analog instruments for monitoring automatic guidance and navigation

The forward flight deck of the NASA 737 near the time of arrival at the Langley Research Center in 1974. Note the profusion of gauges and dials and the yokes used to control the aircraft. The co-pilot's position, however, has received an upgrade of electronic flight displays for research into SST technology.

systems, which was an important consideration in the case of the space shuttle.[3]

Prior to the 1970s, air transport operations were not considered sufficiently demanding to require advanced equipment like electronic flight displays. The increasing complexity of transport aircraft, the advent of digital systems and the growing air traffic congestion around airports began to change that, however.

In order to solve the capacity and noise problems of busy commercial airports, future airline operations were expected to include more complex approaches to airports and more closely spaced air traffic operations. Instead of the 10 mile, straight final approaches that were typical with the Instrument Landing System (ILS) that had been in use since the 1940s, future air traffic operations were expected to rely on steep, curved approach paths with final legs as short as a mile. Airlines were also beginning to look at improving low visibility landing capabilities of their aircraft, including the use of automatic landing systems. In order to accomplish all these maneuvers safely, airline pilots were going to need a much more accurate picture of the airplane's position at all times. They also had to be able to control the airplane's progress precisely and accurately monitor any automatic systems so they could take over if necessary.[4]

This kind of precise knowledge about the aircraft situation would have been difficult, if not impossible, to gather from the instrumentation in most airline cockpits at the time.[5] The average transport aircraft in the mid-1970s had more than 100 cockpit instruments and controls,[6] and the primary flight instruments were already crowded with indicators, crossbars, and symbols. Airline pilots were having to monitor and manage more complex aircraft systems and operations, and there was a growing consensus among research and industry engineers that conventional instrumentation was simply no longer adequate for the job. What was needed were displays that could process the raw

Original configuration of the aft flight deck of the NASA 737 with monochrome flight displays. Note the "Brolly Handle" flight controls.

aircraft system and flight data into an integrated, easily understood picture of the aircraft situation, position and progress, not only in horizontal and vertical dimensions, but with regard to speed and time, as well.[7] This was one of the strengths of CRT displays, and it was the reason the NASA engineers at Langley wanted to include electronic display research in the TCV program.

Electronic Flight Display Research

The overall goal of the TCV experiments with electronic flight displays was to examine how well the displays worked and how they could be used in a transport cockpit. In addition to validating the benefits of the basic equipment, several different display concepts were tried and evaluated to see if they would improve pilots' situation awareness and their ability to compensate and correct for flight path errors.

Much of the development work was actually conducted in the Transport Systems Research Vehicle (TSRV) simulator at the Langley Research Center, but promising display concepts were then incorporated into the 737 airplane's aft flight deck (AFD) for operational testing. There were a number of research flights dedicated specifically to evaluation of display concepts, but because the electronic flight displays were an integral part of the AFD, researchers were able to gather information on the displays in the course of conducting other research, as well.[8] During two years of flight demonstrations of the U.S. microwave landing system between 1976-1978, for example, the TCV program engineers gained valuable information on the impact of electronic displays on pilots' ability to fly complex, curved approaches to airports.[9]

The initial displays in the 737 aft flight deck were 5" x 7" monochrome CRTs. Each pilot position had two displays: an electronic attitude

The TSRV 737 research simulator at Langley.

director indicator (EADI), and an electronic horizontal situation indicator (EHSI). The EADI contained the same basic information available on a conventional attitude indicator instrument; that is, pitch attitude, roll or bank angle, and raw vertical and horizontal (localizer and glideslope) tracking information for an ILS approach. Because of the flexibility offered by the electronic display format, however, the EADI also offered some additional information and options. In an effort to provide the pilot with an improved awareness of the airplane's situation, the screen also displayed the radar altitude of the airplane, symbols that showed if its airspeed was slower or faster than a selected target speed and if the plane was accelerating or decelerating, and an indication of the airplane's actual flight path.

On an electromechanical indicator, the airplane symbol was oriented around a "horizon" line that was drawn across the center of the instrument. If the airplane was level, the symbol would be directly on top of the horizon line. With the additional information being evaluated on the electronic display, however, researchers were concerned about whether they would be able to see individual elements clearly. In order to unclutter the middle of the display screen, the airplane symbol was biased up five degrees, so the symbol appeared five degrees above the horizon line when the airplane was actually level.

The EADI display also came with three pilot-selectable options. A perspective runway and an indication of the airplane's track angle to the runway could be included on the display. A second option was the addition of flight director symbols, which would show the pilot what pitch and bank angles to follow to stay on a predetermined flight path. The pilot could also select to superimpose all the display symbology on a real-time image received from a Lear Siegler Forward Looking, Low Light Level Television camera mounted in the nose of the 737. With this option, the pilot in the aft flight deck could actually "see" the airport and runway during an

The aft flight deck of the NASA 737 in 1987. An upgrade in 1986 replaced four original 5 x 7 monochrome displays with eight 8 x 8 color monitors.

approach. The TV camera also served as a method of verifying the accuracy of the runway symbology used in the display.

The EHSI displayed the same navigational reference information provided by an electromechanical horizontal situation indicator (HSI), but in a much more integrated, pictorial format. The EHSI was a map display that showed a diagram of the airplane's pre-planned flight path annotated with navigational waypoints, geographic reference points such as airports and navigational radio beacons, and the location of selected terrain and obstacle hazards along the route. The display also showed the airplane's current horizontal position on the flight path, represented by a triangle on the map, and dashed lines that indicated what the airplane's location would be in 30, 60, and 90 seconds if no further flight control inputs were made. The actual magnetic compass heading and track of the airplane were indicated at the top of the display. The map could be oriented in either a conventional "north-up mode," or a "track-up mode" which showed the direction the airplane was flying at the top of the screen, regardless of its actual compass heading. The display could also be set for numerous scales, ranging from one to 32 nautical miles/per inch. Additional options included the ability to display altitude or speed targets associated with waypoints, and even time reference information for experimenting with "4-D" navigation.

As with the EADI, the objective of the EHSI display was to provide pilots with integrated, intuitively understandable information that would give them a more accurate picture of the airplane's exact situation at all times. Armed with this information, pilots were expected to be able to monitor and control the airplane's progress much more effectively and precisely in both manual and automatic flight modes.

Manual flight from the aft flight deck was accomplished through a flight mode called "Control Wheel Steering" (CWS). Instead of a

The aft flight deck of the NASA 737 after a 1988 modification. The pilot position's "Brolly Handle" flight controls have been replaced with a McFadden sidestick controller while the co-pilot position has not been modified.

direct linkage from the control yokes (or "brolly handles") to the airplane's flight controls, CWS took the pilot's control inputs and processed them through the airplane's digital flight computer, which, in turn, operated the flight controls. This allowed the pilot to command changes in the airplane's pitch or bank angle while delegating the actual stabilization functions to the computer. One of the concerns often voiced by pilots and human engineering specialists about automated cockpit functions was that they would eliminate the pilot from the control loop entirely, leading to an undesirably low level of activity for the pilot and even a decay in his flying skills.[10] The idea behind CWS was to reduce the pilot's workload without automating the flight control function entirely, so that the pilot would remain "in the loop."

Even in 1974, control wheel steering was not an entirely new concept. The McDonnell Douglas Aircraft Company's DC-10 wide-body airliner had a CWS mode that allowed the pilot to control the autopilot through inputs to the control yoke. The TCV set-up, however, had a couple of slightly different twists. The digital flight control computer that drove the autopilot in NASA's 737 allowed the research engineers to experiment with different control laws and algorithms. So in addition to a more standard "attitude" control wheel steering mode, the 737 could be operated through a second control law concept, called "velocity vector control wheel steering."

Velocity vector control meant that the pilot's inputs commanded changes in the airplane's flight path instead of its attitude and bank angle. The rationale was that the end result a pilot was trying to achieve through attitude and bank angle changes was, in fact, control of the airplane's flight path. With velocity vector CWS, the pilot's control inputs told the computer what flight path he wanted the airplane to follow, and the computer would make whatever attitude and bank changes were necessary to achieve that flight path. With a combination of the CRT

The aft flight deck of the NASA 737 with both sets of "Brolly Handles" replaced with McFadden sidestick controllers and color displays.

displays and velocity vector CWS, the NASA researchers thought it might be possible for pilots to manually fly complex approach maneuvers with a high degree of accuracy and success, even in low visibility conditions.[11]

The NASA research pilots encountered some problems with the velocity vector CWS at first because of the way the control law was implemented and the EADI displays were configured. The displays initially showed the actual flight path of the airplane. When a pilot commanded a change in the flight path, there would be a slight delay as the computer and the airplane responded to the command. During that lag time, however, the flight path on the display would not have moved. So the pilot had to guess at how much of a control input would result in the correct amount of flight path change, and the frequent result was a series of oscillations as the pilot hunted for the correct flight path angle. This made precision control very difficult, so the displays were changed. Initially, the displays were modified to show both the commanded flight path angle and the actual flight path angle. Eventually, the actual flight path angle symbology was removed altogether, because when the commanded flight path symbols reached the position the pilot wanted, he could simply neutralize the controls and the computer would hold that path.

The initial EADI displays were also oriented around the nose of the airplane, regardless of which CWS mode the pilot was using. In cruise flight or in a no-wind situation, this was not a problem, but on approaches with a crosswind, the nose of the airplane would be pointed to one side to compensate for the wind. So although the ground track of the airplane might be straight toward the runway, the display would show the runway off to one side. Pilots found this somewhat disorienting, so the displays were modified. In the attitude CWS mode, the displays were still oriented around the attitude indicator symbol and the nose of the airplane, but in velocity vector CWS, the displays were oriented around the flight path of the airplane.[12]

One of the more significant display concepts the Langley researchers tested in the TSRV simulator and on the 737 was the addition of the perspective runway, extended center line and track angle to the EADI. In essence, this gave the pilot a visual, 3-D picture of the approach on a single display, instead of just the raw localizer and glideslope data. Research experiments tested pilots' performance using the velocity vector CWS, with and without the added symbology on both straight-in approaches and 130 degree curved path approaches with final legs as short as one mile. The results showed that with velocity vector CWS and the pictorial horizontal situation information provided by the runway and track symbols, pilots were able to manually fly the airplane on both types of approaches with the same precision achieved by pilots following conventional flight director commands for a Category II low visibility landing.[13]

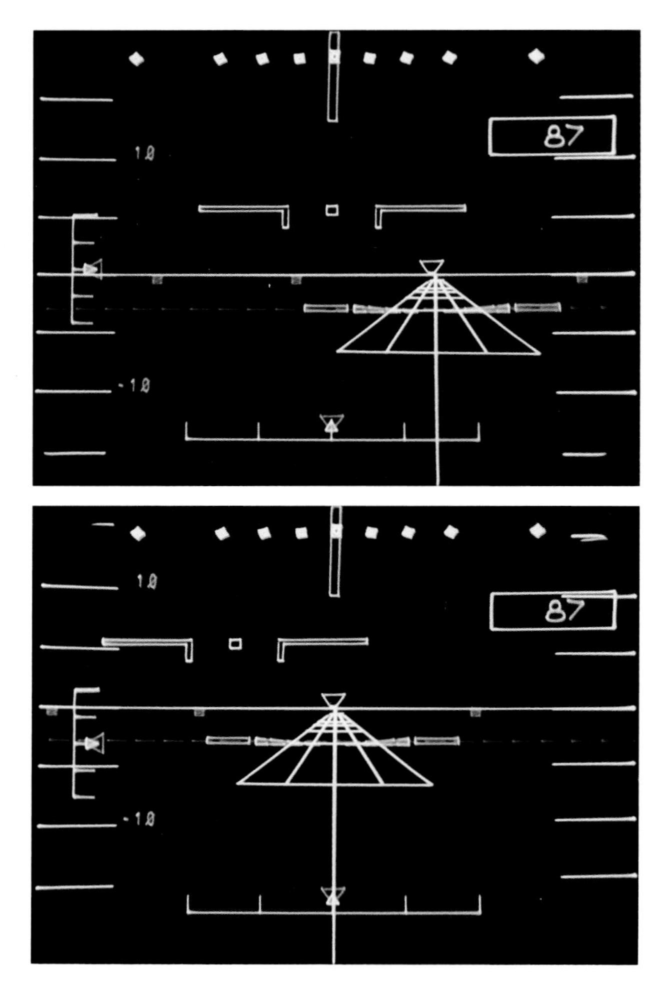

The Electronic Attitude Director Indicator (EADI) on the NASA 737 research aircraft. Top—Attitude Centered EADI format orientation in a crosswind approach. Bottom—Flightpath centered EADI format orientation.

The pilots' mental workload was lower and their performance was significantly better with the added pictorial information than with the basic EADI display. Research pilots commented that the integrated format gave them a better understanding of the airplane's position and trajectory to the runway, which allowed them to more quickly recognize and recover from large course deviations with confidence.[14]

Unlike many research projects conducted by NASA, the electronic flight display work was not a formal research experiment with formal beginning and ending dates. The research began when the airplane arrived, and experiments on better display formats continued throughout the aircraft's 20 year history at the Langley Research Center. By 1978, however, the researchers had proven the viability of the basic concept and had demonstrated some significant potential benefits that integrated electronic flight displays, control wheel steering, and velocity vector control could offer.[15] Consequently, researchers at the Langley Research Center were optimistic that some of the technology would be integrated into the next generation of commercial transport airplanes.[16]

Of course, the TCV program was not the only effort to develop new technology for transport aircraft. Even before 1978, the commercial aircraft industry had begun to incorporate some advanced equipment into transport designs. The Lockheed-California Company, for example, certified an operational flight management system (FMS) for some of its L-1011 wide-body airliners in 1977. The system offered operators approximately 3 percent fuel savings by providing automated 3-D navigation and power management for fuel efficient flight profiles. That kind of improvement might not seem all that significant, but for a fleet with 10 L-1011-1 aircraft a 3 percent savings translated to 1,750,000 gallons of fuel a year.[17]

An order of L-1011-200s sold to Saudi Arabian Airlines even incorporated an 8" square monochrome map display with the flight management system. Unfortunately, the display proved unreliable, the company that manufactured it was unable to support it, and the displays were eventually removed from the L-1011s. Flight management systems, on the other hand, were offered on all L-1011-500 series airplanes.[18]

Flight management computers (FMC) had a couple of distinct advantages over electronic flight displays when it came to gaining acceptance among airframe manufacturers, however. First, they were seen as having a lower technical risk than the CRT technology. Flight management computers were also perceived as having a more compelling benefit, since they offered operators concrete fuel savings in an era of rising fuel prices. Since the financial advantages of electronic flight displays were not as concrete or obvious, the work the TSRV did in developing CRT display formats and demonstrating their benefits in a transport aircraft environment played an important role in gaining acceptance for the "glass cockpit" concept.

The Transfer of CRT Technology

As the NASA researchers working with the TCV program developed new display concepts and discovered some of the benefits CRT displays offered, they disseminated that information in several ways. They wrote and presented technical papers and documents, and Langley even held a small symposium in 1975 to update industry and airline representatives on the progress the TCV program was making.[19]

The most powerful method of technology transfer employed by the TCV program, however, was its cooperative working relationship with the team of engineers and technicians from the Boeing Commercial Airplane Company. The senior managers at Boeing who selected the engineers to work with the TCV program at Langley knew that the technology in NASA's 737 was going to direct the next generation of equipment developed for transport airplanes. So they intentionally sent some of their brightest young engineers to work at Langley, where they could gain experience and knowledge about the systems, in the hope of incorporating some of that technology into the design of the company's next airplane.[20]

In the mid-1970s, Boeing began designing that new airplane, which would actually evolve into two aircraft: the wide-body 767 and the smaller 757. Several of the engineers who had worked on the TCV program at Langley were brought back and put in charge of groups designing different aspects of the 767 airplane. Delmar Fadden, for example, had been the head of the Boeing group at Langley from mid-1975 until January 1977. When he returned to Seattle in 1977, he was put in charge of the flight deck technology staff for the 767, which was responsible for the human performance aspects of the new airplane's flight deck equipment. In other words, Fadden and his group looked at what information the pilots needed to have and how it should be presented to them. Since much of the TCV display work had been concerned with that same issue, his experience at Langley was extremely valuable.

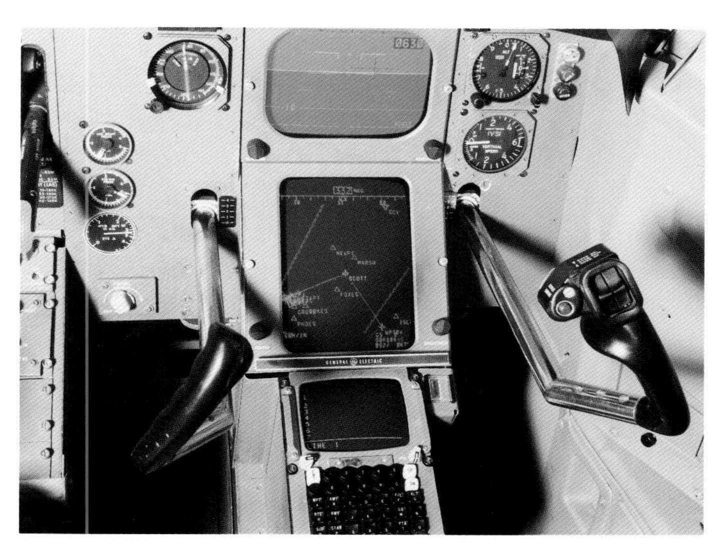

Close-up of co-pilot's position on the aft flight deck of the NASA 737 research aircraft showing "Brolly Handle" flight controls and color CRT displays.

In addition to gaining experience with new technologies and a first-hand understanding of what they could do for pilots, the Boeing employees who worked with the TCV program found their experience at Langley gave more credibility to the work they did at Boeing after they returned. In fact, John Warner, the head of the Boeing group at Langley for the first year of the program and now vice president of Boeing Computer Services, termed the joint Boeing/NASA work on the TCV program "the best example of good technology transfer since the days of NACA."[21] Yet for all that, the Boeing 767 and 757 came very close to being produced with conventional electromechanical flight instruments in the cockpit.

By 1978, the dynamics of airline management and transport aircraft sales was very different from what it had been when World War I ace Eddie Rickenbacker ran Eastern Airlines or even when Juan Trippe and Pan American Airlines ordered the first Boeing 747 jumbo jet in 1966. In the early days of air travel, the presidents of the airlines were often pilots. That began to change in the years following World War II, but the airlines still had large engineering departments which put a high value on technological performance and were very influential in the airlines' aircraft purchase decisions. In 1978, however, the airline industry was deregulated. Suddenly, the air transport industry was a highly competitive business. In a very short period of time, cost became practically the sole driving factor behind the airlines' purchase decisions. New technology now had to earn its way onto airplanes more than it ever had to before.[22]

The flight management computers promised concrete fuel savings for airline operators at a time when fuel conservation was becoming a high priority. But there was no such immediate problem driving the use of electronic flight displays. CRT displays offered advantages like improved situation awareness and more efficient air traffic control system operations, which were much harder qualities to quantify in terms of cost savings. In addition, the acquisition and maintenance costs of CRT displays were still uncertain, and any new equipment raised the possibility of having to train pilots to use it, which would be an additional cost to the airlines.[23]

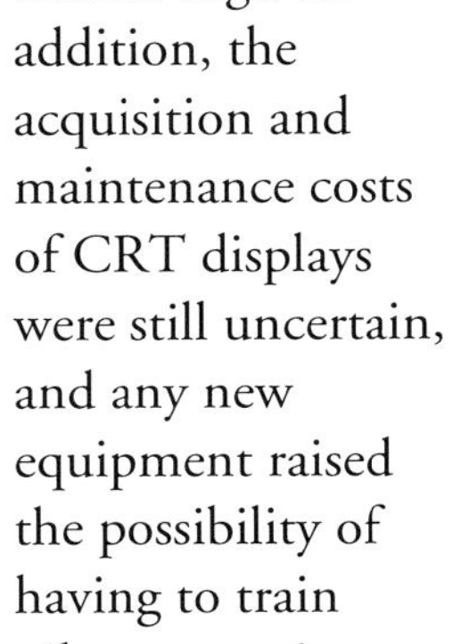

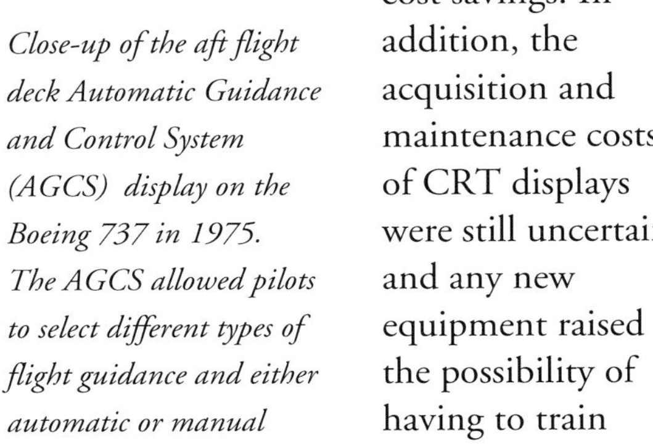

Close-up of the aft flight deck Automatic Guidance and Control System (AGCS) display on the Boeing 737 in 1975. The AGCS allowed pilots to select different types of flight guidance and either automatic or manual flight modes.

CRT technology also was not yet perfected. NASA's 737, for example, had only small, monochrome displays. Color displays were in the process of being developed by several companies, but most had limited capability and were difficult to see in bright sunlight. Yet there was concern that the black and white displays would not be able to differentiate the numerous pieces and types of information the screens would have to display clearly enough.[24]

Initially, Boeing had planned to put electronic flight displays in the 767. But as development progressed, a lack of strong customer demand and the lingering uncertainties about the equipment cost led the company to opt for electromechanical displays, instead. The engineers at Boeing and Langley who had worked on the TCV program were extremely disappointed. They knew what electronic displays could do and how they could benefit pilots, but the inherent capability of the technology was simply not sufficient to win it a place in a commercial airline design.[25]

Then in September 1978, very late in the development cycle of the 767, Boeing reversed its decision and announced that the 767 and 757 would both use electronic flight displays. The simple reason for the change in position was that Boeing had discovered a customer demand for the technology.[26] There were several events and factors that helped to create that demand, however.

In early 1978, Boeing had begun a cost of ownership study and analysis comparing conventional electromechanical instruments against both monochrome and color CRT displays. Cost comparisons were by no means precise, because the result depended heavily on what assumptions were made about how the displays might be used in the future. However, a number of vendors supplied Boeing with figures and, in mid-1978, Boeing presented the study conclusions to its airline customers. The results showed that monochrome CRT displays might actually be more cost-effective than electromechanical instruments, although the cost of ownership for color displays would probably still be slightly higher.[27]

At the same time, NASA's 737 airplane was just finishing a demonstration program of the U. S. microwave landing system. During the demonstrations, a number of airline and industry representatives had been given the opportunity to fly on the airplane and observe the displays in action during curved path, automatic and manual approaches in a real-life air traffic control situation. Between the MLS demonstrations and the other display research flights, the NASA researchers gave a significant number of airline pilots and operators the opportunity to become familiar with the technology and the potential benefits it might have for airline operations. "(The NASA researchers) were very open, answered any questions and provided as much information as they had," Boeing engineer Delmar Fadden said. "I think that was as important as anything we might have done, and maybe more important in the broad scheme of things. Without that happening, I'm not sure that the airline people would have decided to (buy the displays)."[28]

The more favorable economics and the decision-makers' ability to actually see the technology in use and gain an understanding of some of its future potential, tipped the scales. Boeing's customers told the airframe manufacturer that they wanted CRT displays. Since they still had concerns about symbol differentiation on monochrome screens, however, the airlines told Boeing managers they wanted color displays, even if the cost of ownership was a little higher. The Boeing mangers and engineers agreed, but since they were still concerned about the state of color CRT technology, a two-pronged development effort was initiated, with color displays as the primary goal, and monochrome displays as a back-up.[29]

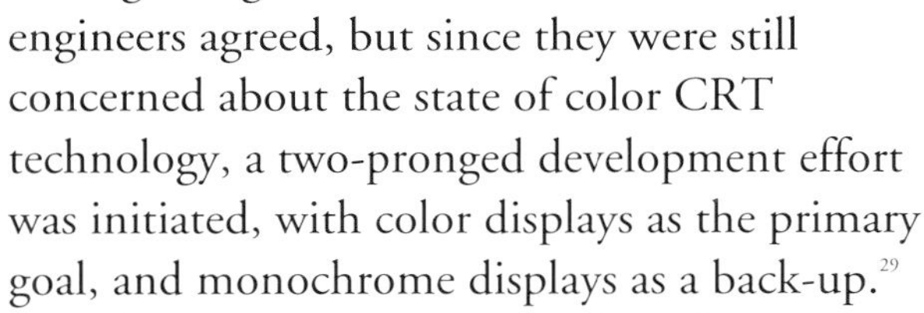

Close-up of EADI CRT flight display showing somewhat steep descent (40 degree flap) to runway. Runway centerline is extended to horizon, the "pole" in the center is to give the pilot something to steer toward. The diamond symbol indicates where on the runway the airplane will touch down if no changes are made.

The Boeing managers need not have worried. While the decision about CRT displays was being debated in Seattle, Rockwell International's Collins Air Transport Division had been quietly working on a type of display the industry had concluded could not be built at the time: a shadow mask, multi-color CRT display, bright enough to be seen in any lighting condition. While this technology was being used for color television sets, none of the avionics companies had been able to develop a "ruggedized" version that could withstand the vibrations and forces to which aircraft equipment was constantly subjected. Collins, however, contacted the Toshiba and Mitsubishi television manufacturers in Japan, who agreed to develop and build a custom, ruggedized version of their color CRT displays specifically for airplane use. In December 1978, Collins unveiled their displays, and the discussion of what kind of CRTs would go into the 767/757 and who would build them was over.[30]

Color electronic flight displays consequently became standard equipment on Boeing's newest airplanes. Both the 767 and the smaller 757 had very similar flight decks, in order to reduce pilot training time and costs for airlines. Both airplanes were covered by a single FAA type rating, which meant that pilots trained in the 757 would also be certified to fly the 767, and vice versa.

Not all of the capabilities of the displays in NASA's 737 were incorporated, however. The CRTs in the 767 and 757 consisted of two 4.7" x 4.2" color EADI monitors, or "Primary Flight Displays," as they became known; two 4.7" x 5.7" color EHSI, or "navigation" displays, (one each for the pilot and copilot positions); and two more 5.7" x 4.7" displays for engine instrumentation in the middle of the instrument panel. The flight critical information displayed on both displays was backed up by electromechanical instruments in the panel.

The EHSI display was actually very similar to the one in NASA's 737. The EADI, on the other hand, was essentially a replication of an electromechanical attitude indicator. It did have a few extra pieces of information displayed on it, such as the airplane's ground speed, radar altitude and decision height altitude for instrument approaches, and indications of what flight modes (such as speed hold, autothrottle, autopilot, lateral navigation or vertical navigation) were activated. The velocity vector,

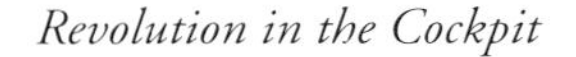

perspective runway and track information tested so successfully in the TCV program were not included, however.

The reason the airlines chose a simple replication of the existing attitude indicator was to help make the step to electronic flight displays an evolutionary change, rather than a revolutionary one. Theorists and futurists often discuss the psychological resistance to change, especially revolutionary change, in organizations.[31] In the case of airline operators and CRT displays, however, the resistance was due more to economic and safety concerns than psychological factors. If an airline wanted to put a revolutionary new technology in a flight deck, it might have to go through a more complex certification process with the FAA, and all its pilots would have to be retrained to use the new equipment. In addition, if the cockpits of different airplanes flown by the same airline were radically different, it would be difficult for pilots to transition back and forth between airplane models, and the chances of pilot error could increase.

Against all of these potential negative consequences of making radical changes in the flight deck, there was not yet a sufficiently compelling need for a velocity vector flight control law or display. The pilot's task had not changed significantly, as it would have with an SST design, and pilots were operating airliners in a perfectly satisfactory manner. NASA and Boeing had developed a solution that lacked a big enough problem to require its use. Nonetheless, several senior Boeing managers remained confident that velocity vector controls and displays would eventually be incorporated into a commercial airplane design.[32]

In the case of the EHSI, the map display was so intuitively easy to understand that pilots required minimal transition training, which is why the airlines elected to use the new display format. The CRT map display still retained the capability of being configured as a conventional horizontal situation indicator, however.

By introducing electronic displays that had the flexibility to be updated later, but could be configured initially with a simple replication of conventional airplane instruments, the airlines hoped to break down what could have been a revolutionary change into a series of smaller, evolutionary steps.[33] But CRT displays were not an isolated advancement. They were part of a new approach to flight deck design that incorporated digital, automated equipment like flight management computers and engine indication and crew advisory systems (EICAS) and forced a re-evaluation the pilot's basic role in the cockpit. By themselves, the electronic flight displays would not have been that dramatic a leap. All of these changes together, however, caused a revolution in the design and operation of commercial airliners.

The Cockpit Revolution

The advent of computerization and automation in the cockpits of commercial airliners allowed the airlines to reap a wide variety of benefits. In addition to fuel-efficient flight profiles, more reliable equipment and greater flexibility for upgrades, airlines were able to certify even large, wide-body airplanes like the

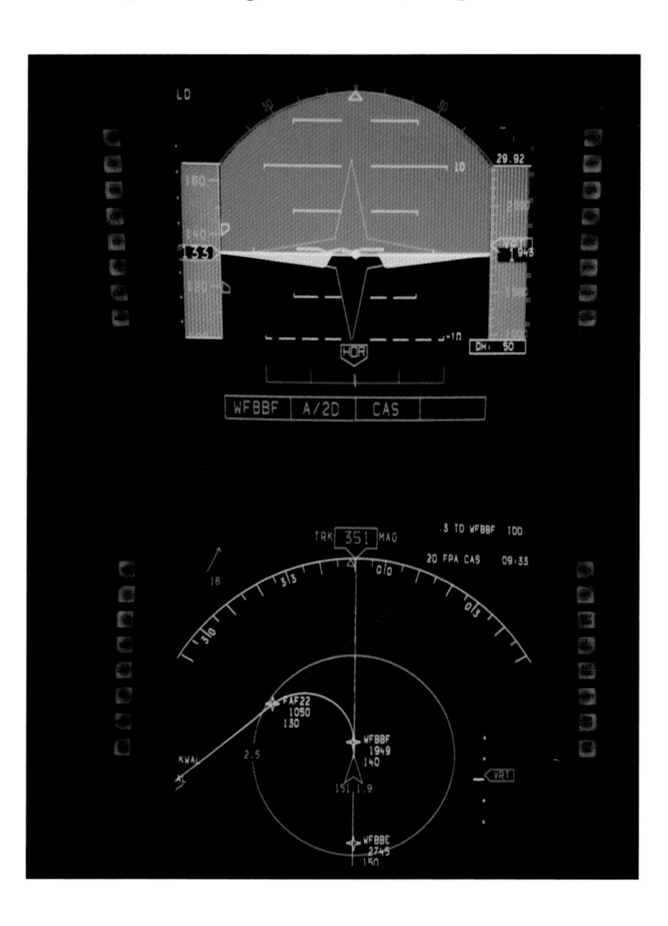

Close-up of aft flight deck CRT electronic display showing flight path for approach to runway and aircraft attitude. The triangle symbol on the map display (bottom) shows the location of the airplane. The dotted line star on the primary flight display (top) indicates the plane is passing a waypoint or approach fix.

767 and the 747-400 for operation with only two pilots. The switch initially encountered fierce opposition from airline pilots' unions, but it had great appeal to airline operators because of the cost savings involved. The crew reduction was approved by the FAA, however, after a presidential task force formed to study the subject[34] concluded it posed no safety threat, primarily because the EICAS technology automated many of the functions previously delegated to the third crew member.[35]

The new cockpit technology also caused some unanticipated problems, however, illustrating the fact that technical advances are not always a simple forward movement. Technology can sometimes cause new problems even as it solves old ones.

Researchers in NASA, academia and industry all recognized that the new cockpit technology and automation could cause some problems, especially with regard to the role of the pilot and pilot-machine interfaces. For the first time, human factors became an integral part of design analysis, and researchers looked closely at optimum levels of pilot workload and ways to keep pilots involved in the computerized systems. Delmar Fadden's flight deck technology group at Boeing, for example, was formed specifically to look at the human performance aspects of the 767's new cockpit technology.[36]

The researchers' main concern was that the automated systems would cause the pilots' workload to become too low, and the pilots would be too far out of the control loop. After the 757 and 767 had been in operation for a few years, however, pilots began complaining that far from being too low, their work load was actually too high. The main culprit was the control and display unit (CDU), which was the pilot interface with the flight management system.[37]

The Sperry Flight Systems CDU consisted of a complete alphanumeric keyboard with 15 additional "mode" keys and a series of "select" keys on either side of a small CRT screen that displayed navigation and performance data, all on 5.75" x 9" unit.[38] As early as 1977, researchers acknowledged that the CDU was designed for "navigation, not for man-machine communication,"[39] but it was the best technology available at the time. The unit was difficult to operate because every command or piece of information had to be typed into the computer with a specific sequence and coding that was difficult to remember.[40] When pilots tried to input new commands during phases of flight that were particularly demanding, such as during approaches or immediately following departure, they were finding themselves overloaded. Sometimes both pilots would get engrossed in trying to operate the computer, leaving nobody looking outside the windows for possible conflicting traffic.

Close-up of the Sperry Flight Systems Control and Display Unit (CDU). These were the least user friendly elements in the new computerized "glass cockpit," and caused a number of unanticipated problems when the equipment was put into commercial use.

The problems caught the engineers who had researched the technology and designed the systems by surprise. NASA and Boeing engineers concluded they had "underestimated how aggressive pilot crews would be in trying to use the flight management equipment." Gradually, airline training programs began to teach pilots not to use the flight management computer at altitudes under 10,000 feet, but to hand-fly the airplane instead. Second and third generation CDUs are also somewhat simplified, but the problem still exists to some extent today.[41]

The experience with the flight management technology taught the researchers at Langley an important lesson about technology application. Computer technology was a new, emerging technology when the TCV program started its experiments with flight management systems and electronic flight displays. Nobody could have guessed how quickly the technology and its use would spread and progress. Now, however, researchers caution that "if you put technology in (a cockpit), you'd better know all the ramifications, because pilots will want to use it."[42]

In an effort to improve the manner in which new technology was implemented and to better anticipate the ways pilots would try to use it, NASA developed the Aviation Safety/ Automation Program in 1989. The program, which was a joint effort between the Langley Research Center and the NASA Ames Research Center in California, set out to take a second look at the impact of the automation that is coming into cockpits. Then, using advanced concepts flight simulators (ACFS) at Ames and Langley, researchers planned to explore concepts that would lead to more "human centered automation," in which the automation would be designed to assist pilots in their jobs instead of trying to do their jobs for them.

In 1992, NASA also joined with the FAA and the Air Transport Association's Human Factors Task Force to develop a National Plan for Aviation Human Factors. The task force objectives included correcting some of the current deficiencies in automated cockpits, furthering human-centered automation, and encouraging development of advanced displays and controls that are more "user-friendly."[43]

Even with the unanticipated problems that arose with automated cockpits, however, pilots' overall opinions about the technology were favorable, and the enthusiasm for electronic flight displays was very high. Pilots liked the improved situation awareness the displays provided, and according to the National Transportation Safety Board, as of 1993 there had not been a single accident involving an electronic map display-equipped airliner where the pilot became confused as to his location and flew into terrain. In two surveys of 757 pilots conducted by the Ames Research Center in 1986 and 1987, 85-90 percent of the pilots said they considered the "glass cockpit" displays and instruments a "big step forward."[44] Furthermore, all new transport aircraft designs since the Boeing 767 and some new models of existing airplanes, including the 300, 400 and 500 series of the Boeing 737, incorporated electronic flight displays.

The fact that not all the elements of the electronic flight displays tested in NASA's 737 were used in commercial transport airplanes illustrates the complexity of the technology transfer process. Nevertheless, the aircraft and the TCV program played a very important role in allowing CRT displays to be incorporated into aircraft designs as early as they were. In a June 6 1979 letter to John Reeder, who was then the chief of the TCV program at Langley, the Boeing Commercial Airplane Company's vice president of engineering, Mr. H. W. Withington, described the contributions the Langley research program had made to the development and acceptance of electronic

flight displays.

Withington noted that the instruments "were expected to contribute to both the safety and efficiency of flight through a better comprehension by the pilot of the airplane's situation relative to its environment," and he credited the TCV program with the development of several specific aspects of the displays, including the EHSI format and symbology. But the program's most significant contribution, he concluded, was that it "provided the vehicle to bring electronic vertical and horizontal cockpit display instruments from the laboratory to industry acceptance" by demonstrating the technologies to the point "where both the aircraft manufacturer and the user had sufficient confidence to incorporate them into the new airplanes."[45]

In other words, had the TCV program research been conducted in simulators and disseminated only through technical reports and conferences, the Boeing 767 and 757 might very well have been built with conventional flight instruments. Certainly, there were other factors involved. If the displays had proved cost-prohibitive to include, for example, the discussion would have gone no further. As it was, the technology still had to gain the confidence and acceptance of Boeing and the airline industry against concerns over any new cockpit technology and the lack of a clear, quantifiable cost advantage of using the displays. The TCV program's close working relationship with rising young engineers at Boeing, and the fact that the program had an actual transport airplane with which to test and demonstrate the technology, allowed electronic flight displays to gain that acceptance.

Time exposure of the NASA 737 on the ramp at Orlando, Florida.

NASA
515
Langley Research Center
NASA

Chapter 4

A Technology Eclipsed: The Microwave Landing System and the Dawn of GPS

Prior to World War II, aircraft approaches and landings in poor weather conditions were often high-risk endeavors. Early civilian air navigation systems provided only basic lateral position information, and 1930s airline pilots flying in low visibility conditions had to take a heading off a radio navigation station and then use speed, time and distance calculations to figure out when they should see the runway at their destination. Safe descents were dependent on the accuracy of their calculations and all final approaches had to be visual, because there was no instrument guidance system that could direct a pilot on a safe, precise descent profile clear of terrain.

Left—The NASA 737 Advanced Transport Operating Systems (ATOPS) Program aircraft landing at Wallops Island in 1992. Right—The NASA 737 research aircraft on the Wallops runway in 1987 with the Microwave Landing System equipment in the foreground.

The successful demonstration of a full Instrument Landing System (ILS) in 1937,[1] therefore, marked a significant advancement for air transport operations. For the first time, pilots could tune in a radio signal emanating from an airport runway and receive precise lateral and vertical guidance on an approach and landing. The ILS broadcast a straight, narrow VHF/UHF signal beam that started at the runway and rose at a steady, three degree angle. By centering the vertical and horizontal needles on his ILS instrument, a pilot could fly down the ILS "beam" to the airport, descending on a gentle, three degree glide slope that was lined up perfectly with the runway centerline and clear of any terrain or obstacles. The system not only improved the safety of airline operations, but also increased the reliability of air carrier service, since it allowed airliners to operate in a wider range of weather conditions.

U.S. airlines began using ILS approaches on a regular basis after World War II, and by 1949, the ILS had become the world standard for landing guidance systems. By the late 1960s, however, air traffic congestion and the need for more noise-sensitive approach paths to airports had begun to demand a more capable and flexible landing system. One problem with ILS was that the VHF/UHF frequencies in which it operated had a limited number of channels. As air transportation became more popular, planners began to see a time when certain areas of the country would have more airports requesting instrument landing systems than the ILS frequency range could accommodate. The

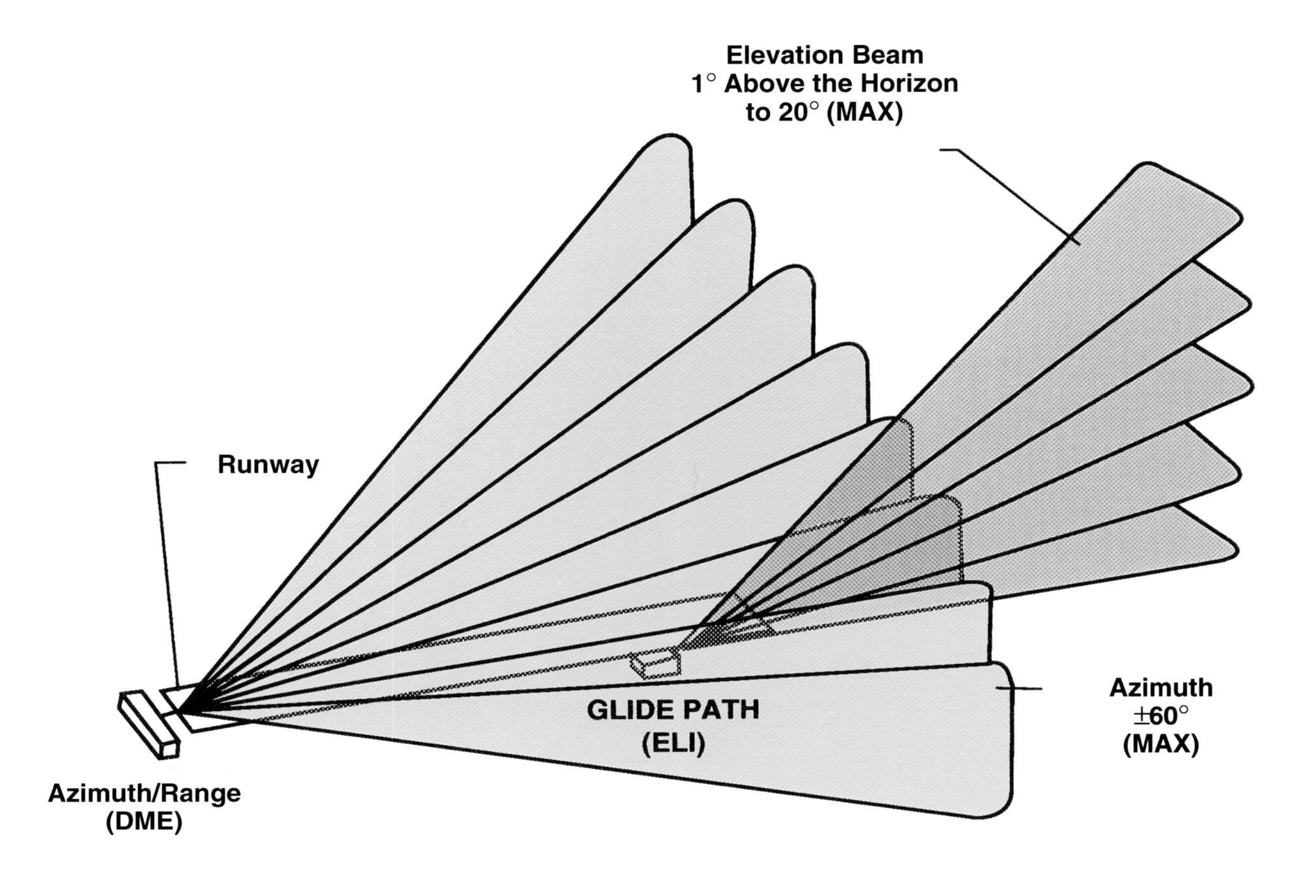

The Microwave Landing System approach vectors. The expanded coverage of the MLS tracked signals within an area 120° wide and 20° high from the runway centerline.

relatively low frequency range of the ILS was also susceptible to signal reflection, or "multipath," errors.

Another limitation of the ILS was that it allowed only one approach path to a runway. Airplanes would lock on to the ILS horizontal "localizer" and vertical "glide slope" up to 10 miles away from the runway, and fly a straight course in for a landing. Two of the top priorities identified by the Department of Transportation/ NASA "CARD" study in 1971, however, were to increase the air traffic capacity of airports and to develop approaches that avoided noise-sensitive areas.[2] The curved, segmented approach paths suggested by Jack Reeder and others in NASA and the FAA[3] could accomplish both of those goals, but they would require a more flexible landing guidance system than the ILS.

In 1968, Special Committee 117 of the Radio Technical Commission for Aeronautics (RTCA)[4], representing both military and civil U.S. airspace users, was formed to develop the requirements and specifications for a new aircraft approach and landing system.[5] Four years later, the International Civil Aviation Organization (ICAO), an agency of the United Nations that oversees international civil aviation procedures and standards, began the official selection process for a new precision approach and landing guidance system standard. Member states were invited to submit system proposals, and ICAO's All Weather Operations Panel (AWOP) was given the responsibility of evaluating the proposals and making a recommendation to the organization as to which system should be adopted as the standard.[6]

By this time, the U.S. Federal Aviation Administration, working with the RTCA special committee, had already evaluated several types of technologies and had decided that a microwave frequency-based, scanning beam format would make the best landing system. The higher frequency microwave band would alleviate the frequency allocation and some of the multipath signal problems, and a scanning beam technique would provide broader signal coverage, allowing more flexible airplane approach paths. There were two ways of designing a scanning beam microwave system, however. One, called a "Doppler Scan" technique, used modulations in frequency to tell a pilot where he was in relation to the runway. The other, called the "Time Reference Scanning Beam" (TRSB) technique, used time-referenced sweeps of a single frequency to pinpoint an airplane's location.

In 1973, the FAA awarded feasibility and demonstration contracts for two separate industry teams to evaluate each of the two systems. ITT/Honeywell and Hazeltine/Sperry each developed a Doppler system, while Texas Instruments and Bendix Corporation each developed a TRSB system. The systems were evaluated by a 17-man steering committee of the Microwave Landing System (MLS) central assessment group, made up of representatives from the Federal Aviation Administration, the Department of Transportation, the National Aeronautics and Space Administration and the Department of Defense. In early 1975, the TRSB microwave landing system was chosen as the U.S. candidate for international standardization.[7]

The performance and the cost of the TRSB and the Doppler designs were both actually very close, but the TRSB appeared to have slightly better performance at sites that were particularly susceptible to signal reflections, such as airports surrounded by high buildings or terrain. In the TRSB system, an airplane's horizontal and vertical location was determined by two separate microwave beams with very precisely timed scanning patterns. The first beam swept back and forth across the runway centerline (plus or minus 60 degrees on each side) at a rate of 13.5 times per second. The second swept up and down from the runway elevation to a position 20 degrees above that at a rate of 40 times per second. The airplane's horizontal and vertical position could be determined by measuring the time difference in between each signal transmission received by the aircraft. By integrating that data with distance information from a conventional distance measuring equipment (DME) transmitter on the airport, a receiver on board an airplane could accurately pinpoint the plane's location in relation to the runway. A third beam, scanning up and down over a 7.5 degree arc from the runway elevation 40 times a minute, could also be installed to provide flare guidance for automatic landings. The net result was a system that could provide precise manual or automatic landing guidance to an airplane anywhere in a wedge-shaped area that stretched 120 degrees wide and 20 degrees high from the airport runway.[8]

The TRSB system was not the only one submitted to ICAO, however. Australia also proposed a TRSB microwave system, but the United Kingdom was strongly advocating a Doppler Scan MLS. The Federal Republic of Germany proposed a dual DME system, and France submitted a plan based on a Ground Controlled Approach (GCA) technique. The U.S. representatives to ICAO had known that there would be other proposals. But after a couple of meetings, the FAA realized that the British were going to put up a very tough fight against the U.S. choice. To win acceptance for the U.S. candidate system, the FAA MLS program managers decided they needed to "look at all the assets available to us and see if we could exploit those in ways we hadn't exploited them before."[9] One of the assets they found was NASA's Boeing 737 Transport Systems Research Vehicle (TSRV).

Although the creators of the TCV program had not anticipated using the 737 for official demonstrations of the microwave landing system, they had hoped to test curved path and variable glide path angles with two demonstration MLS systems the FAA had installed at NASA's Wallops Flight Facility,[10] across the Chesapeake Bay from the Langley Research Center. In fact, several people in Langley's Flight Instrument Division (FID) had already begun to gather data from the microwave systems at Wallops Island before 1975. The researchers wanted to model the MLS signals in order to experiment with ways to process the information for the advanced aircraft displays and guidance systems they were developing. Langley did not have access to any actual airborne MLS receivers, so the data collection was conducted with a MLS receiver Langley engineers built out of off-the-shelf high frequency receivers and high speed recorders and installed in a DeHavilland DH6-C Twin Otter airplane. The makeshift receiver consisted of "a huge rack, three bays wide, full of equipment," but it allowed the Langley researchers to get the MLS signal data they wanted.[11]

Several people in the antenna and microwave research branch at Langley had also begun experimenting with MLS aircraft antennas as early as 1974, evaluating designs and placement locations on an airplane that would create the broadest coverage and the least signal interference.[12] As a result, researchers at Langley already had some basic groundwork accomplished by the time the FAA asked Langley to support its efforts to sell the TRSB system to ICAO. This was fortunate, because the job the FAA wanted the 737 to perform was not an easy one.

The FAA's navigation division had originally asked the NASA researchers to provide 10 to 25 hours of MLS data collection flights on straight approach paths in the summer of 1975.[13] When the FAA MLS division realized how tough a fight the ICAO selection process would be, however, its managers decided that what they really needed was not just data, but a way to actually demonstrate some of the more impressive capabilities of the TRSB system. In the spring of 1975, the FAA asked the TCV program office if the TSRV 737 could perform a demonstration of curved path approaches and automatic landings to the ICAO All Weather Operations Panel. There was initially some concern within the TCV program office that the workload involved in preparing for a demonstration that complex would cause too many other research projects to suffer, but in July 1975, NASA agreed to participate in the demonstration.[14]

The task ahead of the Langley engineers was considerable. The demonstration was scheduled for May 1976, only 10 months away, and the 737 was not yet equipped to process MLS information or perform curved path approaches. In addition, the airplane was designed to use inertial navigation system (INS) data for

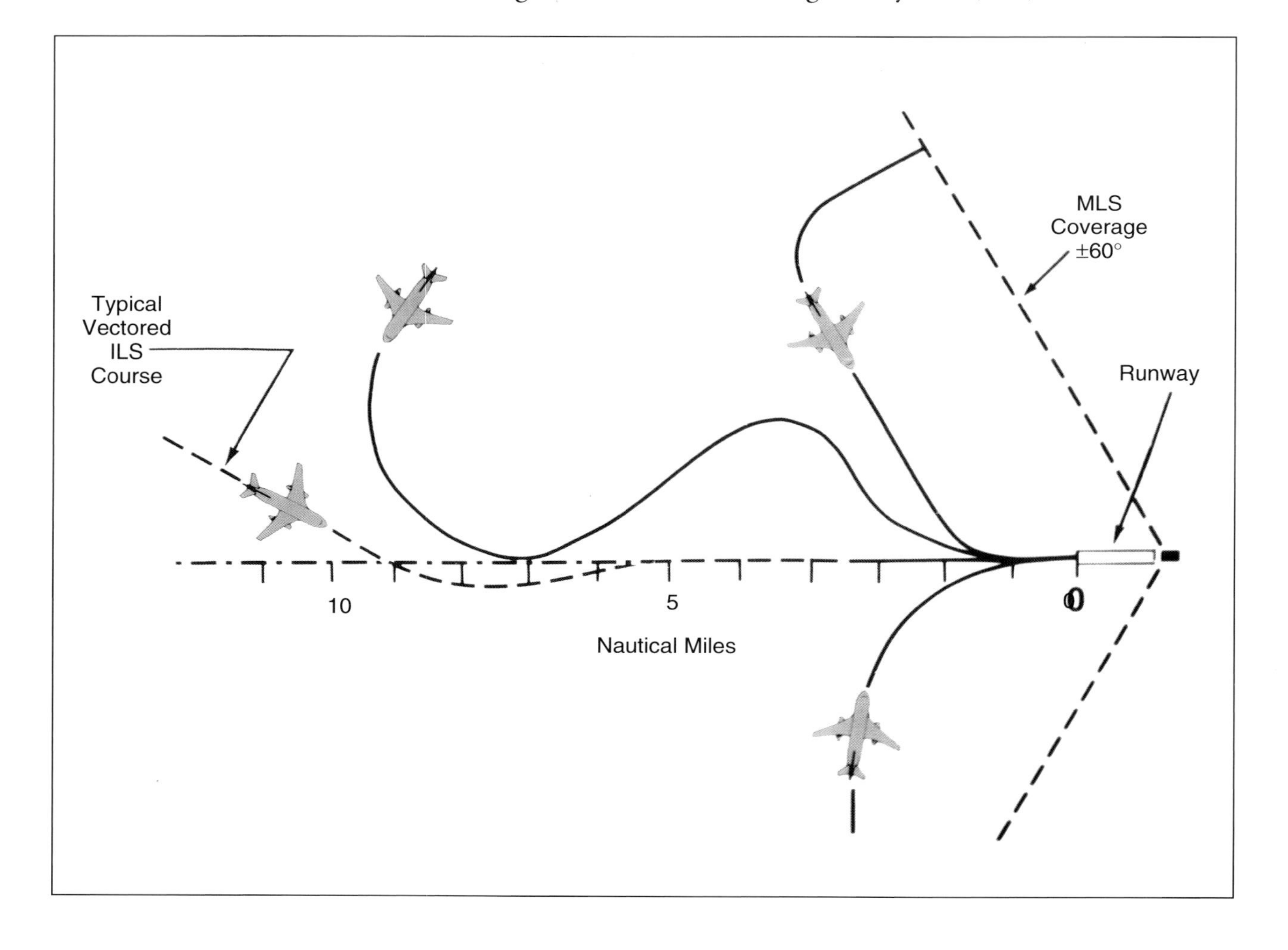

Map of vectors flown for research with the Microwave Landing System flight tests in 1978. Demonstrates three different curved paths possible instead of the straight line path used for ILS.

autolands, which used internal gyros to determine movement from a known starting point. The FAA, however, wanted the ICAO demonstration autolands to be done without the use of an INS.[15]

There was not enough time to develop a new automatic control system that would operate off of MLS signals, so the engineers decided instead to convert the MLS information into a more conventional signal format the airplane's computers could recognize. A separate Singer Kerflot 2000 digital computer was installed to reformat the data from the MLS receivers and convey the translated information to the airplane's existing navigation and flight control computers. Curved approach paths that would line up precisely with the runway were designed into the navigation computer and the autoland system was adjusted to use MLS signals for its navigation and guidance cues, although it still needed acceleration information from a secondary source for smooth control of the airplane.[16]

The engineering and design challenges of creating all the various pieces of the system and integrating them together and with the other equipment in the airplane would have been formidable in any event. But this particular research endeavor had the added pressure of a very public and non-negotiable deadline. If the system was not ready to go when it came time for the demonstration, it would reflect badly not only on NASA, but on the FAA and the United States itself. As a result, many people involved in the project put in extremely long hours throughout the fall and winter of 1975-1976.[17] The TCV team put the concepts, calculations and systems through three different levels of sophisticated simulations before they even put the equipment on the actual airplane. They then took the 737 up to the FAA's National Aviation Facilities Experimental Center (NAFEC) in March 1976 for more than five weeks of flight testing to work out any remaining problems in the equipment before the demonstration.[18]

Wind tunnel model tests of placement of the antennae for Microwave Landing System research in 1974.

Considering how quickly the system had been developed, the flight tests went well. They were not entirely without incident, however. Several days before the ICAO demonstration, for example, the flight crew was monitoring an automatic MLS-guided landing in the airplane. Normally, when the flight path reached the point where the glide slope guidance began, the airplane would pitch down slightly as it began its final descent. Yet on this occasion, only 600 feet or so off the ground, the nose pitched up and kept rising. The safety pilots in the front cockpit took over, forced the nose down again and landed the airplane. Upon investigation, the researchers finally discovered that the problem was an incorrect algebraic sign on one of the computer tapes. Since the system was all experimental, the computer tapes were full of "patches" where programming modifications had been made. Every time the flight computers "crashed" (which happened often when the airplane hit a sharp bump on a runway), each patch would have to be reloaded individually. To try to simplify the process, a new tape had been made that incorporated all the patches, but a single algebraic sign had been transposed in the process, causing the pitch-up problem.

On another occasion, a disconnected computer lead caused the airplane to initiate a roll as it approached the runway on crosswind landings. There were problems with the MLS receiving equipment overheating and breaking down. The crew operated in horrendous wind and weather conditions throughout the month of March. But when the all weather operations panel of ICAO arrived for the demonstration, everything came together.[19]

The TCV program's demonstration at NAFEC consisted of repeated automatic flight demonstrations of two basic MLS approaches, followed by automatic landings. The first path was an "S-turn" approach, which incorporated a 90 degree turn to the right followed by a 180 degree turn to the left, rounding out onto a final approach leg 3 miles from the runway. The second path was a descending 130 degree turn to the runway with a straight, three mile long final approach. The demonstration lasted for 10 days, during which time 11 flights were completed. Each flight carried approximately 10 observers who rotated positions so that everyone got to see an automatic landing from both the aft flight deck, where the electronic displays were located, and the forward cockpit. Although the demonstration was conducted in severe wind and turbulence conditions, the results were impressive. The mean overshoot error of the airplane when turning final was about 30 feet, decreasing to 10 feet one mile before the runway. The mean vertical error at one mile was less than five feet. The performance of the second "EL2" elevation transmitter for flare guidance compared favorably with that of a radar altimeter, which was what airlines were using at the time for automatic ILS landings.[20]

Even more significant than the exact numbers in the research reports, however, was the fact that the ICAO panel members had not just observed a static viewgraph presentation, or even a flight demonstration of standard, straight-in approaches using the new kind of guidance system. They had seen for themselves, with the help of the 737's vivid, visual electronic displays, a transport airplane perform maneuvers that no other transport airplane had ever been able to accomplish. The ICAO panel didn't have to imagine what the U.S. microwave landing system could do for air transport operations. They had already experienced it.[21]

Researchers in the TCV program continued to perform some additional experiments with the MLS at the New Jersey technical center during the summer of 1976, including manually flown, curved path approaches with even shorter final legs, but they thought their involvement in the MLS selection process was essentially finished. In fact, however, it was just beginning.[22]

One of the methods the FAA had used to evaluate the four candidates for the U.S. microwave landing system was computer simulation. A computer could model adverse effects that were not currently present at any airport, but were anticipated in the future as traffic and real estate development expanded. The agency had hired the Lincoln Laboratory, from Lexington, Massachusetts, to do the simulation work. So by the time the international evaluation of systems began, Lincoln was experienced in modelling MLS signals and diagnosing potential "multipath," or signal reflection, problems, and its work had a lot of credibility with ICAO members.

In July 1976, the Lincoln Laboratory presented a report to a technical working group of ICAO that indicated the British-supported Doppler Scan MLS might be more susceptible to multipath errors in some future situations than anyone had previously thought. The British modified the system's antenna scan pattern and alleviated the problem, but a new evaluation by Lincoln Laboratory indicated that the modification might make the system more susceptible to other multipath problems at certain sites. In March 1977, the FAA asked Lincoln Laboratory to look more closely at one such potential location, in Brussels, Belgium. Using the official map of the Brussels airport, the lab ran a new simulation of standard and low aircraft approach paths and determined that there might, indeed, be a significant multipath problem with the Doppler MLS. The results were presented to a meeting of the all weather operations panel of ICAO in Montreal, Canada, eight days before its crucial vote on which landing system to recommend to ICAO for adoption as the international standard. The decision of the 10-person panel was close, but the United States-backed TRSB microwave landing system was approved by a 6-4 vote.

Even before the AWOP vote, the British contingent promoting the Doppler system had been pushing for a competitive flight demonstration of the Doppler technique versus the TRSB system, arguing that regardless of what computer simulations showed, the real-life performance of the two systems was comparable. The British company that manufactured the Doppler system, Plessy Company, Ltd., also hired a lobbyist to promote the Doppler system to other elements of the U.S. government outside the FAA. The lobbyist conducted a campaign with Congressional representatives, the Department of Transportation, the White House, and the U.S. media to try to cast doubts on the TRSB system, and put pressure on the U.S. ICAO representative to delay the AWOP vote. These actions did not sit well with the FAA, of course, and by the time the Montreal vote was held, the debate between the two contingents had become heated.

The controversy took on new proportions immediately after the ICAO vote, however, when the British decided to test the Doppler system at the Brussels airport in order to prove the Lincoln Lab simulation wrong. Upon arriving at the airport, they discovered that one of the key buildings that had caused the multipath problem in the Lincoln Lab simulation did not, in fact, exist. It had been planned, so it was on the airport map, but it had never been built. When Lincoln Lab representatives travelled to Brussels and gathered their own on-site information about the airport configuration, and the lab reran the simulation, the results showed no significant difference in performance between the Doppler and TRSB systems.

Accusing the FAA of intentionally misleading Congress and ICAO and subverting the scientific process, the British lobbyist intensified his campaign to pressure the U.S into comparative flight tests of the two systems. He also implied that the reason the FAA did not want to conduct the tests was that they knew the demonstrations would show no difference between the two systems. The controversy was approaching the dimensions of an international incident, and after the issue reached the level of hearings before the House Government Operations Committee's government activities and transportation subcommittee in September 1977, FAA Administrator Langhorne M. Bond agreed to a series of international demonstrations.[23]

Once again, the aid of the TSRV 737 airplane was enlisted.[24] The first demonstration was held October 31 - November 7, 1977 in Buenos Aires, Argentina, during a conference sponsored by the Organization of American States (OAS).[25] The demonstration flights were conducted at the Aeroparque Jorge Newbery, which had many approach path restrictions due to the fact that it was only 4 kilometers from the city center of Buenos Aires. The MLS equipment the FAA installed at the airport was more limited than that at the New Jersey technical facility, with an azimuth (lateral position) coverage of only 40 degrees on either side of the runway centerline. The FAA also did not install a second elevation transmitter for flare guidance, so the TSRV used a conventional radar altimeter for that portion of the autolands.

The TCV program researchers designed two descending, curved path approaches to the Buenos Aires airport that followed the Rio de la Plata river, minimizing the noise impact on the heavily populated areas under the long, straight-in ILS approach. One of the paths had a 1.6 nautical mile final approach leg, while the other had only a 1.1 mile final. During the demonstration, a total of 56 automatic approaches and landings were made, with accuracies similar to those achieved during the NAFEC flights in May 1976. As important as the statistical results, however, was the fact that the demonstration allowed ICAO representatives from the different OAS countries to observe the U.S. system in action on board NASA's 737. Once again, the electronic flight displays gave the observers an impressive, visual illustration of the complex, automatic maneuvers that contributed greatly to the impact of the demonstration.[26]

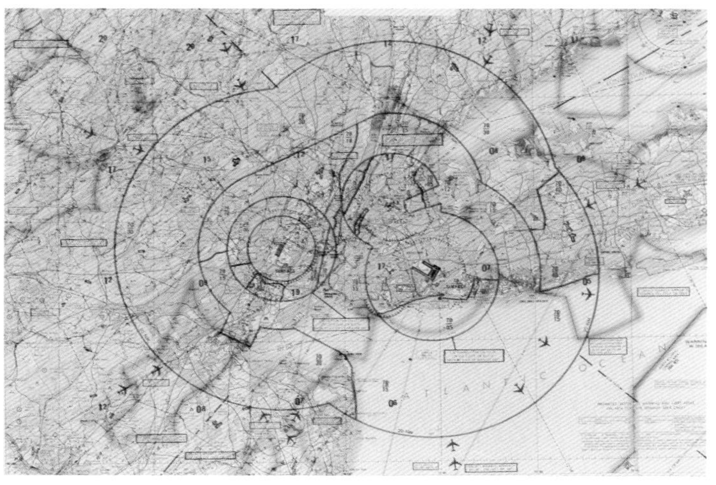

Aeronautical chart of crowded New York airspace. The MLS would help prevent conflicts between airport flight areas.

Less than a month later, the NASA team took the airplane to the John F. Kennedy airport in New York City, where the U.S. TRSB system and the British Doppler MLS would both be tested. The New York metropolitan airspace was extremely congested, because there were three major airports (JFK, LaGuardia, and Newark, New Jersey) all located in close proximity to one another. As a result, some of the ILS approach paths for one airport overlapped the air traffic control zones of another. This was an area where curved path approaches could make a tremendous difference in airport safety and capacity.[27]

The demonstration flights lasted from December 5 - 13, and the weather conditions were harsh throughout the week. On five of the eight days, the approaches had to be flown with tailwinds exceeding 20 knots, and below freezing temperatures played havoc with the computer equipment on the airplane. On the first morning, for example, the electronic flight displays would not work. After an hour and a half of troubleshooting, the displays seemed to be fixed, but the same problem occurred again the next morning. The technicians in charge of the equipment finally figured out that the root of the trouble was simply that the display computers were getting too cold at night. They fixed the problem the first day by borrowing a hair dryer to warm up the affected computer component, and ended up taking that piece out of the airplane every night to store it in a heated trailer. In truth, the electronics technicians had one of the toughest jobs during the demonstrations, because in addition to flying on the airplane during the day, they had to fix any problems with the research equipment at night so the flights could be kept on schedule.[28]

The path the TSRV 737 demonstrated at JFK was the most demanding yet. It followed the "Canarsie" VOR approach to runway 13L, which was normally used only in visual flight conditions because the final leg was less than half a mile long.

The TSRV flew a total of 38 automatic approaches during the official demonstration at JFK and successfully completed 30 autolands. The safety pilots had to take over and land the airplane on eight approaches, but the performance of the airplane was considered "very successful," considering the adverse weather conditions and the fact that the .44 mile final leg left the autoland system very little time to capture the final approach segment.[29]

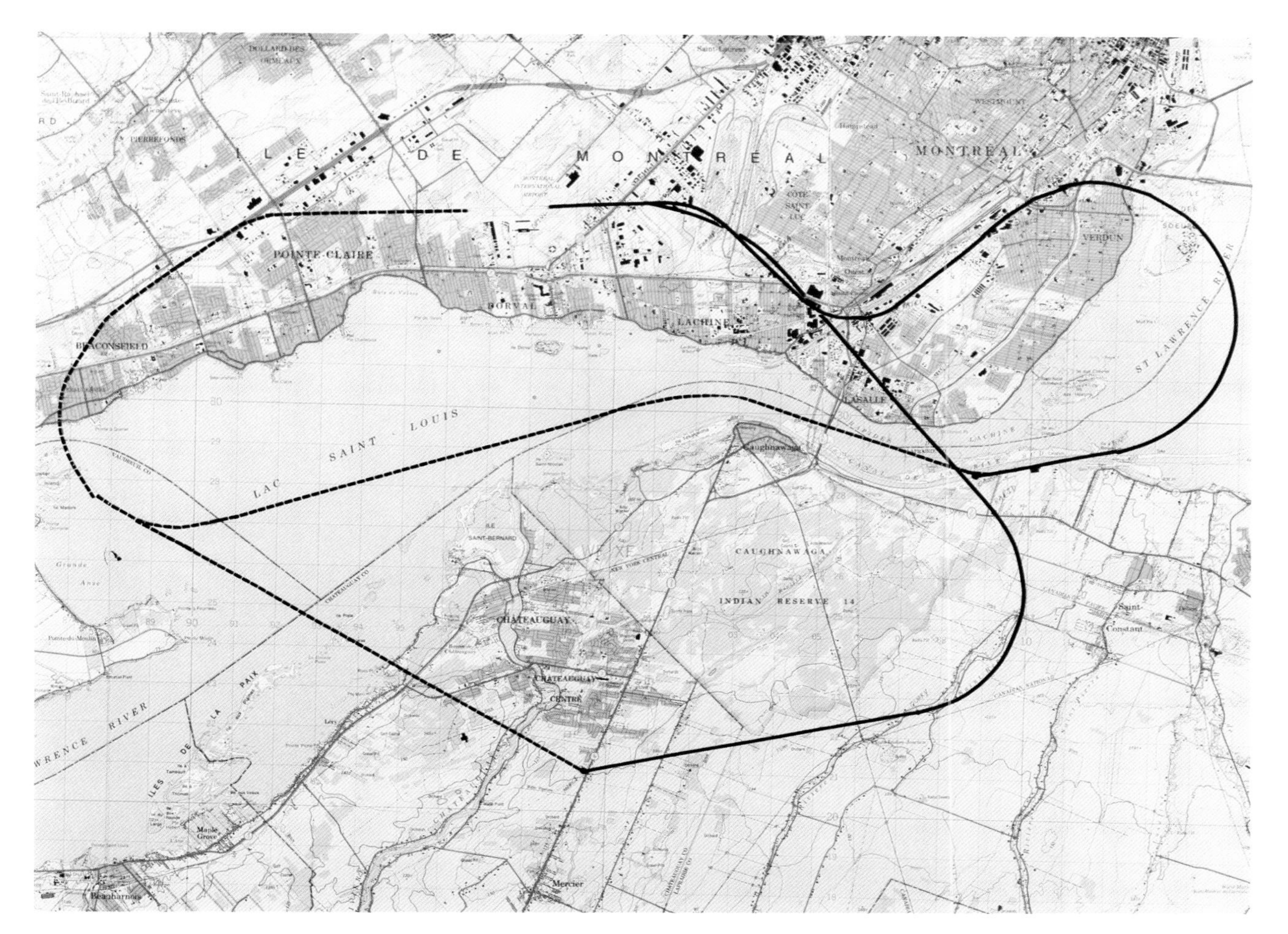

The Microwave Landing System flight demonstrations at Montreal, Canada. The map depicts two curved-path MLS approaches demonstrated by the Langley 737 during the 1978 ICAO meeting.

The British tested the Doppler system on the same runway two months later, but the British Aerospace (HS) 748 airplane had neither an autoland system nor the capability to fly curved approach paths. So although the British airplane performed numerous automatic straight-in approaches to a 50 foot decision height without any difficulty, the effect was not as dramatic as the 737's autoland performance on the difficult Canarsie approach.

The final MLS demonstration involving NASA's 737 was for ICAO's All Weather Operations Division, which had to approve or overrule the recommendation of the All Weather Operations Panel to adopt the TRSB design as the world standard for precision approach and landing guidance systems. The division meeting where the MLS vote would be taken was held in Montreal, Canada in April 1978, and both the British and the U.S. set up demonstrations of their respective systems.

The 737 demonstrated a curved path and an S-turn approach, designed to keep the airplane clear of an Indian reservation just south of the airport. One of the paths also had a glide slope angle of over four degrees, as opposed to the three degree descent angle used for ILS approaches. As in New Jersey, Argentina and New York, the FAA had observers ride on board the 737 so they could see for themselves, with the help of the aft cockpit's electronic flight displays, how well the airplane performed the curved, complex maneuvers and automatic landings.[30]

On April 19, 1978, the all weather operations division of ICAO voted 39 to 24 (with eight abstentions) in favor of the TRSB system. The decision remained politically charged up until the end, however, and the final vote was taken by secret ballot to protect the member countries from undue political pressure.

In truth, there was actually little technical difference between the British and U.S. systems. The TRSB design was a little more advanced, but the Doppler scan probably could have matched the TRSB performance with a little more development.[31] By using the TSRV 737 for the flight demonstrations, however, the FAA gained a couple of distinct advantages in the competition. First, it gave the U.S. system what Frank Frisbie called the credibility of "the NASA logo." Second, the fact that the TSRV airplane could not only perform complex automatic approach and landing maneuvers, but could also display them visually on electronic flight instruments, gave observers a dramatic and vivid impression of the TRSB system's capabilities that the British could not match.[32]

After the April 1978 ICAO decision, the organization began developing Standards and Recommended Practices (SARPs) for MLS. The target date for switching over to MLS as a primary landing guidance system was changed from 1985 to 1995, but the future of the TRSB microwave landing system seemed assured. The technology was proven, the ICAO world organization had given its stamp of approval, and after the SARPS were written, all that remained was to produce and install the equipment.

Yet 15 years later, only a handful of MLS installations had been completed, and it was uncertain whether the microwave landing system would ever be implemented, at least in the United States. In a telling example of how complex the technology application process can be, the MLS encountered so many delays and obstacles in the 10 years following the ICAO decision that it finally began to be overshadowed by an even newer technology: the Global Positioning System (GPS).

The FAA awarded the first production contract for 178 of the 1,250 planned microwave landing systems to the Hazeltine Corporation in Commack, New York, in January 1984. The specifications for the equipment required only a Category I level of performance, however, because the FAA planned to put the first systems at small airports which had only Category I ILS equipment, or no instrument landing capability at all, to help ease the transition to MLS.[33] Category I conditions were the least severe of the three low-visibility condition categories, requiring at least 200 foot cloud ceilings and a half mile of visibility. Actually, the guidance signal of the MLS equipment did not change from Category I to Category III, but Category II and III installations required a much higher level of redundancy in the equipment.

The FAA planners hoped that by installing the first microwave landing systems at outlying airports, they would prove the flexibility of the system to provide coverage in areas unable to incorporate a standard ILS and begin to build a consensus of support for MLS among regional airlines and corporate aircraft operators. Interestingly enough, although the major airlines had initially pushed for the development of MLS in the late 1960s, they were less enthusiastic as the time came to implement the system. Some of the problems with the ILS had been rectified, and the growing financial concerns of the airlines following deregulation made them reluctant to purchase new avionics for their entire fleets unless they could see some immediate benefit from the new equipment.[34]

The problem with the FAA's strategy was that installing Category I equipment at outlying airports offered no opportunities to show the airlines any of the more impressive advantages the MLS could offer them, such as more efficient approach procedures or better automatic landing capabilities.[35] Nevertheless, had the 178 Category I systems been installed as planned, there might have been enough momentum to support the production and installation of the more capable Category II/III MLS equipment at airports used by the major airlines. But as it turned out, those first 178 systems were never delivered.

Hazeltine Corporation had promised it would begin delivering the MLS systems 18 months after its contract with the FAA was signed. The company ran into problems with software, however, and the delivery date was pushed back repeatedly. Four years later, Hazeltine had only delivered two systems, and the FAA finally cancelled the contract in 1989.[36] By this time, numerous questions were being raised about the necessity of MLS, not only by the airlines, but also by Congress and even the General Accounting Office.[37] More importantly, however, MLS technology was no longer the only alternative to ILS.

In 1983, the United States decided to make its satellite navigation network available to the world. The system, which was developed originally by the Department of Defense for military purposes, was based on a constellation of geosynchronous satellites. By using satellite-transmitted radio signals to measure the distance from a receiver to several different satellites, the exact position of the receiver could be determined at all times. The Global Positioning System (GPS), as the U.S. satellite network was called, offered so much more capability and flexibility than any other navigation system that it was described as "the greatest opportunity to enhance aviation system capacity, efficiency and safety since the introduction of radios and radio-based navigation."[38] GPS was not dependent on any ground navigation aids, which meant that it could provide guidance in a much wider variety of locations than navigation systems based on radio transmissions from particular ground positions. GPS could also provide precise position and velocity information in three dimensions, at any instant in time, which other navigation systems could not do.

There were limitations on the system, however. To keep the defenses of the U.S. from being compromised, the Department of Defense intentionally degraded the accuracy of the satellite signals for civil use. As a result, the position accuracy was only within 300 feet, which was acceptable for navigation, but not precise enough for a landing system. These position errors could be corrected and the inherent accuracy of the satellite signals could be improved further through the use of "differential" techniques, although this approach did require ground installations. In a differential system, a stationary GPS receiver was placed at a surveyed location near the airport. The ground site would receive the satellite transmissions, compute how much correction was needed to match its surveyed location, and transmit that correction factor to approaching airplanes through a real-time data link. There were still questions about the capability of GPS to provide enough accuracy for the most demanding instrument approaches, however.[39]

Representatives of the airlines' Air Transport Association (ATA) began to advocate the use of GPS, perhaps in combination with the current ILS system, as a possible alternative to MLS. Some simulation research had also started to evaluate the use of GPS for landing guidance systems, but there was still tremendous momentum within the FAA and the international community for the microwave landing system. The GPS movement got a tremendous boost, however, from a series of flight tests conducted in the fall of 1990 by NASA's TCV/ATOPS program and the TSRV 737 airplane.[40]

Ironically, the TSRV research was not even directed toward civil aviation use of GPS. Honeywell, Inc. had developed a GPS receiver integrated with an inertial reference unit (IRU) that it wanted to test to see if it was accurate enough to be used as a landing aid for returning space vehicles, such as the shuttle or an emergency crew rescue craft. Space vehicles generally land in good weather, on very long runways, however, so the accuracy requirements are not quite as stringent as those for commercial airline operations in extremely low visibility conditions.[41]

Because the ATOPS 737 had extensive experimentation and data collection capabilities, Honeywell proposed testing its GPS/IRU system on the NASA airplane. One of the NASA managers suggested integrating the GPS/IRU equipment with the airplane's existing autoland system, to gather some additional data on the performance of the equipment all the way through landing. The autoland portion of the experiment was almost dismissed, however, because from a research standpoint, there was little to be gained. The Langley engineers knew that the autoland system on the airplane worked, so performing autolands with Honeywell's GPS/IRU equipment appeared to be simply demonstrating a capability that was already obvious.[42] What the research engineers at Langley failed to appreciate was that while that capability was obvious to them, it was not yet obvious to the rest of the world.

In October and the early part of November 1990, the 737 performed a total of 25 hours of flight tests with the GPS/IRU system, using a differential GPS station at the Wallops Island flight test facility. Initial tests with just the GPS/IRU guiding the autoland system showed an unacceptable vertical error, so a radar altimeter was integrated, as well. With that combination, the airplane performed a total of 36 successful

Aerial view of Wallops Flight Facility, where many of the 737 research flights have been conducted.

GPS/IRU automatic landings. The airplane's performance did not meet the most stringent precision landing requirements, but it met Category I specifications (within 112.2 feet horizontal and 27.2 feet vertical accuracy) and came close to the 33.8-foot horizontal accuracy requirements for a Category II landing.

To the researchers at Langley, the results were interesting, but not earth-shattering. In addition to the 36 successful autolands, there were others that had to be completed by the safety pilots, although that was typical of Category I landings. The accuracy of the GPS/IRU/radar altimeter system also still fell substantially short of the microwave landing system.[43] To the outside world, however, the specific error levels and the combination of equipment that the landings required were secondary. The ATOPS program had just demonstrated, in an actual transport airplane, that a GPS-guided autoland was possible. In a few test flights, the ATOPS researchers had changed the face of the GPS debate from a basic question of whether GPS could ever be used for landings to more specific questions about the degrees of accuracy and reliability that could be achieved.[44]

The results achieved in the NASA/Honeywell tests in 1990 were not nearly good enough to support using GPS instead of MLS, but they helped build momentum for further research and development efforts. By 1993, GPS technology had already advanced so far that the ATOPS program began another series of test flights with equipment that, in theory, could achieve accuracies not only adequate for Category II/III landings, but within 10-19 centimeters.

The 1993 research effort used an Ashtech, Inc. P12 12-channel, carrier phase tracking receiver, with additional processing software developed by Ohio University. The Honeywell equipment tested in 1990 was a much earlier generation GPS receiver that used code tracking reception and only two channels. The carrier phase tracking receivers were more accurate, because instead of just locking on to a code associated with the GPS signal, a carrier phase receiver locked onto the actual GPS frequency wave itself. The Ohio University software was designed to improve the accuracy of the equipment even further by locking on to not only the frequency wave pattern, but the exact frequency cycle associated with the airplane's position.[45]

Even if the Ashtech/Ohio University system performed flawlessly, some questions about GPS would remain, especially within the ICAO community. To be acceptable as a landing system, GPS would not only have to have high reliability, it would have to be able to alert pilots instantaneously if a satellite signal was flawed. There were also uncertainties about how easy it would be to jam a GPS signal, and concerns among the international community about relying on a satellite system owned and operated by the U.S. military.[46]

In 1988, the Soviet Union also agreed to make its GLONASS satellite signals available for international civil use, which reduced some of the concerns about satellite availability and U.S. control of the system. ICAO designated an international satellite system, including GPS, GLONASS and any other country satellites that might be added to it in the future, the "Global Navigation Satellite System," or GNSS.[47] The political upheaval in what had been the Soviet Union following 1991 left some uncertainty as to when or if the full complement of GLONASS satellites would be operational, however.

ICAO finally decided to wait until 1995 before determining whether or not to alter its plan to implement MLS. The original deadlines called for installation at all international airports by 1998 and transition to MLS as the primary navigation system by 2000. By 1995, the FAA and NASA were expected to have substantially more information on the potential and limitations of GPS, and ICAO members could determine whether they wanted to extend the deadline for MLS, shift the main navigation and landing system focus to GNSS, or look at some combination of the two.[48]

The landing system decision remained a highly charged issue, however, and there were split opinions both within ICAO and within the United States itself. The United Kingdom, for example, decided to proceed to MLS implementation without waiting for additional research into GPS. The poor visibility conditions in the U.K. made the ability to perform Category III landings a necessity, and ILS frequency congestion and interference problems were more severe in Europe than they were in the United States. The British reasoned that even if GPS technology could be developed far enough to provide the accuracy for Category III operations and the questions regarding system integrity, reliability and availability could be resolved satisfactorily, development and implementation of the system would take too long.[49]

The United States looked much more favorably upon a GPS or GNSS system, but there were still strongly divided views within the FAA, NASA and the aviation community about what the next landing guidance system should be. Most people agreed, however, that even if the MLS system was implemented, it would probably be in a much more limited capacity than originally envisioned.[50]

The 25 year controversy over a new landing guidance system underscored just how much political, financial and other external factors can influence the acceptance and application of new technology. In the mid-1970s, the microwave landing system clearly demonstrated its superiority over the existing instrument landing guidance equipment. Yet almost 20 years later, the old ILS system was still in use, and MLS was being overshadowed by an even more advanced technology.

The landing system debate also showed once again the impact an airplane like the TSRV 737 could have on the acceptance of new technology. With the use of the NASA 737, the backers of both the TRSB microwave landing system and the global positioning system were able to go beyond simply describing or simulating the capabilities of the technology. They could physically demonstrate its performance, in an actual air transport class airplane and in realistic flight situations. In the case of the MLS competition, this gave the U.S. candidate an edge the British entry could not match. In the case of GPS, it forced a re-evaluation of the system's possible applications and generated momentum for further research and development efforts. The NASA 737 was continuing to prove that actual flight demonstrations could give new technology a level of credibility that no amount of laboratory testing or simulation could achieve.

Chapter 5

"The Best That We Can Do": Taming the Microburst Windshear

The TSRV (Transport Systems Research Vehicle) 737 made numerous contributions in many different areas during its 20 years at the Langley Research Center. But no effort involving the 737 was more successful, or had a greater impact, than the airborne windshear detection and avoidance program.

Members of the Aeronautics Advisory Committee that oversees the research efforts of NASA called the windshear program "NASA at its best."[1] The windshear program was, indeed, a classic research success story, and its achievements were even more extraordinary because of the significant organizational and technical challenges the program involved. The windshear research effort required an unusual number of cooperative relationships, not only among several different directorates at Langley, but between NASA and both the FAA and industry manufacturers. The research was subjected to a high degree of public pressure and scrutiny, with a deadline by which results had to be achieved. The technical obstacles were substantial, and many knowledgeable sources doubted they could be overcome at all. If technical solutions could be found, the flight testing would still be unusually challenging, and potentially dangerous if not planned and executed extremely well.

Yet the NASA and industry researchers and technicians involved with the program rose to the challenge. In a remarkable seven-year effort, the windshear research team at Langley developed, demonstrated, and successfully transferred the technology to tame an aviation weather hazard that had caused 26 airline accidents and claimed more than 500 lives since 1964.[2]

The immediate catalyst for the NASA/FAA windshear program was a tragic event at the Dallas-Ft. Worth (DFW) airport on the afternoon of August 2, 1985. Thunderstorms were in the area of the Texas airport as Delta Flight 191, a L-1011 jumbo jet with 163 passengers and crew on board, approached runway 17L for landing. There was a rain shaft and scattered lightning coming from a thunderstorm cell in the airliner's final approach path, but the pilots decided the weather was passable and continued the approach. Fifteen to 30 seconds after the L-1011 entered the weather, however, the rain and lightning intensified, and the airplane was buffeted by a violent series of up and down drafts. The headwind increased

Left—Microburst windshear research in Colorado in 1992. The photo was taken from a tail-mounted camera that photographed the aircraft's upper fuselage and the horizon.
Right—Forward flight deck of the NASA 737 at the time the aircraft entered a microburst windshear cell in 1992.

rapidly to 26 knots, and then, just as suddenly, switched to a 46 knot tailwind, resulting in an abrupt loss of 72 knots of airspeed. The jet was only 800 feet above the ground when it encountered the severe weather, leaving the pilots little room to maneuver when the airplane began to lose airspeed and altitude at the same time. Thirty-eight seconds later, Delta Flight 191 crashed into the terrain short of the runway, killing all but 26 of those on board.[3]

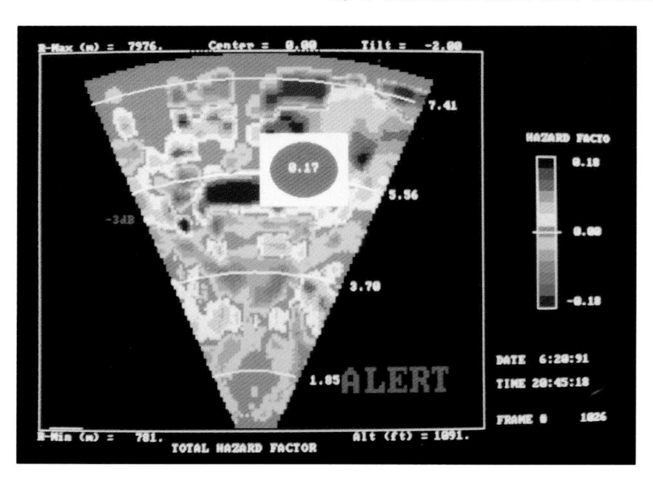

The crash of Flight 191 jarred the nation. Just three years earlier, a Pan American World Airways Boeing 727 departing the New Orleans International Airport had also encountered a severe windshear and crashed, killing 145 people on the airplane and eight more on the ground.[4] Two such accidents in three years, with the loss of almost 300 lives, was too much. With the wide publicity the Dallas crash received, "windshear" suddenly became a household term and the safety of air travel began to be questioned. Members of Congress were deluged with phone calls from constituents asking that something be done to prevent any more accidents.[5]

Actually, the FAA, NASA and other organizations had been working on the problem of low level windshear for some time. As early as 1949, researchers had begun to explore some of the potentially dangerous characteristics of thunderstorms, and in 1971 the FAA started a joint program with several research organizations to work on improving the forecasting and detection of windshear. The issue received renewed emphasis, however, when an Eastern Airlines Boeing 727 crashed on approach to runway 22L at the John F. Kennedy International Airport in New York on June 24, 1975, killing 112 people.[6]

Information from meteorological measurements and another aircraft in the area

Left—Windshear display used on the NASA 737 research aircraft; displays the location and intensity of the weather hazard. The aircraft's position is at the bottom of the cone; the dark red areas indicate the greatest shear intensity. The red dot shows the F-Factor. Right—The 737 crew conducting windshear research from the aft flight deck. Clockwise, from lower left, Roland Bowes, program manager; Lee Person, research pilot; Michael Lewis, deputy program manager; experimenters Emedio Bracalente and David A. Hinton.

ALERT
ALERT

indicated that the airliner had encountered a strong downdraft of air and an abrupt switch in wind direction just prior to the crash. Researchers analyzing the accident looked more closely at the thunderstorm conditions the airliner had encountered and concluded that a particularly violent, deceptive, and deadly kind of windshear, which one researcher named a "microburst," had caused the Eastern Airlines jet to crash.[7]

Meterologist Dr. Fred H. Proctor on the ground directing the NASA 737 toward microbursts using a Terminal Doppler Weather Radar.

Windshear, defined as a sudden change in wind velocity and/or direction, was not always dangerous. Aircraft often experience a shift or drop in winds in cruise flight, but at that point they have enough speed and altitude to compensate for the loss of airflow over their wings. If an airplane encountered windshear during a takeoff or landing it was more serious, because the plane was close to the ground and had very little extra speed. A microburst windshear, however, was a unique phenomenon that posed a particularly deadly threat to airplanes.

A microburst occurred when the precipitation in a column of rising air evaporated, cooling the air very quickly. Since air became more dense as it cooled, the column of air would fall rapidly, spreading out in all directions with a great deal of force as it neared the ground. The phenomenon could occur in a variety of conditions, and not all microbursts had any rainfall associated with them. However, the strong, convective air currents in thunderstorms and towering cumulus cloud build-ups were particularly conducive to the formation of microbursts.

Low altitude encounters with microbursts were especially hazardous to aircraft because the first effect a pilot would notice was a performance-enhancing headwind (as the plane first encountered the outflow of the burst). If an airplane was on a landing approach, the pilot would typically respond by reducing the engine power to maintain the proper glide path angle and speed. As the plane progressed into the center of the microburst, however, the plane would be hit with severe downdrafts. Then, as it passed into the far side of the burst, the headwind would be replaced with a strong tailwind, causing a sudden loss of performance and airspeed. If the pilot had reduced power during the first stage of the microburst, this loss in performance would be intensified even further. Turbine engines take several seconds to spool up to provide additional power, and by the time a pilot realized the nature of the problem, it was often too late.[8]

Another reason microbursts posed such a danger to pilots was that they were extremely difficult to detect. A microburst was usually less than 2.5 miles in diameter and lasted only a few minutes. To help give pilots better warning of potentially dangerous shear conditions, the FAA developed a Low Level Windshear Alert System (LLWAS) in 1976. LLWAS consisted of an array of wind velocity measuring instruments that were installed at various locations around an airport. The LLWAS compared the wind direction and velocity readings from the different sensors and, if a 15 knot or greater difference existed, transmitted an alert to the air traffic controllers, who could then notify pilots in the area. The system had a number of limitations, however. The instruments could not measure winds above the ground sensors and could not record vertical wind forces. An extremely localized microburst on a final approach path might not even be recorded by the sensors. Even alerts that were recorded took a couple of minutes to reach the controllers.

Nevertheless, the LLWAS was an improvement over the existing detection methods, which consisted of weather forecasts and pilot reports of weather conditions they had just encountered. By 1983, the FAA had installed LLWAS at 59 major airports and had plans to install the system at an additional 51 locations.[9] The FAA also issued special Advisory Circulars in 1976 and 1979 that contained information for pilots on windshear recognition and recovery techniques. In 1977, the FAA amended Part 121 of the Federal Aviation Regulations to require air carriers to adopt an approved system for obtaining forecasts and reports of adverse weather conditions, including low altitude windshear. The agency even issued an advanced notice of proposed rulemaking (NPRM) in 1979 that proposed making airborne windshear detection equipment mandatory for scheduled airlines, but the regulation was not enacted. [10]

In truth, the technology for airborne windshear detectors and the level of knowledge about the phenomenon itself were still very limited, although researchers were working on the problem. For example, engineers and meteorologists at the Langley Research Center began to explore windshear and microburst behavior in more detail in the early 1980s as part of a simulation technology program. In order to simulate the weather hazard accurately, the engineers had to first understand how it operated and how it affected aircraft performance. Understanding windshear behavior was a difficult challenge, however. The NASA researchers first had to study the basic meteorology and atmospheric physics associated with windshear and then, using extremely high fidelity fluid dynamics models run by super computers, try to model the phenomenon's characteristics.[11]

In another effort known as the Joint Airport Weather Studies (JAWS), the National Center for Atmospheric Research (NCAR) conducted windshear experiments in the Denver, Colorado, area during the summer of 1982. Researchers concluded that some of the microbursts recorded during the JAWS program created windshear too severe for landing or departing airliners to survive if they encountered it less than 300-500 feet above the ground.[12]

Yet even as the JAWS researchers were collecting microburst data in Denver, Pan American World Airways Flight 759 crashed in New Orleans, Louisiana. The airport's LLWAS did trigger an alert, but not in time. The tower controller's first broadcast warning of possible windshear came two seconds after the Pan Am Boeing 727 hit the trees off the end of the runway.[13] The accident prompted Congress to pass Public Law 97-369, mandating the FAA to contract with the National Academy of Sciences (NAS) to "study the state of knowledge, alternative approaches and the consequences of windshear alert and severe weather condition standards relating to take off and landing clearances for commercial and general aviation aircraft."[14]

Researchers aboard the NASA 737 during windshear detection flight tests.

The NAS report was issued in May 1983 and concluded that low altitude windshear presented an "infrequent but highly significant hazard to aircraft while landing or taking off." Among the report's recommendations was continued research into airborne windshear detection systems.[15] That November, the FAA cleared the way for certification of airborne windshear detectors by issuing Advisory Circular No. 120-41, "Criteria for Operational Approval of Airborne Windshear Alerting and Flight Guidance Systems." [16]

The crash of Delta's L-1011 in Dallas in August 1985, however, provided a dramatic catalyst that suddenly turned the search for an effective weapon against the microburst into a top priority, organized program. In addition to the fact that it was the second windshear accident with a large number of fatalities in three years, the Delta crash highlighted just how inadequate the detection and warning technology still was. The Dallas-Ft. Worth airport was equipped with a Low Level Windshear Alerting System, but none of the system's five sensors issued an alert until several minutes after the Delta airplane hit the ground. [17]

Among the Congressmen who were swamped with concerned calls from constituents following the Dallas crash was Representative George Brown from California. A couple of

The hazard that NASA tackled: aircraft approaching a runway are especially at risk from sudden and intense downdrafts brought on by abrupt temperature changes. Developing a reliable warning system was the only answer.

weeks after the accident, Congressman Brown visited the Langley Research Center and asked for a presentation on windshear. An FAA manager named George "Cliff" Hay and Dr. Roland L. Bowles, a Langley research engineer, had been working on a plan for an airborne windshear detection research program for six months prior to the Dallas crash, but the only concrete research that was actually underway at the Langley Research Center at the time was the work on microburst and windshear modelling. Dr. Jeremiah F. Creedon, head of the new Langley Flight Systems Directorate, put together a quick briefing on the windshear problem and potential technologies that might be able to combat it. Congressman Brown asked how much money it would take to develop a solution. Nobody at Langley had thought that far down the road, but Dr. Creedon gave the Congressman a rough estimate of at least several million dollars. Brown reportedly commented that the amount of money Creedon had quoted was nothing. "It's a lot of money if you don't have it," Creedon replied. The Senator whispered to an aide, and as the contingent left the briefing, the aide told one of the Langley managers that NASA had just gotten itself a windshear program.[18]

Actually, it was not quite that simple. Congressman Brown, who was a ranking member of the House Science and Technology Committee, certainly had a lot of influence with both the FAA and NASA. But the Delta crash had created a tremendous amount of public and political focus on the windshear problem. The media coverage following the Dallas accident, public concern, and the interest of high-ranking Representatives and Senators all helped garner support for a substantial, coordinated interagency research effort to address the windshear problem.

In April 1986 the FAA announced the formation of a National Integrated Windshear Plan. The plan was an umbrella program that incorporated numerous independent research efforts, some of which were already in progress.[19] Even before the Dallas crash, for example, the FAA had begun working on a Windshear Training Aid for the airlines. The project was a joint effort by all three major commercial transport airframe manufacturers (Boeing, Lockheed, and McDonnell Douglas), and the training program and techniques they developed to help pilots handle severe windshear situations proved extremely effective.[20]

In addition to the training aid, the FAA National Plan incorporated LLWAS, research into an improved ground detection method called Terminal Doppler Weather Radar (TDWR), plans to improve terminal area communications of windshear threats, more detailed characterization of the windshear threat, and an airborne windshear detection research program.[21] This airborne system research program would be conducted by the Langley Research Center. In addition to its aeronautics expertise and the microburst modelling work that had already been done there, Langley had one other asset that made it a logical choice for the windshear research: a fully instrumented air transport test plane, with advanced displays, that could take the sensor technology development through a test flight stage. On July 24, 1986, NASA and the FAA signed a Memorandum of Agreement formally authorizing the start of a joint Airborne Windshear Detection and Avoidance Program. A Windshear Program office was created in the Flight Systems directorate at the Langley Research Center, headed by Dr. Bowles.[22]

The FAA/NASA airborne windshear research program had three major goals. The first was to find a way to characterize the windshear threat in a manner that related to the hazard level it presented for aircraft. The second was to develop airborne remote-sensor technology to provide accurate, forward-looking windshear detection. The third was to design flight management concepts and systems to transfer that information to pilots in such a way that they could respond effectively to a windshear threat.[23] The program also had to pursue these goals under unusually tight time constraints.

Part of the pressure came from the fact that both Congress and the general public were demanding a solution to the windshear threat as soon as possible. An even greater motivating factor, however, was a proposed FAA regulation that would greatly aid the transfer of any new technology developed in the NASA program if the research could be completed quickly enough. Since 1979, the FAA had contemplated requiring air carriers (operating under Part 121 of the Federal Aviation Regulations) to install airborne windshear detectors in their airplanes, and the proposed regulation was brought up again after the Dallas accident. It was finally enacted in September 1988 and required Part 121 air carriers to install airborne detectors in all their aircraft no later than December 1993. The minimum requirement was only for a reactive system, but Northwest Airlines, American Airlines, and Continental Airlines obtained exemptions that allowed them two more years to explore forward-looking detection systems.[24]

In order for the technology being researched by the NASA/FAA windshear program to have a real impact, the airlines, who were the ultimate customers, would have to support forward-looking detection systems. Three major airlines had already expressed an interest in forward-looking systems, but if NASA's research was not completed until after the airlines had outfitted their entire fleets with reactive systems, airline support for the new technology would be greatly reduced.

The emphasis on forward-looking systems reflected a growing realization of how severe the microburst threat could be. The JAWS research in Denver in 1982 discovered microbursts too strong for an airplane to fly through safely, no matter what kind of immediate recovery techniques the pilots used.[25] In its official report on the 1982 New Orleans Pan Am crash, the National Transportation Safety Board (NTSB) noted that although reactive systems could help improve pilot performance, "programs must be pressed to develop airborne and ground systems with greater lead time predictive capabilities."[26] The FAA Windshear Training Aid also warned that the maximum windshear capability of jet transports in some situations was 40 to 50 knots wind speed change, and that "some windshears cannot be escaped successfully (once they are actually entered)."[27]

Advance warning would give pilots the ability to increase the engine power and, if necessary, level the airplane before entering the microburst, so the airplane would have more energy, altitude, and speed with which to combat the effects of the windshear. Or, if traffic permitted and the shear was strong enough, the pilots could elect to maneuver around the microburst altogether. One of the first questions the Langley windshear researchers had to answer, however, was exactly how much advance warning was required to prevent an airplane from getting into a shear situation that it could not fly through safely. The Langley simulation technology program had already yielded significant insights about the characteristics of windshear and microbursts. The researchers integrated this information with analyses of aircraft energy states, tested their results in piloted simulations of microburst recovery techniques, and concluded that even 15-20 seconds of advance warning was enough for an airliner to avert or survive an encounter with a microburst windshear. In fact, simulations indicated that aircraft with 10-20 seconds of advance warning could fly through even relatively strong windshears without losing any altitude.[28]

A flat plate airborne radar used in the microburst windshear detection research program was housed in the nose of the NASA 737 aircraft.

In order to allow the pilots to take appropriate corrective action, however, the warning had to convey how much of a hazard the impending shear posed for the airplane. Some windshears could be penetrated safely with only small power additions; others were more dangerous and required immediate full thrust or evasive maneuvers. The solution devised by Roland Bowles, manager of the Langley windshear program, was a hazard index that he called the "F-Factor."

The F-Factor was a dimensionless number that interpreted the vertical and horizontal strength of a windshear in terms of the amount of climb performance it would take away from

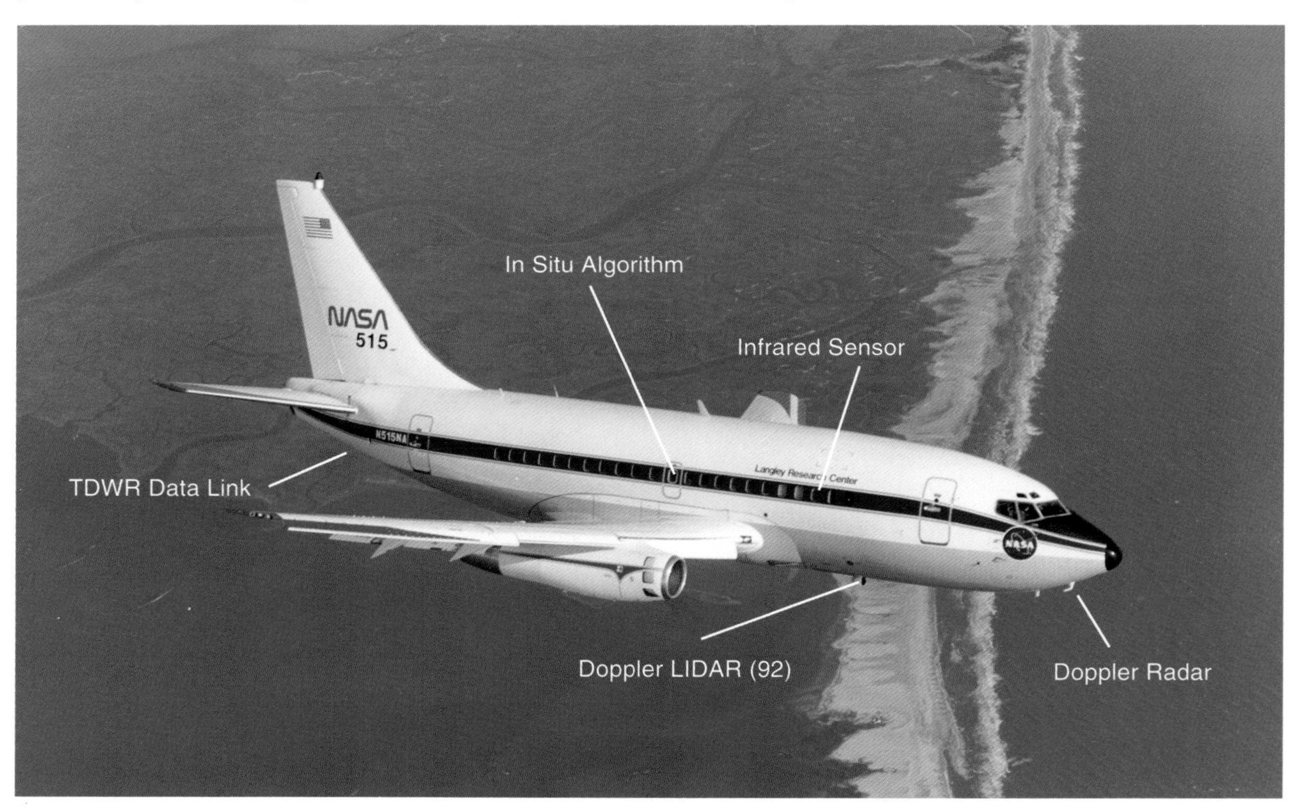

The placement of the windshear airborne sensors used on the research aircraft.

the airplane. Or, to put it another way, the F-Factor of an windshear would indicate how much excess power an airplane would have to have to fly through it without losing airspeed or altitude. A typical twin engine jet transport plane, for example, might have engines capable of producing .17 excess thrust on the F-Factor scale. So if a windshear registered higher than .17, the airplane would not be able to fly through it, even at full power, without losing airspeed or altitude. Information from past windshear accidents indicated that the warning threshold for most jet transports in landing or take-off configurations should be an F-Factor of .1. Consequently, a cockpit warning display could be preset to only show alerts for windshears with an F-Factor of .1 or more to eliminate nuisance or unnecessary warnings.[29]

The invention of the "F-Factor" was an important step in the development of windshear detection systems, because it provided a way for information from any kind of sensor to be presented to the pilot in a relevant and easily understood form. But the hazard index was only one of five basic requirements the windshear research team at Langley had identified for an effective forward-looking detection system. The technology also needed to identify hazards while rejecting non-threatening information, locate the position and track the movement of a potentially dangerous air mass, and annunciate the hazard to the flight crew. In addition to an "F-Factor" type of hazard index, the display also needed to provide information on the proximity and volume of the windshear.[30]

By 1986, Boeing and the Sperry Corporation were already in the process of developing reactive airborne windshear systems that would alert pilots to windshear once it was actually encountered. But technology with the capability the Langley researchers wanted, especially in a forward-looking system, did not yet exist.[31] In fact, although the NASA/FAA windshear program listed the design of forward-looking windshear detection systems as one of its three primary goals, it was still not known whether such technology was even possible. The 1983 National Academy of Sciences (NAS) report on "Low-Altitude Windshear and Its Hazard to Aviation" discussed three different potential techniques for remote sensing of windshear, but found problems with all three that made them impractical.[32] Even the 1986 memorandum of agreement that initiated the FAA/NASA windshear program noted that "there is no assurance that a practical airborne forward-looking system capable of detecting both wet and dry severe windshear 'microbursts' can be achieved."[33]

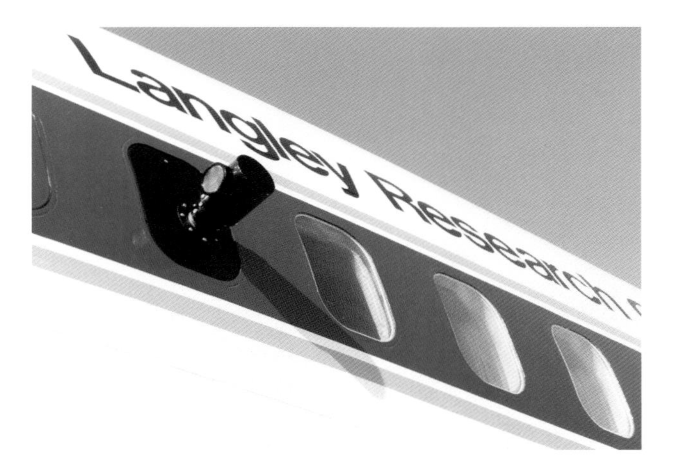

Close-up of the side-mounted infrared sensor used in the windshear detection program.

Despite their drawbacks, the forward-looking technologies that seemed to have the most potential were the microwave Doppler radar, Doppler light detecting and ranging (LIDAR), and passive infrared radiometry systems discussed in the 1983 NAS report. Microwave Doppler radar operated by transmitting radio waves of uniform frequency ahead of the airplane. The waves would be reflected back to the plane when they hit water particles, and the frequency shift of the return signal would indicate the direction and velocity of the raindrops and, therefore, the wind. Just as the whistle of a train would be a high pitched noise as it approached and would become a lower and lower pitched sound as it went further away, the frequency of the radar return signal differed in direct proportion to the speed and direction of the water particles. If they were coming toward the airplane, as in the case of a headwind, the frequency would be high. If the particles were going away from the plane, the frequency would

Close-up of the Light Detection and Ranging (LIDAR) radar mounted on the lower fuselage.

During the microburst windshear detection research laser beams, shown here, were used to align the optical hardware of the infrared and LIDAR systems.

be proportionately lower. A variation of the frequency, and therefore the velocity and direction of the water particles, would indicate the presence of a windshear.

The Terminal Doppler Weather Radar (TDWR), which was a microwave Doppler radar system, was proving very effective in ground detection of windshear, but there were several problems with trying to adapt the technology for an airborne system. First, the ground Doppler radars were much larger and more powerful than the size equipment that would fit on an airplane, so an airborne version might not be as effective. The radar would also be looking not only ahead, but also down toward the ground as the airplane descended. As a result, the radar would be reflected off objects on the ground, creating "clutter" in the return signal. In addition, not all microbursts contained rain, and microwave signals typically received few returns from dry air.

Doppler LIDAR operated in much the same manner as Doppler radar, except that it used a laser light beam instead of radio waves. The LIDAR system also used reflections off tiny dust particles in the air instead of raindrops to determine wind direction and velocity. The size of existing LIDAR equipment posed a potential problem for its use in an aircraft environment, but the biggest concern about LIDAR was that its signal tended to be absorbed by raindrops. Consequently, its signal was weak, or "attenuated," in the presence of the kind of heavy rain that was often found in thunderstorm microbursts.

Passive infrared radiometry was based on the premise that since microbursts were formed by a column of cooler, rapidly descending air, their presence would be marked by a sharp temperature shift in the air ahead of the airplane. The technology was simpler, less expensive and lighter than the other systems, but it had several potential problems. First, there was no firm evidence that microbursts or gust fronts were the only weather phenomena containing temperature shifts, so there was a potential problem of nuisance alerts with an infrared system. Even if the nuisance alert problem was solved, there would have to be a direct relationship between the amount of temperature change and the severity of the windshear in order for the system to be an effective warning device.[34]

To try to overcome the technical obstacles to the different types of forward-looking airborne sensors, NASA enlisted the help of several industry manufacturers. Lockheed Missiles and Space was given a contract to develop an airborne forward-looking LIDAR detection system, and funds from NASA's Small Business Innovative Research (SBIR) program were awarded to a Boulder, Colorado, company named Turbulence Prediction Systems to develop an infrared radiometry sensor.[35]

The radar windshear detection technology was developed by the researchers at Langley, but the system's basic component was a specially modified Model 708 X-band weather radar built by Rockwell Collins, Inc. The NASA engineers had developed a radar and ground clutter simulation model at the beginning of the windshear program, which they had been using to explore various radar design and signal processing methods. Their work indicated that by making some design modifications to the radar, using filtering in the signal and data processing, and managing the tilt of the radar antenna, the ground clutter problem could be eliminated without diminishing the radar's ability to detect windshear.[36]

The NASA researchers also designed two additional warning systems that did not use forward-looking airborne technology. The first was an improved "in situ" reactive system that used airspeed, accelerometer, angle of attack, groundspeed, and other data from aircraft sensors to verify when windshear was actually encountered. Although reactive systems were already being developed by commercial manufacturers, the NASA version had more comprehensive, three-dimensional capabilities. A comprehensive and precise reactive system was critical to the windshear research because the "In Situ" detector was the "truth" measurement against which the accuracy of the forward-looking systems would be judged.

The final detection system was simply a VHF radio data link that would allow information from a ground Terminal Doppler Weather Radar (TDWR) to be transmitted to the airplane directly. The standard TDWR design transmitted the information from the radar to a tower controller, who then had to transmit a verbal caution to flight crews. Clearly, a data link would improve the timeliness of windshear warnings to any airplane landing at an airport equipped with a TDWR. But the NASA researchers also planned to use TDWR information, uplinked to the TSRV 737 airplane and processed to indicate the "F-Factor" hazard level of any indicated windshear, to help them locate microbursts for flight testing the forward-looking sensor systems.[37]

Technicians service the tail-mounted reciever on the NASA 737 used in the windshear detection research project.

Developing the various sensor technologies took several years. In the process, the researchers made extensive use of computer models and piloted simulations developed by engineers at the Langley Research Center. Potential versions of the different detection systems were "flown" against computer models of past windshear accidents many times to determine how accurately the hazards were detected and measured. Yet especially with tricky, unstable phenomena like windshear and microbursts, computer simulations could only go so far. In order to get a true sense of the accuracy and performance of the sensors, they had to be tested in actual windshear conditions. In May 1990, a second Memorandum of Agreement was signed between the FAA and NASA to support a flight test program for demonstrating and validating the advanced windshear detection systems.[38]

Flight testing this particular technology raised some significant safety considerations, however. The microburst windshear that was so lethal to aircraft occurred only close to the ground. To flight test the windshear sensors, NASA's 737 test plane would have to intentionally fly into microburst conditions at low altitude. At best, the tests would be intense, turbulent encounters with an extremely severe weather environment. But if the sensors underestimated the severity of a microburst,

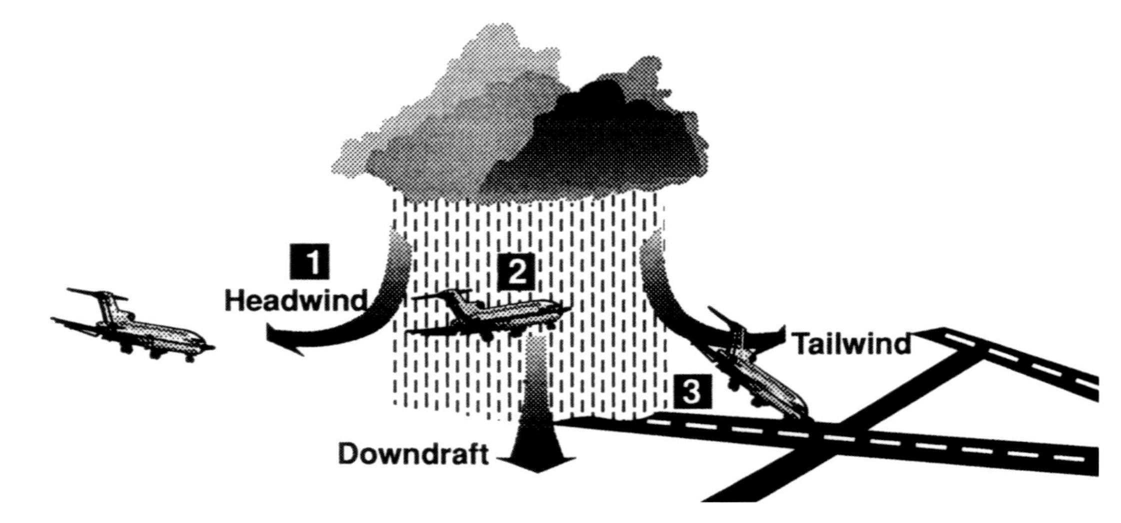

Schematic of microburst windshear and its threat to aircraft. 1: During a landing a plane entering a microburst encounters head winds that increase airspeed. To maintain airspeed and rate of descent the pilot will normally reduce power. The plane flies through the headwind and 2: encounters a downdraft followed by a 3: tailwind. These rapidly reduce airspeed and climb potential and, because of the earlier cut in power, can cause the plane to crash.

there would be much less margin than usual to correct for the error.

To minimize the risks, the researchers at Langley conducted an unusually thorough examination of the flight test plan before it was approved. First, research pilots "flew" possible flight test scenarios in the Transport Systems Research Vehicle (TSRV) fixed base piloted simulator to establish operating procedures with adequate safety margins. After experimenting with numerous parameters and procedures, the researchers drew up a list of guidelines to ensure flight safety during the tests. The first was to minimize weather exposure. The team would work with isolated thunderstorm cells, but would avoid cells embedded in frontal systems. Furthermore, although the penetrations would be flown by the safety pilots in the forward flight deck, who could see the actual conditions the airplane was encountering, they would be guided by the pilots monitoring the electronic windshear and navigation displays in the 737's experimental aft flight deck (AFD). Before each microburst was entered, the AFD pilots would give the safety pilots an escape vector in case the cell was stronger than expected. Ground obstacles that might be a factor at low altitudes would be programmed into the moving map display in the aft cockpit, as well, so the crew there could make sure the airplane stayed clear of them.[39]

Some weather risks could not be completely eliminated, however. It was going to be impossible to conduct microburst experiments, for example, without running some risk of a lightning strike. The biggest danger posed by lightning was that a spark might ignite the airplane's fuel, triggering a catastrophic explosion. So before the flight tests began, NASA called in specialists to thoroughly inspect and seal the 737's fuel tanks and system. Lightning could also severely damage the research equipment on board the airplane, so Langley technicians tried to harden the equipment against strikes as much as possible. While lightning still posed a threat to some of the equipment, the researchers felt the risks had been reduced to an acceptable level.[40]

Second, the researchers set firm operating limits for microburst penetrations. For cells with an "F-factor" greater than .1, they set a minimum flight altitude of 750 feet above the ground and a minimum indicated airspeed of 210 knots. Microbursts with an F-factor greater than .15 would be avoided. The plane would also stay clear of weather cells with extremely high levels of "reflectivity," or dense precipitation, to minimize the risk of hail damage. Even in less dense rain, however, the igniters in the 737's JT8D jet engines would be left on to minimize the chance of a flame out due to water ingestion. The researchers also planned a phased approach to the microburst experiments, starting with mild shear conditions and working up to the more severe storm cells.

Third, an extensive training program was developed for pilots and researchers who would be taking part in the flight tests. Flight crews were put through literally hundreds of simulated windshear penetrations so they could practice appropriate responses. The flight and research crew then underwent two weeks of rehearsal flights in the vicinity of the Langley Research Center and the Wallops Flight Facility before the team deployed for the actual microburst experiments.

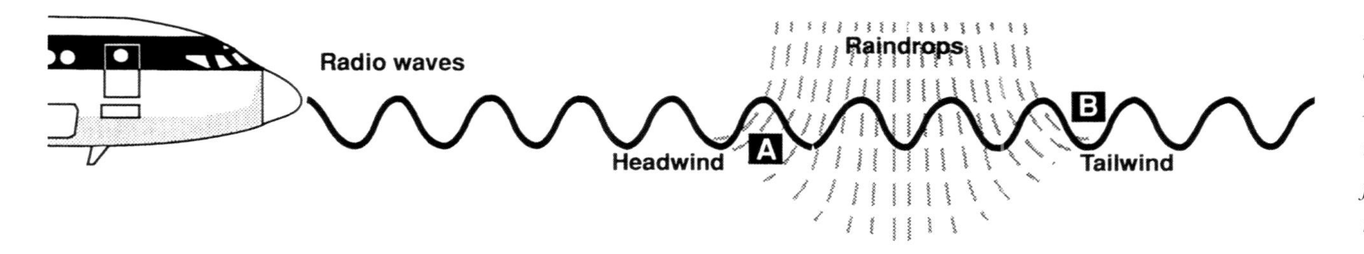

How the microwave detection system works. Microwave radar emits radio waves at a uniform frequency and wavelength that are reflected back by raindrops. The returning signals' frequency is measured and compared with the emitted frequency to determine the direction and speed of the raindrops. A Doppler reading of varying wavelengths can indicate a wind shear condition. A: The raindrops borne by headwinds return a shorter wavelength. B: The raindrops borne by tailwinds return a longer wavelength.

The 737 was outfitted with some additional equipment for the windshear flight tests. The radar sensor used the flat plate Doppler weather radar that was already in the nose of the airplane, but a whole pallet of processing equipment for the system had to be installed in the cabin. The LIDAR also required a pallet of equipment in the cabin, in addition to a sensor that was attached to the underside of the 737's fuselage. The infrared sensor was installed in a window on the left side of the plane. Changes were also made to the research flight deck to allow the windshear data to be displayed. The electronic map and primary flight displays in the left seat position of the aft cockpit were left alone, but three of the cathode ray tube (CRT) screens on the right side were modified to display windshear information, and two additional CRT displays were installed above the standard instrument panel. Each of the two monitors above the instrument panel could be configured to show a real-time forward-looking image from a television camera in the nose of the plane, the radar sensor display or the LIDAR sensor display. Another CRT screen showed information from the infrared and in situ sensors, and two additional monitors displayed the data linked information from the TDWR.

The display formats were created primarily by Langley engineers. Sensor data from the infrared and in situ detection systems was displayed in simple bar graphs indicating the "F-factor" level of the hazard. The radar and LIDAR sensors were capable of detecting a much more comprehensive picture of the airspace ahead of the airplane, however, so the information from those sensors was processed into graphic, multi-color displays, coded to indicate levels of windshear severity. If the sensors detected a windshear over a .1 threshold, both displays would highlight the threat area with either a box, in the case of the radar display, or a diamond in the case of the LIDAR. The highlighted area would also display the numerical "F-Factor" of the shear, and a large "ALERT" signal would appear on the screen.

The TDWR displays, which were the primary navigation aids in finding microbursts, integrated all the windshear detection information. The basic TDWR display would indicate microburst hazards with oval, race track-shaped icons. The icons were color coded, depending on the severity of the microburst, and a numerical indication of the F-factor of each particular microburst accompanied the icons. When the radar or LIDAR forward-looking sensors detected the shear, the warning box or diamond, with the F-factor, would be replicated on the TDWR screen. Warnings from the infrared sensor were displayed in numerical format in a corner of the TDWR screens. When the airplane actually entered the microburst and the in situ sensor detected an F-factor hazard over a .1 threshold, a red dot appeared over the microburst icon on the TDWR displays. The accuracy of the forward-looking sensors could be verified by comparing the numerical data recorded from all five of the sensor systems.[41]

The initial flight tests were conducted during the summer of 1991, in Orlando, Florida, and Denver, Colorado. The locations were picked for two reasons. First, Orlando and Denver each had an TDWR system in the vicinity of the airport. Second, microbursts in Orlando tended to be "wet" cells, while a majority of those in Denver were "dry." By flight testing the sensors in both places, researchers could find out how well each system performed across a full range of microburst conditions.

The LIDAR equipment was not yet ready for flight testing in 1991, however, so the initial experiments involved only the radar and infrared systems. The first tests took place around the Orlando International Airport from June 10th through June 20th. A team of more than 50 researchers, technicians, and meteorologists was involved, including researchers from the Massachusetts Institute of Technology's Lincoln Laboratory, who operated the Orlando TDWR equipment.

On a typical flight day, the research team received its first weather briefing in the late morning, since microbursts typically did not develop until the afternoon or evening hours. After the briefing, the researchers often had to endure hours of waiting before the right weather conditions materialized. When the meteorologists saw promising signs of microburst activity, the flight crew of nearly 30 researchers and pilots boarded the 737 and took off.

The flight operations themselves were complicated, because in order to use the TDWR to help locate microbursts, the NASA plane had to stay in the immediate vicinity of the airport. The researchers discussed the flight test plans and procedures with the airport air traffic controllers in advance, but the flight crew still had to stay in constant communication with controllers throughout the flight to avoid conflicts with other airport traffic. The crew also had to be in constant contact with the TDWR ground personnel for microburst and other weather information. Added to these communications were numerous other conversations over the airplane's internal intercom between the two flight decks and between the different research stations and the crew viewing the displays in the aft flight deck. Communication was actually one of the toughest challenges of the flight tests, as the work often required as many as five different voice channels to be active at the same time.

A test run began when the ground TDWR personnel notified the flight crew of a potential microburst target. Lee H. Person, the primary aft flight deck pilot for the 737 throughout its 20 years at the Langley Research Center, usually flew the airplane onto a final approach path to the microburst, because he had the advantage of the CRT navigation and TDWR displays. The team had to maneuver quickly, because microbursts were a short-lived phenomenon, lasting only five to 10 minutes. On approximately a two mile final approach to the microburst, Person would turn control of the airplane over to research pilot Kenneth R. "Dick" Yenni in the forward cockpit. Yenni, like Person, had been with the airplane since it arrived at NASA and was the primary safety pilot on the 737. Test runs were flown in level flight at altitudes between 750 and 1,000 feet above ground level, and before entering a severe microburst, the 737's airspeed was stabilized at 210 knots. The procedure was to enter each microburst with an indicated airspeed of 210 knots and then, as the plane encountered the initial headwinds, add power as necessary to maintain at least a 210 knot groundspeed. That way, the airplane would have enough power and airspeed to safely transit the microburst, no matter how great the windshear.

As the 737 approached the microburst, the activity in the airplane became highly focused and intense. The forward flight deck pilots were watching for air traffic, obstacles and unacceptable conditions, such as severe lightning. At the same time, they were keeping up a running conversation with the air traffic controllers, and listening for course corrections, hazard and escape vector information, and groundspeed reports from the pilots in the aft flight deck. In addition to the constant reports they were giving to the safety pilots, the crew in the aft flight deck was talking continually with the ground TDWR personnel to make sure the windshear and reflectivity levels in the target microburst were still within acceptable safety limits and no other hazards had arisen. On two different intercom channels, researchers were giving status reports or positioning requests for the different sensors. Meanwhile, the weather around the airplane would deteriorate rapidly as the 737 entered the kind of rain-filled thunderstorm cell typical of Florida microbursts. The plane was buffeted by turbulence and rain pounded at the windows. The world outside the cabin became dark and threatening, lit up only by lightning flashes, which were sometimes so close the researchers could "hear thunder inside the airplane." The first few times out there were reportedly some wide eyes throughout the cabin, but after a while, the flights became almost routine to the research crew. Even during the first few flight tests, however, the sensor monitoring, status reports, and communications among crew members continued uninterrupted through even the most turbulent storm encounters.

In all the flight testing in Orlando, there were no "safety of flight" issues, but there were more than a few tense moments. Once, the weather conditions around the airplane suddenly closed in, and the 737 crew found the airplane headed up a blind canyon of thunderstorm cells that were all beyond the safety limits set for the flight experiments. Fortunately, the safety pilots found a slightly lighter section of clouds between two cells and were able to steer the plane through the hole without incident. On several other occasions, the plane came close to being hit by lightning, but it never actually took a lightning strike. It did, however, run into hail in one of the more severe microbursts it penetrated.

Following the Orlando experiments, the plane and its research crew travelled to Denver Colorado for two more weeks of flight testing on July 8 - July 24, 1991. The flight tests were staged out of Denver Stapleton Airport and used the NCAR "Mile High" Doppler ground radar in nearby Boulder to help locate the microbursts. The procedure was similar to that followed in the Orlando tests, although the conditions were expected to be somewhat different. The researchers were hoping to encounter "dry" microbursts in Denver, which would present severe windshears without the heavy rainfall of the Florida storm cells. Unfortunately, the weather refused to cooperate. The only

To obtain the data required, NASA windshear researchers intentionally flew in conditions most pilots try to avoid.

windshears the researchers found in the two weeks at Denver were generated by gust fronts. The gust front shears were still quite strong, however, and they caused some unique flight conditions. Several of the fronts threw up dust clouds from the ground, and some of the 737's low-level test flights were at or below the tops of the dust clouds. As a result, the research crew found that they had discovered a new and unusual way to get the bottom of the airplane dirty.

The Langley crew boarding the Boeing 737 research aircraft in preparation for a windshear detection flight at Orlando, Florida.

The results of the 1991 flight experiments showed that the forward-looking radar detection system successfully identified and tracked high hazard areas in flight, although the low moisture microbursts that were expected to present the greatest challenge to radar were not tested. The in situ warnings also correlated well with the other detection systems. The infrared sensor did not fare anywhere near as well, but another round of flight experiments was scheduled for the summer of 1992, when the LIDAR equipment would also be tested.[42]

The 1992 flight tests very nearly did not happen, however. The plan was to repeat the basic 1991 schedule, with flight tests first in Orlando and then in Denver. Everything was going according to schedule until two months before the Florida tests, when several problems arose that should have cancelled the entire summer's test flights. First, both of the 737's engines developed problems and had to be overhauled or replaced. Then, even before the engine work had begun, maintenance technicians discovered some de-bonding in certain lap joints of the 737's fuselage skin. This same problem had caused an Aloha Airlines 737 to lose a section of its fuselage in flight, so the NASA airplane was grounded until all the affected areas could be riveted together. This was a major maintenance project, and under ordinary circumstances, the airplane would have been down for several months.[43] But this was not an ordinary airplane or program.

Throughout the history of the flight research program at Langley, the 737 and its research projects had attracted a unique type of person. Taking research all the way to flight required much more detail work and presented a lot of unknowns and obstacles that were never encountered in laboratory tests. Projects that included flight testing also forced researchers to focus on real world, practical applications of their ideas. It took an enthusiastic, pragmatic and resourceful person to enjoy working on flight test research programs, and the people who worked with the TSRV 737 were often characterized as having an energetic, "can do" attitude about their projects and the airplane. But the power of their resourcefulness and dedication was never more evident than in the 1992 windshear test program.

When the 737 technicians and researchers got the bad news about the airplane, most people assumed the summer windshear experiments would have to be cancelled. That would set the research back a full year, since microbursts occurred primarily during the summer months. In addition to being frustrating, a year's delay could make it more difficult for airlines to use forward-looking detection systems, because it would leave little time for industry to incorporate the technology before the FAA deadline for installing windshear detectors.

Some of the people involved with the program refused to give up so easily on the flight tests, however. Artie D. Jessup, an electronics technician who worked on the plane's research systems, came up with the idea of leaving the research pallets and wiring in the airplane during the airframe repair. There was some risk that the wiring could be damaged during the riveting process, but if it worked, it would eliminate weeks of work. Jessup argued that the risk of damage could be minimized, and the repair technicians could probably work around most of the experimental equipment. So the equipment was left in place. The determination of the

Langley crew also seemed to rub off on the workers at the repair facility in Birmingham, Alabama, because they put extra people on the project, worked round the clock shifts, and returned the airplane a week ahead of schedule.

Even then it appeared that, at best, the airplane would only be able to complete one of the windshear flight tests before the end of the summer. Although the program managers thought they might be able to gain a little extra time by conducting the Denver flight tests first, since the Florida microburst season tended to last a little longer, they were still doubtful that the airplane and its equipment could be ready in time. But then Michael Basnett, the airplane's crew chief, took up the challenge. He told the program managers that if they could get the research equipment ready, he and his crew would do whatever it took to make sure the airplane was also ready in time for both deployments. The positive attitudes exhibited by Jessup and Basnett began to spread. After all, if the crew chief was willing to make that kind of commitment, with all the maintenance problems the airplane was having, the other team members decided they could do no less. A growing conviction began to emerge from the windshear team that they might just be able to get the job done, after all. That conviction was backed by the managers of the Flight Systems directorate, who authorized the funding and overtime the effort required.

Over the next few weeks the researchers and technicians worked long hours, including weekends and holidays, to get the airplane and the research equipment ready. As Dr. Bowles described it, "Nobody wanted to be pointed to as the guy holding up the program." Problems that arose were handled quickly and quietly, with as little disturbance to other work areas as possible. A strong team spirit developed among those working on the project, and morale remained extremely high throughout the flight test program. The team even printed up colorful "Burst-busters" patches that they wore with pride alongside the NASA insignia on their flight suits. Finally, the long hours, dedication, and effort paid off. On July 13th, two months to the day after the airplane arrived back at Langley from the Birmingham repair facility, the windshear team departed for Denver.[44]

The Denver flight tests were held on July 14–18, 1992. This time, the researchers found the dry microbursts they were seeking and were able to get solid data on the performance of all three forward-looking sensors. Two weeks after returning to Virginia, the team flew to Orlando for a second round of flight tests in "wet" microburst conditions. The flight tests ran from August 11 - 25, 1992. Aside from a two-day hiatus when the airplane had to be flown back to Langley to avoid Hurricane Andrew, the research went extremely well. Weather conditions cooperated, and the researchers were able to get excellent data on the radar, LIDAR and infrared systems.

Video display of a windshear research flight undertaken by the NASA 737 aircraft in 1991. Although the aircraft was not hit by lightning, it came very close.

The flight tests showed that the radar system accurately and reliably detected and tracked hazards in both wet and dry microburst conditions. The advance warning given by the radar was impressive, sometimes alerting the pilots to a hazard as much as a minute in advance. The LIDAR detected the dry microbursts well in Denver, but was less effective in the heavy rain conditions encountered in Florida. The LIDAR was the least developed of the technologies, however, and was still considered to hold some promise for the future. On the other hand, the researchers finally concluded that the infrared technology, was unable to reliably detect windshear activity.[45]

Throughout the course of the FAA/NASA windshear program, researchers had kept in close contact with potential commercial manufacturers of the technology. The Langley Research Center held yearly conferences to update industry on the progress in the program and made all the computer modelling and simulation technology developed by the NASA

Ground radome at Boulder, Colorado, providing data for windshear detection research project from the Center for Atmospheric Research.

researchers during the program available to any interested company. The Westinghouse Electric Company, the Bendix/King Division of Allied Signal Aerospace and the Collins Air Transport division of Rockwell International were all acutely interested in forward-looking windshear detection technology, especially since the FAA was going to require some kind of detectors in all future airliners. Representatives from these three companies visited Langley often and talked to researchers almost weekly over the telephone. Consequently, the manufacturers knew as much about the technology as the NASA researchers by the time the test flights were completed. In perhaps the most telling measurement of the program's success, all three companies had commercial radar-based forward-looking windshear detection systems almost ready for FAA certification less than a year after the NASA windshear research was completed.[46]

In fact, the NASA/FAA windshear program was an almost classic example of a successful government/industry research effort from the very start of the project. Like many of the early National Advisory Committee for Aeronautics (NACA) research projects, it was a very focused, mission-oriented program that took a proven, significant threat to aviation and air transportation and developed new technology that could defeat it. At the same time, the windshear program illustrated how complex a technology development effort could be. The program structure was a joint venture between NASA and the FAA, and the airborne detection program was only one component of an even bigger National Integrated Windshear Plan. Within NASA itself, the program involved numerous different research directorates, including electronics, engineering, aeronautics, and flight systems. In addition, the program involved researchers from industry and academia, as well as agencies like the National Center for Atmospheric Research (NCAR).

The windshear research itself was also complex. It incorporated physics, meteorology and engineering and consisted of theory, analysis, simulation, and flight testing. The work also had to be completed in a relatively short period of time. In addition, the flight tests were unusually demanding, and in order to complete them successfully, the researchers had to pull together as a team to overcome some significant obstacles. Yet despite the difficulties, the research was highly successful. There were several scientific and technological breakthroughs made during the windshear program, including the invention of the "F-factor" and the development of a Doppler radar-based ,forward-looking windshear detector. As a result, the program was able to develop new technology to finally tame the microburst windshear threat. Furthermore, since the NASA engineers had worked with potential commercial manufacturers of the technology from the start of the program, the transfer of the technology occurred smoothly, quickly, and effectively.

Of course, there were other factors that influenced the success of the windshear program, as well. The research might not have been done at all, and certainly would not have been completed in such an expeditious manner, if it had not been for the airline accidents in New Orleans and Dallas and the public and political pressure that followed them. By the same token, no matter how impressive or worthwhile the research results were, the information might not have been applied quite as quickly by industry manufacturers if it had not been for the FAA regulation requiring airliners to install windshear detectors. The FAA regulation created an automatic market for windshear detection technology, which made commercial companies more willing to develop forward-looking detection systems. The manufacturers still had to compete with reactive systems, but they did not have to argue the basic cost-benefits of windshear detectors.

The NASA 737 also played an important role in gaining acceptance for the forward-looking detection systems among manufacturers and airlines. The fact that the windshear research included flight tests in the 737 meant that the technology was developed further than if the program had been limited to computer simulations. Consequently, there was a much smaller gap for the manufacturers to close between the NASA research effort and the commercial applications of the technology. In addition, the NASA test data, collected in a transport airplane and in realistic microburst conditions, presented unassailable proof that an airborne Doppler radar could reliably and accurately detect windshear 40 seconds or more before the airplane entered it. This conclusive evidence gave both the manufacturers and their customers a critical boost of confidence in the new technology.

The 737 flight tests were only the final, visible step in a complex, seven-year research effort, however. Without the wide diversity of research talent both at the Langley Research Center and in the companies, universities, and other government agencies that participated in the program, the support of managers at NASA and the FAA, and the remarkable dedication of all the research team members, the flight tests would not have happened. In recognition of the extraordinary effort put forth by those involved and the significance of what they achieved, the NASA/FAA airborne windshear research program was nominated in 1992 for a Collier Trophy — the highest honor an American aviation research effort can receive. Industry evaluations of the program by NASA's Aeronautics Advisory Committee were full of praise, describing the research effort as a "perfect role for NASA in support of national needs" and "NASA at its best."[47] The windshear research team at NASA agreed. "This was the best we can do," Dr. Creedon said. "We might get that good again, but we can't get any better." [48]

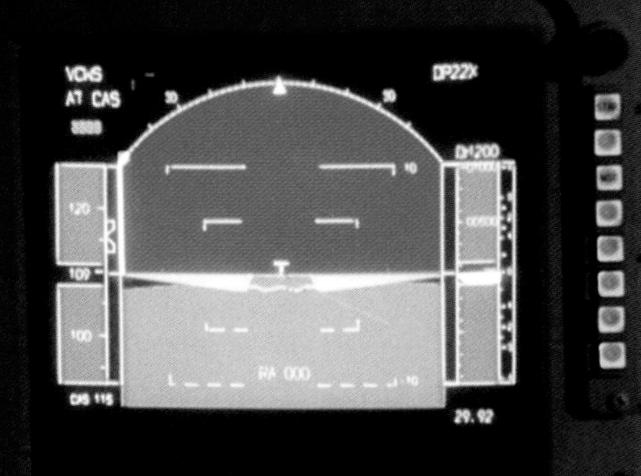
AT CAS
RA 000
29.92

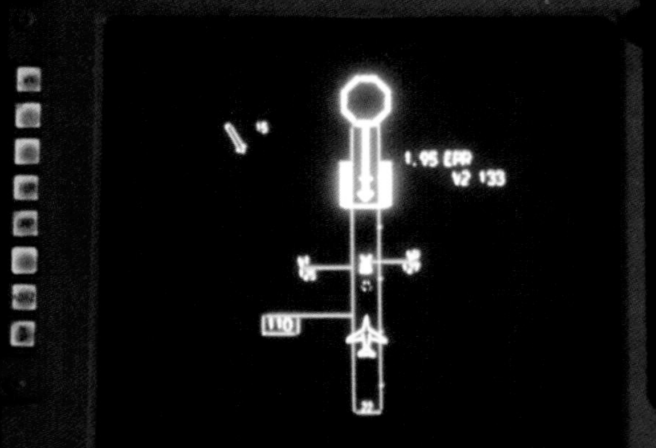
V2 133
110

Chapter 6

Improving Aircraft Systems

When the NASA Terminal Configured Vehicle (TCV) program began in 1973, the goal was to develop airborne systems and flight procedures that could improve the safety, efficiency, and capacity of terminal, or airport, operations. As the program evolved into Advanced Transport Operating Systems (ATOPS), the research expanded. Instead of concentrating only in the terminal area, the goal became improving the efficiency and safety of flight operations throughout the National Airspace System.[1] One area the NASA researchers targeted to help accomplish this goal was the development of more capable and efficient aircraft systems.

Left—A heads-up electronic flight display tested at NASA's Langley Research Center to improve aircraft performance and safety. Right—NASA Langley's "flying laboratory" at sunset.

The ATOPS program and the Boeing 737 Transport Systems Research Vehicle (TSRV) conducted several different technology research projects during the 1980s and early 1990s that were geared toward improving the internal systems and operation of transport aircraft. A Digital Autonomous Terminal Access Communication (DATAC) data bus and experimental optical engine control technology offered improved control and operation of basic aircraft systems. A Total Energy Control System (TECS) allowed aircraft to fly more efficiently and comfortably by integrating autopilot and autothrottle controls. An Engine Monitoring and Control System (E-MACS) showed that safety could be increased and pilot workload decreased by redesigning engine instrumentation displays. A Takeoff Performance Monitoring System (TOPMS) provided pilots with visual information on the progress of a takeoff roll to help them make the critical "Go/No Go" decision.

All these technologies offered significant improvements in various aspects of aircraft systems and operations — at least in theory. Yet while the research results for all the technologies were positive, the degree to which they were incorporated into commercial aircraft varied widely. DATAC was so well accepted that it became the basis of an industry design standard. TECS was incorporated into a remote piloted vehicle designed by the Boeing Commercial Airplane Company, but it was not designed into any of the company's transport aircraft. E-MACS was not immediately adopted by the air transport

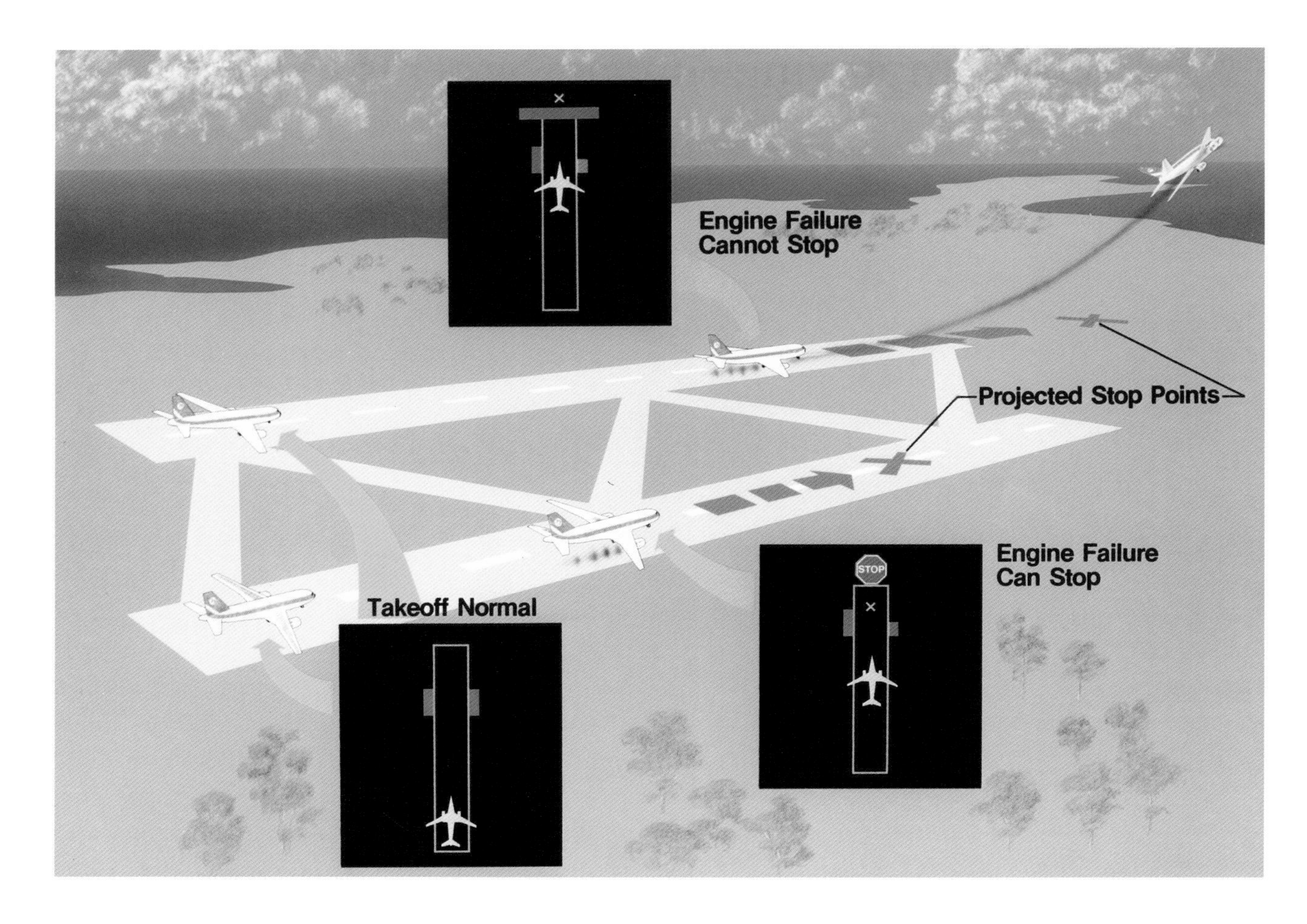

Briefing concept for Langley's research effort to develop a takeoff performance monitor for use on commercial aircraft.

industry, but the technology was enthusiastically accepted by a general aviation manufacturer, and it garnered enough industry interest to make it a potential addition to future transport aircraft designs. TOPMS, on the other hand, was popular with pilots but was not widely supported by the commercial air transport airframe manufacturers or airlines, although McDonnell Douglas decided to research the technology further to see if its deficiencies could be resolved.

The ATOPS research showed several ways technology could improve aircraft systems. But it also illustrated the complexity of the technology application process. To a researcher at NASA's Langley Research Center, a technology with improved performance was clearly better than an old method. But the commercial manufacturers and airlines who would use the technology had to take more complex factors into account. Just because a technology appeared worthwhile to researchers did not necessarily mean that manufacturers or the airlines would view it the same way.

DATAC

The ATOPS program did not actually conduct any dedicated research into data bus design. But in 1983, the aerospace engineers who were responsible for the 737's research systems began looking for a better way to integrate the various system components. To make the experimental systems work, the flight control, navigation and display computers and any experimental equipment being tested on the airplane had to communicate with each other. Up until that point, each separate computer or component that needed to exchange information with any other system or equipment had to have a dedicated wire for each connection. In other words, if a computer had to give information to three other components and receive information from three others, it had to have a total of six cables connected to it. This limited the number of elements that could be integrated into the system, and made the installation of any experimental equipment a time-consuming job.

David C. Holmes, who was chief engineer of the Experimental Flight Systems Section (EFSS), came across an experimental concept that he thought might be a great improvement to this cumbersome system. The new technology, called Digital Autonomous Terminal Access Communication (DATAC), was being developed at Boeing by an engineer named Hans Herzog. It was a design for a single, global data bus that would carry all the information between the different components of the airplane systems. The data bus consisted of a single twisted pair of wires, to which all the components that needed to exchange information were connected. Instead of mechanical splices, all the coupling was magnetic, and each "box" or computer needed only a single clip connection to the data bus. To keep the data from each component from getting jumbled with the other information being exchanged, each component's data was coded and "broadcast" in a synchronized order. All the information was transmitted on the data bus, and each computer or component could be programmed to pull off whatever information it needed.[2]

The DATAC system was a perfect design for the NASA 737. It would allow a far greater number of components to be integrated into the aircraft systems, and it would greatly reduce the amount of time required to add or exchange experimental equipment. Since the data bus had fewer wires and components, it would also be lighter and would require less maintenance than a conventional system. The only problem was that in 1983, DATAC existed in concept only. Herzog was working with it in a lab at Boeing, but the technology was far from fully developed. Nevertheless, Holmes presented the potential benefits of the system to William E. Howell, who was the chief of the Langley ATOPS program at that point, and Howell approved the idea.[3]

Putting experimental equipment on the TSRV airplane was nothing new. But this case was different. The data bus was part of the airplane's basic infrastructure. If it did not work, none of the experimental systems, including the navigation, flight control and display computers, would be able to function. In addition, there was a time element to be considered. The 737 was expected to be grounded for the upgrade and an engine repair for about a year. But that was not very much time to develop the technology for a new data bus, build aircraft-compatible equipment, design whatever software it needed to operate and install it in the airplane. If the airplane was ready and the data bus was not, it would set all the ATOPS research projects behind schedule. Yet the potential benefits seemed worth the risks involved.

The development of the DATAC data bus became a joint effort between Boeing and NASA. Herzog and his team designed and built the data bus itself and the terminals that provided the interface between the data bus and the computers or components using the system. NASA engineers designed interface boxes and software that would convert the data from the format needed for transmission on the data bus to a format the 737's computers and experimental systems could understand.

Boeing first had to create crude laboratory versions of the terminals to send to the Langley Research Center so the engineers there could begin developing the software. The Boeing researchers then worked on designing aircraft versions of the terminals, which had to be smaller by two thirds than the laboratory equipment. In the summer of 1984, after a year-long effort, the data bus, the magnetic couplers and the aircraft versions of the terminals were ready. Herzog and several of his co-workers travelled to Langley with the equipment to help integrate it with the NASA-designed interface boxes and software and install the system in the airplane.

The equipment still needed a fair amount of fine-tuning, however, and time was getting short. The rest of the upgrade was nearly finished, and the 737 was scheduled to begin flight testing again in a few weeks. As a result, the Boeing-NASA crew spent many long hours in Langley's Experimental Avionics Simulation and Integration Laboratory (EASILY) working out bugs in the system, including one memorable weekend when the power went out in the building. Time was too precious to wait until maintenance crews could fix the problem Monday morning, so the crew set up a generator in the parking lot and continued working with flashlights and small work lights throughout the weekend.[4]

By the beginning of August 1984, DATAC was installed and working in the airplane. The 737 made an excellent test bed for a new data bus, because the equipment in the front cockpit remained conventional. If the DATAC system had ever developed a problem in flight, the safety pilots could have taken over and flown the airplane. The system never had any such problems, however. The Langley engineers and technicians were extremely pleased with its operation and reliability, as well as the ease with which new experiments or systems could now be integrated into the airplane.

In September 1985, after the DATAC system had flown on the 737 for over a year, a team of engineers working on Boeing's new transport design, designated the "7J7," visited Langley to look at some of the new technologies the ATOPS program was exploring. Howell was giving them a demonstration of the equipment on the TSRV airplane, when one of the engineers asked if DATAC was being used for data recording. Howell told him it was being used not only for data recording, but for the full experimental flight control system. The Boeing engineers became more interested, and asked how many problems the NASA crew was experiencing with the data bus. "None," Howell replied. In that one simple interchange, a significant amount of the NASA work on DATAC was successfully transferred to industry.[5]

Boeing actually owned the DATAC technology. But the system might not have been developed enough to use in the 7J7 design had NASA not supported Herzog's work. By the same token, the design team working on the 7J7 might not have had the confidence to use a dramatically new technology for something as important as the basic system architecture of a new airliner if it had not proven itself first on the TSRV airplane. Although the 7J7 was never built, the DATAC technology was incorporated into Boeing's next jet transport design, the B-777.

DATAC worked so well, in fact, that Aeronautical Radio, Inc. (ARINC) used it as the basis of a new industry data bus standard. ARINC is a not-for-profit organization owned and supported by the airlines that sets standard specifications for technology, so the products developed by different manufacturers will be compatible with all commercial transport aircraft. The specification for the new data bus, called ARINC 629, was adopted in September 1989.[6]

The DATAC research was a somewhat unusual joint partnership between Boeing and NASA. The bulk of the development work was done by a Boeing engineer, and the work was supported by NASA primarily because the data bus could give NASA's own B-737 test airplane enhanced capability. In the process, however, the TSRV 737 played a crucial role in gaining acceptance for the data bus in not only Boeing's newest airliner, but the entire next generation of transport airplanes.

OPMIS

Six years after the DATAC system was installed on the 737, the ATOPS program researchers began working on a joint project with the McDonnell Douglas Aircraft Corporation that showed potential of someday usurping the ARINC 629 standard. The project was called the Optical Propulsion Management Interface System (OPMIS), and it represented a first step toward a concept called fly-by-light technology. Fly-by-light systems would use fiber optic cables instead of electrical wires to transmit signals to operate the flight and engine controls of an airplane.

Fiber optic technology had several potential advantages. The most significant one was that it could eliminate problems with electromagnetic interference (EMI) that often occurred with closely grouped electrical wires. Fiber optic cables could also carry much more information than electrical wires, so a fly-by-light system

Front view of NASA Langley's 737 Flying Laboratory.

Heads-up visual displays of the Take Off Performance Monitoring System tested on the Langley 737 aircraft. Left—An acceptable acceleration error. Center—An unacceptable acceleration error with an abort advisory sign. Right—A single-engine failure without an abort advisory.

would have expanded capabilities. In addition, the technology was lighter weight than comparable electrical systems, which would translate into increased efficiency in aircraft performance.

McDonnell Douglas had been working on fly-by-light technology since 1987 and wanted to test the concept on an airplane. The McDonnell Douglas engineers decided to start with a fiber optic engine control system, because it would be a manageable project and it would be safer than experimenting with an entire flight control system. Even if a fly-by-light system failed, the test airplane would still have at least one good engine and all its flight controls functioning, so it could land safely.

The OPMIS project was actually a joint effort among several entities. McDonnell Douglas worked with United Technologies, Inc. to develop the basic fly-by-light technology. The big hurdle in the fly-by-light system, however, was the development of optical sensors to interface with the engine itself, and five different companies built experimental sensors to test during the research program. NASA engineers at Langley then integrated the OPMIS technology into the TSRV 737 airplane.

OPMIS used optical sensors installed in a bracket on the throttle controls to pick up any changes in throttle position. That change would be transmitted by fiber optic cable to the engine, where an engine controller would translate the optical signal to an electrical one which, through an actuator, would move the engine controls to correspond with the throttle position. Data on the operation of the OPMIS equipment would then be sent via fiber optic cables, but in the ARINC 629 data bus format, to the research pallets in the back of the 737 airplane. Although the point of the research was not to investigate data bus technology, the OPMIS research was the first time an optical ARINC 629 data bus had ever been flown on an airplane.

Developing the system presented some new technical challenges, because fiber optic cables had to be handled differently than electrical cables. Working with fiber optics required new techniques, as well as different connections, harnesses, and hardware. The NASA engineers also decided to incorporate shear fuses into the system that would allow the safety pilots to physically disconnect the OPMIS system from the engine in case of a problem or equipment failure. If the OPMIS equipment was disconnected, the engine control would revert to its baseline mechanical system.

Finally, in the spring of 1993, an operational OPMIS system was installed on one of the TSRV 737's two Pratt & Whitney JT8D-7 engines. The research flights began in May 1993, and the researchers planned to fly OPMIS on the airplane on all its research flights.[7] Results would not be available for some time, but the TSRV 737 was continuing to play an important role in exploring the frontier boundaries of advanced aircraft systems.

TECS

The Total Energy Control System research was, essentially, an effort to make an autopilot/ autothrottle system perform more like an actual pilot. In most transport aircraft, the autopilot, which operated the aircraft flight controls, and the autothrottles, which managed the engine power settings, were designed as totally independent systems. If the pilots wanted to fly the airplane through its automatic controls, they would set a desired speed, heading, and altitude into a control panel. The autothrottles would correct deviations in speed by increasing or decreasing the power settings of the engines, and the autopilot would compensate for deviations in either altitude or heading by changing the pitch or bank angle of the airplane.

The systems were designed separately so that if one failed, it would not affect the operation of the other. The approach was not very efficient, however. The autopilot functions always had priority so, for example, if the airplane hit turbulence, the autopilot would be making constant pitch corrections to try to keep the airplane on the correct altitude. The autothrottle had no way of knowing that the pitch changes were temporary, so it would continually increase and decrease the throttle settings to try to keep the speed constant. The problem was even worse in other situations, such as when the airplane was trying to stay on a descending glideslope into an airport.

If the airplane was high and slow, on its approach, the autopilot would pitch the nose of the airplane down to get back to the proper descent path, and the autothrottles would increase the power settings to correct the speed. As the airplane pitched down, however, the plane would speed up, and the speed would increase even further because the autothrotttles had raised the engine power levels. Suddenly, the airplane would be too low and too fast. The autopilot would then pitch the airplane up, and the autothrottles would retard the engine settings. But that combination would cause the airplane to slow down too far, so the autothrottles would have to increase the power settings again. As the engines came up in power the airplane would start to climb, so the autopilot would tell the airplane to descend, and the whole cycle would start over again. The net result was that in automatic modes, the autothrottles were moving constantly, and the autopilot had to make an excess number of pitch adjustments. It was a system that was not only potentially uncomfortable, but also extremely wasteful of fuel.

A human pilot intuitively took a more coordinated approach to controlling an airplane. Upon realizing he was a little high and slow on a descent path, for example, he would simply point the nose of the airplane down, correcting both the alitutude and speed errors without adding power. In doing so, the pilot would be using the stored energy in the airplane's excess altitude and converting it into speed as he descended, instead of relying solely on the energy of the engines to adjust the airplane's speed.

The Total Energy Control System was an attempt to design a more efficient, integrated autothrottle/autopilot system that would make better use of an airplane's stored energy. Studies at the Langley Research Center had indicated the potential advantages of such a design, and in 1979-1981, NASA contracted with engineers at the Boeing Commercial Airplane Company to develop the control laws the system would require. After pursuing several design strategies that did not work, the engineers finally focused on how the different controls affected the energy of the airplane. The throttle, they realized, controlled the energy state of the plane, and the elevator controlled the distribution of that energy from flight path to speed.

Within six months of that realization, the Boeing engineers successfully completed the design of the Total Energy Control System (TECS). When making decisions about how to correct errors in the aircraft's flight path or speed, TECS would first look at the energy state of the airplane. If it was correct, TECS would simply use the elevator to redistribute the energy to achieve the desired flight path or speed. For example, if the airplane was high and slow on an approach, TECS would recognize the potential energy in the extra altitude, and use the elevator to pitch the airplane down, just as a human pilot would. When a maneuver demanded a significant climb or descent rate and/or a very large speed change, of course, it might exceed the energy capabilities of the airplane. In that case, TECS would first insure that the engine settings were within the pre-set limits programmed into the system. It would then give priority to meeting either the speed or flight path target, depending on which mode the pilot had selected. In an aborted landing and go-around situation, for example, speed would be critical, so that would take precedence. If the pilot selected flight path priority, the airplane would give up speed to maintain the flight path target within the safety limits of the airplane's stall and maximum speed limits.

TECS was first tested in the real-time B-737 fixed base simulator at the Langley Research Center. The concept worked well in simulation, so the NASA engineers then programmed it into the TSRV's flight computers and conducted 20 hours of flight testing with the system in 1985. The objective was not only to test the performance of the technology, but also to give pilots an opportunity to fly and evaluate the integrated autopilot/autothrottle system. The flight test results showed that TECS met or exceeded all of its performance objectives, and pilots liked the system.

Yet by 1993, TECS had not been incorporated into any of Boeing's commercial transport aircraft, and the decision had been made not to include it in the new B-777 airliner the company was building. The primary reason was that implementing TECS required a complete redesign of the automatic control system. While the control laws the Boeing engineers used to develop TECS had been kept generic on purpose, to make the concept easily adaptable to new aircraft, designing a new control system from scratch would still entail significant costs for Boeing. In order to make that investment worthwhile, there would have to be a compelling need for the change, or significant cost savings involved. While TECS would result in fuel savings, the fuel crisis of the late 1970s that had helped spur the start of the research had subsided by the mid-1980s. The bottom line was that while TECS was an excellent concept, there was not yet a great enough need for it for Boeing to justify the expense of developing it into a commercial application. Nevertheless, Boeing engineers who worked on the project remained optimistic that a commercial transport application for it would eventually develop.

Actually, an application for TECS had already developed, although it was not in a commercial transport airplane. After the TECS research was completed, Boeing began building a high altitude, long endurance, unmanned airplane, called the Condor, for defense and/or other uses, such as patrolling the antarctic for holes in the ozone layer. As it was unmanned, the aircraft had to be flown entirely on autopilot. Since it was also designed for maximum endurance, that autopilot system had to be operating at peak efficiency, at altitudes where the speed envelope between its maximum speed and its stall speed was only two or three knots.

By a fortunate coincidence, one of the Boeing engineers who had worked on the early TECS research was assigned to the Condor project. The other engineers had heard of TECS, but having someone on the project who knew the technology intimately helped convince them to pursue it. It was easier to introduce new technology to the Condor project, of course, simply because of the aircraft's nature. It was unmanned, so there was no concern about having to re-train pilots. There were no human factors problems to consider. It was already being designed from scratch, so incorporating a new control system did not entail as many additional costs, and it was not a commercial airliner, so the new control system did not have to be re-certified by the Federal Aviation Administration.

Nevertheless, TECS still might not have been incorporated into the Condor if it was only a paper theory. The fact that the technology had already been successfully flight tested in NASA's 737 gave the Boeing designers a crucial level of confidence in its performance and reduced the risk level enough that Boeing was willing to use the new technology in an operational aircraft. [8]

E-MACS

The advent of computers in the cockpit and electronic flight displays had opened up tremendous new opportunities for conveying information to pilots. In the 1970s, the TCV program had conducted a lot of research into different display formats, but the focus had been primarily on flight and navigation displays. In 1987, however, a NASA researcher in Langley's Aviation Safety/Automation program, Terence S. Abbott, began working on a new format for displaying engine instrumentation information. The display was called the Engine Monitoring and Control System (E-MACS).

Abbott's focus was actually on developing a more effective format for any kind of display. As opposed to electromechanical instruments, which could only present raw sensor information, computerized, electronic displays had the capability of processing that information into a more useful form for the pilot. Specifically, Abbott wanted to evaluate the advantages of "task-oriented" displays, which would, as the name suggested, take the end task the operator needed to perform with the information and design the display to support that task. He chose an engine instrumentation display as an application with which to experiment because the tasks pilots had to perform with engine information were relatively simple, but they still involved both monitoring and control functions.

The primary control task pilots had to perform with aircraft engines was choosing and setting the power level. Conventional, electromechanical engine instruments gave the pilot direct readings of the engine pressure ratio (EPR), which measured the difference in pressure between the engine inlet and outlet, the speed of the low pressure engine compressor (N1), and the speed of the high pressure engine compressor (N2). The pilot would use these readings to interpret and adjust the amount of power, or thrust, the engine was developing. Abbott's design, on the other hand, used a computer to process all that information for the pilot. Using a model of the engine's performance and vertical bar graphics, E-MACS showed the pilot the actual thrust commanded (presented as a percentage of full take-off power), as well as the thrust the engines were putting out at the moment.

The second aspect of E-MACS addressed the engine monitoring functions pilots had to perform. To insure that the engines were operating properly, pilots had to constantly monitor readings of exhaust gas temperature, engine oil pressure, oil temperature, and fuel flow, in addition to the EPR, N1 and N2 gauges. The conventional, round electromechanical instruments showed the numerical value for each parameter and would indicate if that number was in a caution or alert range. The only way for a pilot to detect small deviations from a normal reading, however, was to know, from past experience, what a normal reading at that power setting should be. Small deviations were significant because they were often early indications of engine trouble.

The E-MACS format was based on the assumption that knowing the actual numerical value of any engine parameter was not as critical to the pilot as knowing whether the reading was normal or not. To give the pilot that information, E-MACS presented the engine readings in a format called a "column deviation graph." The display represented each engine parameter as a separate vertical column on a common graph. The readings were synchronized so that, regardless of the actual numerical value, the middle line of the display represented zero deviation from a "normal" reading at a given power setting. The first lines above and below that line represented a caution level, and the lines beyond that signalled a warning level. The column graphs for each parameter would extend up or down from the middle line for any high or low deviation from the ideal value. For more specific information, each column was labelled and the numerical value of each parameter was displayed in digital form above the appropriate column.[9]

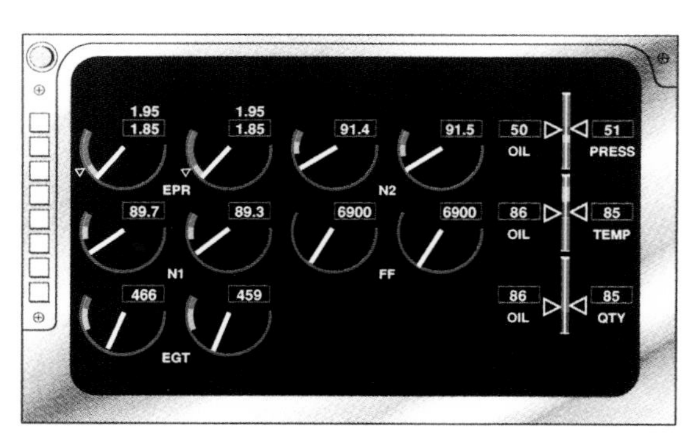

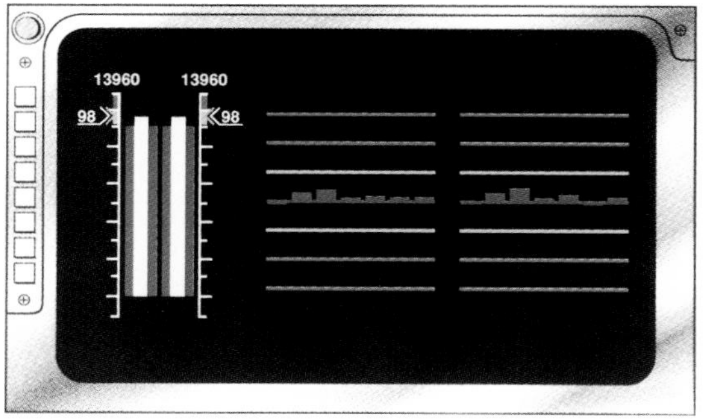

Displays of normal engine power-up for takeoff; top-traditional display, bottom-Engine Monitoring and Control System (E-MACS) display, designed for easy reading.

This display had several potential advantages. First, it enabled pilots to detect even small deviations in engine behavior easily, before they reached a caution level. Second, it allowed pilots to scan all the instrument readings quickly and almost instantaneously determine if all the parameters were within limits. Several behavioral studies had indicated, in fact, that a column deviation graph format allowed a user to process up to 18 different elements in the same amount of time it took to process one, because the entire graph was perceived as a single item.[10]

Abbott started work on the concept in 1987 and began tests of the system in the TSRV fixed base simulator at Langley in the summer of 1988. A total of 16 NASA, airline and United States Air Force pilots participated in the study, which used the cathode ray tube (CRT) displays in the simulator to compare modern, conventional engine instrumentation displays against the E-MACS concept. The results were striking. Using the conventional instruments, the pilots missed 43% of the engine faults introduced into the system. With the E-MACS display, however, every single fault was detected, no matter how small.

In a particularly dramatic aspect of the experiment, the researchers introduced a similar kind of fault as the one identified as the cause of the Air Florida crash on the 14th Street Bridge in Washington, D.C., January 13, 1982. The problem on the Air Florida B-737 jet was that the forward probe for the engine pressure ratio was blocked by ice. As a result, the EPR reading in the cockpit was erroneously high. Since pilots use the EPR gauge to set the engine power, the pilots of the Air Florida jet thought they had full takeoff power when, in fact, they did not. While the other gauges, such as the fuel flow, N1, and exhaust gas temperature, would have shown lower than normal readings because of the low power setting, they were not low enough to indicate a caution level, and the Air Florida pilots did not catch the problem in time. Using the conventional display format, the evaluation pilots in the NASA simulation study all missed the error, as well. With the E-MACS display, however, the pilots caught the problem in time on every single run.

The pilots in the study reported that the E-MACS display was significantly easier to use for both engine control and monitoring, and they showed an overwhelming preference for the E-MACS format for fast detection of fault conditions.[11] Clearly, the technology had promise. The system was put on the TSRV 737 airplane in February 1991 to see if it would still work in realistic flight conditions. Since the objective of the flight tests was validation of the basic technology only, the tests did not include any industry pilots. Further flight tests were scheduled, but the push to finish the airborne windshear detection flight testing forced the E-MACS research to be rescheduled.

Although the technology showed significant promise, the major airframe manufacturers still had some concern about the system's ability to judge ideal engine performance accurately over the life of an engine. Typically, as an airplane engine aged, its maximum performance would deteriorate, so the "normal" readings would change. Although NASA researchers believed that the parameters between a "normal" reading on the display and a cautionary one were sufficiently broad enough to allow for engine degradation, the concern remained. Nevertheless, the McDonnell Douglas Corporation did include an E-MACS concept in the tentative baseline cockpit design for a future air transport airplane it planned to build, designated the MD-XX.[12]

Interestingly enough, the most rapid application of the E-MACS concept was not in the air transport industry at all, but by a general aviation avionics manufacturer. Representatives from ARNAV Systems, Inc. saw a NASA display of E-MACS at the Experimental Aircraft Association annual convention in Oshkosh, Wisconsin in 1989. They liked the idea so much that they adapted the concept into a design for general aviation piston engines, and began marketing it as a component of the company's MFD 5000 Cockpit Management System in 1992. To cope with the problem of engine performance degradation over time, ARNAV developed an artificial intelligence-based computer program that would modify the ideal values as the engine aged. Although the initial version of the MFD 5000 did not incorporate all the elements of the E-MACS display, it included the basic column deviation graph, and the company eventually planned to implement the entire E-MACS concept.[13]

The E-MACS research illustrated an interesting aspect of technology transfer. Although the major manufacturers considered putting the technology on a next-generation airplane, that application process would take five or more years and would still be dependent on whether or not the technology proved itself cost-effective enough to be included in the final cockpit design. E-MACS was accepted immediately and enthusiastically, however, by a smaller company outside the mainstream air transport industry. Ever since Thomas S. Kuhn introduced his concept of "paradigms," theorists have argued that new ideas are often accepted first at the edges of an organization or industry. Smaller companies could generally move faster, had less inertia supporting the status quo, and had less to lose by incorporating new technologies or concepts.[14] While the theory did not necessarily apply in every case, the rapid transfer of the E-MACS technology to ARNAV illustrated at least one example where the theory held true.

TOPMS

NASA's research into a takeoff performance monitoring system (TOPMS) originated as the doctoral thesis of a Kansas University student named Raghavachari Srivatsan. Srivatsan believed the number of takeoff-related accidents could be reduced if pilots were given more information on the airplane's progress throughout the takeoff roll. In 1984, Srivatsan began working with researchers at the Langley Research Center on display concepts that might be able to give pilots this kind of information.

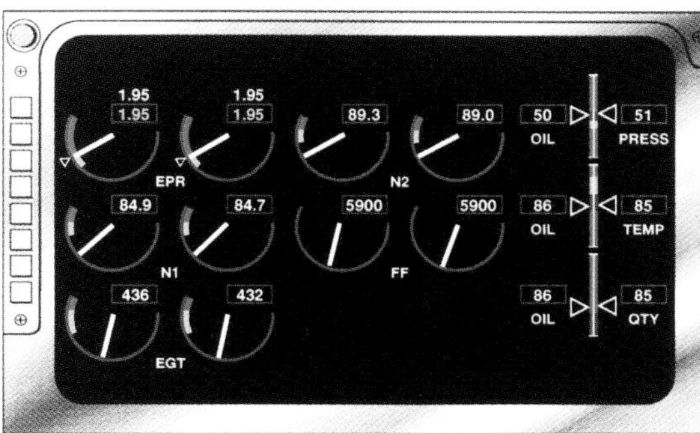

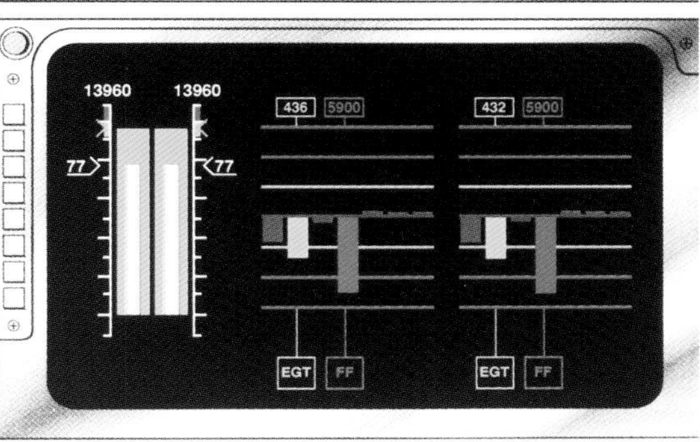

Displays of incorrect sensor readings during engine power-up for takeoff, similar to that experienced during the 1982 Air Florida accident at Washington National Airport. traditional display, Top— Traditional display. Bottom—Engine monitoring and Control System (E-MACS) display. Note the visual superiority of E-MACS to warn flight crews of hazard.

The basic TOPMS information was designed to be displayed on the navigation CRT screen in the cockpit. The pilot would input the airplane's weight, the outside temperature, wind conditions, runway length and the basic runway condition (dry, wet, icy, snow-covered, etc.) into the flight management computer. The computer would then create a display of the departure runway that showed the predicted takeoff point of the airplane, the point at which the airplane had to rotate in order to clear a 35-foot obstacle at the end of the runway, and where on the runway the critical reference speeds should occur. The airspeed was displayed in digital form in a box beside the runway. The display also incorporated two moving bars that indicated the engine pressure ratio (EPR) for each of the two engines. If either or both of the engines failed during the takeoff roll, the corresponding EPR bar would turn red, alerting the pilot to the engine problem.

Three seconds after the pilot stopped advancing the throttles on the takeoff roll, the computer would compare the predicted acceleration of the airplane against the actual movement its on-board accelerometers were reporting. If the two rates did not agree, the computer would adjust its equations and show a new predicted takeoff point on the TOPMS display. During the takeoff roll, the computer would also be running a series of tests on the airplane's condition and modifying the display accordingly. The first test was whether or not both engines had failed. If they had, not only would both EPR bars turn red, but a red stop sign would appear at the top of the display. If both engines had not failed, the computer went on to the next test, which was whether or not the airplane had reached the critical decision speed, known as V1. Once the airplane had passed V1 speed, it was committed to the takeoff, and a large green arrow would appear at the top of the screen, indicating to the pilot that the takeoff should be continued.

If V1 speed had not yet been reached, the computer tested to see if one engine had failed. If an engine failure was detected before the airplane reached V1 speed, a red stop sign would appear on the screen, advising the pilot to abort the takeoff. If both engines were still operating, the computer next evaluated the acceleration of the airplane. If the acceleration rate was below a predetermined threshold, a red stop sign appeared on the display. If the acceleration rate was still within acceptable limits, the computer looked to see if the predicted takeoff point had progressed beyond the point on the runway where the airplane could rotate and still clear a 35-foot obstacle, even if one engine failed. If it had, the stop sign appeared. The final test was to see if the predicted stopping point of the airplane would still be on the runway if the pilot aborted. Once the stopping point was beyond the runway, the display showed a green arrow at the top of the screen. If the pilot aborted the takeoff at any point, all the takeoff information disappeared, and the display indicated only the predicted stopping point of the airplane at its current deceleration rate and with maximum braking efforts.[15]

Most of the TOPMS research was actually performed in the TSRV fixed-base simulator at Langley. The first simulator study, conducted in 1985-1986, consisted of 32 pilots from NASA, the FAA, the United States Air Force, airline companies, and airframe manufacturers. The pilots liked the display, but were concerned about the pilot looking down to monitor the information, instead of looking out the window. As a result of the study recommendations, the NASA researchers organized a second simulator study in 1986-1987, in which 17 pilots were asked to evaluate the TOPMS on both a "heads-down display" (HDD) and a "heads-up display" (HUD). The pilots rated the heads-down display as "good" and the heads-up display as "very good." All the pilots reported, however, that they would like to have at least a heads-down TOPMS display in their cockpits, because the information provided "valuable safety information not currently available during takeoff."[16]

Following the second simulator study, TOPMS was installed on the TSRV 737 to evaluate how well it would operate under actual flight conditions. In April, 1988, the ATOPS crew took the airplane down to the Kennedy Space Center to test the system on the same 15,000 foot runway the Space Shuttle used for Florida landings. The researchers wanted to test the accuracy of the system's predicted stopping points for high-speed takeoff aborts, and the long, wide runway at Cape Canaveral provided a reassuring extra safety margin. After the predictions proved accurate during 80 knot and 100 knot aborted takeoff runs in Florida, the crew conducted similar experiments back at the Wallops Island flight facility in Virginia. Between other research projects, maintenance and scheduled upgrades to the 737's experimental systems, however, only six days of TOPMS flight testing were completed over a two year period. In addition, all the test runs were on dry runway conditions.[17]

In October 1989, NASA held a workshop on TOPMS that was attended by representatives from manufacturers, airlines, avionics companies, flight safety groups, and industry associations. Despite the positive reviews by the test pilots in the simulator studies, the industry response to the concept was mixed. One concern was that the sudden appearance of the "STOP" and "GO" flags on the display might be interpreted by pilots as a command instead of an advisory caution. Another concern was that the predicted information on the display might not always be accurate, because there were too many potential variables. For example, conditions could change from one end of the runway to the other, so although the display might indicate to the pilot that he had enough room to stop, that might not actually be the case.[18]

To try to address some of the concerns raised at the workshop, Srivatsan and the Langley researchers conducted a third simulation study with six pilots in 1991-1992. This study evaluated three different TOPMS display options. The first showed a predicted takeoff point but had no advisory symbols and did not include information on the predicted stopping point in the case of an aborted takeoff. The second option was the original TOPMS display, and the third contained the same predictive and advisory information as the second option, with one additional feature. In the third option, the appearance of an preliminary abort symbol indicated a developing acceleration problem before a firm "STOP" advisory appeared on the screen. Four of the pilots preferred the third display option, while two preferred the format without any advisory information, although all the pilots reported that they would prefer any of the options to no TOPMS display at all.[19]

The different display formats still did not address the industry concern of runway variables, however, and one other significant problem remained. In manufacturing a warning system to be used in circumstances where the consequences of a missed alert could be serious, such as in a critical takeoff situation, the alert tolerances had to be made very tight. Tight tolerances could easily lead to nuisance alerts, however. Nuisance alerts would not only prompt unnecessary takeoff aborts, which were in themselves somewhat hazardous, but they could also lead pilots to pay less attention to alerts when they were triggered. As a result, the pilots might ignore a warning in a situation that was actually critical, negating the value of an alert system that had cost a lot of money to install.[20]

In short, safety from a manufacturer's or operator's standpoint was not as simple as it might appear to research organizations.[21] TOPMS seemed to give pilots valuable safety information, and the test pilots who participated in the demonstration all thought it was a beneficial system. But TOPMS would need a lot more work before it would be acceptable to the airline industry, which had to take different and more complex factors into account. As a result, Boeing elected not to include a takeoff performance monitor in the B-777 design.[22] McDonnell Douglas, on the other hand, saw at least enough potential in the technology to continue internal research on the concept. Based on the expectation that additional research might be able to overcome the technology's perceived deficiencies, McDonnell Douglas also included a takeoff performance monitor in the tentative baseline design for the MD-XX cockpit.[23]

Summary

The ATOPS program research into airplane systems showed that new technology could make significant improvements in the safety and efficiency of flight operations. The research also underscored, however, that manufacturers looked at the potential risks associated with new technology as much as they looked at its potential benefits. If the risks were low, the technology would probably find ready acceptance. But if some level of risk remained, or if there was not enough of a driving economic benefit to balance out the risk, the technology might not be as easily adopted, especially by the major industry manufacturers.

NASA
NASA

Chapter 7

Improving Aircraft Operations

Developing better equipment and systems for individual aircraft was an important step toward increasing the safety and efficiency of air transport operations. But the Terminal Configured Vehicle (TCV) program grew out of a realization among researchers and policymakers that simply improving airplane components was no longer sufficient. Gaining a few extra knots of airspeed or better efficiency in cruise flight was useless if the airplane was then vectored around for 20 minutes at low altitude because of terminal area congestion. Researchers needed to focus not only on improvements to individual airplanes, but also on technology that would allow the airplanes to operate more efficiently within the air traffic control system.

Several of the TCV/Advanced Transport Operating Systems (ATOPS) program research projects focused on flight operations in the ATC environment. In 1979-80, NASA researchers conducted experiments with a four-dimensional (4-D) navigation system to try to streamline descent and approach procedures into crowded terminal areas. Another research effort explored the use of a cockpit display of air traffic to help pilots maneuver more efficiently onto an approach course. A third series of experiments looked at the use of a two-way data link to improve and simplify communications between pilots and air traffic controllers.

The TCV/ATOPS researchers also worked on concepts to increase the efficiency of landing operations. If technology could be developed that could reliably reduce the length of time an airplane spent landing and taxiing off the runway, arriving airplanes could be spaced closer together by air traffic controllers. Closer spacing would, in turn, decrease delays and increase capacity at airports. In one joint effort between the Langley Research Center and the Boeing Commercial Aircraft Company, engineers developed and tested precision flare control laws that improved the ability of airplane autoland systems to land the aircraft at a specific point along a runway. The touchdown point could then be planned to coincide with runway turnoffs so the airplane could land and get off the runway in a minimum amount of time. A separate research project tested the use of a magnetic cable buried in the runway and taxiway surfaces to help guide airplanes off the runway quickly in low visibility conditions.

Improving the efficiency of transport operations within the air traffic control system offered significant benefits in terms of fuel savings and airport capacity. But improving operations in a system was a much more complex task, involving many more variables, than simply improving elements of a single airplane. Technology oriented toward system operations required not only the support of airframe manufacturers and airlines, but the Federal Aviation Administration (FAA), as well. Several of the airborne systems also relied on guidance or information from ground facilities, and all of the technology had to work in concert

Ground crew member directs the Boeing 737 "flying laboratory" to its ramp position after a research flight at Orlando, Florida.

with air traffic controllers and other aircraft operating in the ATC environment.

As a result, some of these technologies proved very difficult to implement or transfer to industry. Changing technology or procedures in the air traffic control system, where the penalties for errors or malfunctions could be disastrous, was a slow and complex process. And airlines would not buy the technology if the ATC system could not support its use. Nonetheless, some of the concepts developed and tested with the NASA 737 Transport Systems Research Vehicle (TSRV) were adopted by manufacturers, and by the early 1990s, the FAA was working on updated air traffic control equipment that could support more advanced and efficient airborne technology.

Profile Descents

As fuel prices rose in the late 1970s, airlines became increasingly concerned with improving the efficiency of their operations. Jet engines were designed to operate best at high cruising altitudes, and they ate up fuel very quickly in the denser air close to the ground. Consequently, the profits from a flight could evaporate quickly if an airliner had to spend a lot of time maneuvering at low altitude as it approached its destination. Unfortunately, the growing congestion around many commercial airports meant that airline flights were often vectored around other air traffic or put into holding patterns as they neared the terminal area, wasting significant amounts of fuel.

In an effort to improve this situation, the FAA began testing a new system called Local Flow Management/Profile Descent (LFM/PD) in the late 1970s. Local Flow Management was designed to reduce the need for low altitude vectoring or holding patterns by matching the arrival rate of all the airplanes coming to an airport to the number and frequency of arrivals the airport could accept.[1] LFM sequenced arrivals through one of four metering fixes 30-40 nautical miles from the airport, at a specific time and in an order that would allow the airplanes to fly directly to the airport and land. The profile descent portion of the system allowed pilots to descend at their discretion, so they could plan a more fuel-conservative descent profile to the metering fix using an idle thrust, clean (flaps and speed brakes retracted) configuration.

The LFM/PD system was first installed on an experimental basis at the Denver, Colorado, and Dallas-Fort Worth, Texas Air Route Traffic Control Centers (ARTCC). The system was a vast improvement over existing arrival procedures, but it still had a couple of significant drawbacks. The computerized program gave the controllers the time each aircraft was to cross its metering fix, but the controllers had to manually compute how to get the airplanes to that fix at the correct time, speed, and altitude. The pilots were given the speed and altitude, or altitude range, at which they were to cross the fix, but controllers had full responsibility for modifying the cruise speed and/or descent profiles of arriving aircraft to meet the time requirements of the schedule. Using various manual calculations, controllers managed to achieve metering fix arrival accuracies as good as plus or minus two minutes. To do that, however, profile descents were often interrupted and aircraft speeds usually had to be modified. Consequently, there was still a significant gap between the fuel efficiencies obtained through LFM/PD and an optimum fuel-efficient flight and descent profile.[2]

In an effort to close that gap, researchers at the Boeing Commercial Airplane Company and the NASA Langley Research Center in the late 1970s began working on profile descent equations, using the four-dimensional, or "4-D," capabilities of the TSRV 737's flight management system (FMS). Two-dimensional navigation only managed an airplane's horizontal path. Three-dimensional navigation controlled the aircraft's vertical flight path as well as its horizontal direction, and four-dimensional navigation included a time element, as well. In a 4-D navigational mode, the airplane would not only hold to a specific horizontal and vertical path, but it would also speed up or slow down to hold to a specific route or arrival time. The controller could simply give the pilot an altitude, speed and time to cross a metering fix, the pilot would enter those parameters into the flight computer, and the computer would calculate the most fuel-efficient flight path to follow to arrive at the fix as instructed by the controller.

The software to give the 737 flight management system 4-D navigation capability was developed and tested first on a fast time computer and then incorporated into the TSRV real-time, piloted simulator. But the true test of the concept was whether or not it would be acceptable to pilots and controllers in a realistic ATC environment. So the software was installed in the TSRV 737 for a series of flight tests in the Denver LFM/PD system. Denver was chosen because it was the FAA's lead center on the LFM/PD concept and had been given a certain amount of leeway to make minor changes to the ATC software as necessary to improve its operation.

The plan was for the air traffic controllers to assign a metering fix time to the 737, and both the NASA researchers and the ground personnel would monitor how accurately the airplane met the fix time and how well the profile descents used by the 737 mixed with other air traffic in the area. The NASA researchers initially expected only a basic level of cooperation from the FAA, but the Denver ARTCC personnel contributed so much assistance in planning and conducting the flights that they became, in essence, a third partner in the research effort. In fact, the cooperation and involvement of the Denver ARTCC was a critical element in the success of the flight tests.

The research flights took place June 19-28, 1979. A total of 19 test runs were made from a cruise altitude to one of the metering fixes for Denver Stapleton airport. At approximately 110 miles from the metering fix, the 737 crew was given a target arrival time, which was programmed into the flight computer. From the top of descent point to the metering fix, the pilot flew the airplane at idle thrust and without speed brakes, following computer-generated path and speed cues on the electronic flight displays in the 737's aft cockpit. Once the airplane crossed the metering fix, it broke off the approach and circled around to begin another test run. The flying duties were divided among two NASA pilots and four airline pilots, and each flight carried numerous FAA and industry observers, as well.

There were a few initial compatibility problems, such as the fact that the initial metering fix times assigned by the LFM system required airspeeds slower than the 737 was physically capable of flying, but a few software changes corrected the difficulties. After that, the flight tests proved extremely successful. The 737 was able to make the metering fix arrival times with a mean time error of only 6.6 seconds, altitude error of 33.6 feet, and airspeed error of .3 knots. In comparing the FMS-computed profile descent flight paths with conventional LFM/PD approaches used by airline pilots at Denver, NASA engineers found that pilots without the advantage of the precise guidance provided by the FMS tended to descend earlier, to ensure their arrival at the metering fix at the correct altitude and airspeed. The arrival time between the two differed only slightly, but the FMS-controlled profile descent used 28% less fuel.[3]

Assessments of the NASA profile descent flight tests from FAA observers were very positive, as well. Their evaluations included comments such as "Fantastic accuracy at metering fix and landing time. Will definitely reduce controller work load, save fuel and much frustration on part of the controller and the pilot," and "Has potential for real capacity improvements." The FAA observers also noted, however, that although NASA's single airplane had performed extremely well, there were additional issues that widespread use of airborne-controlled profile descents would raise. What would be the consequences, for example, of different airplanes using specific, but different, climb and descent paths and speed profiles while still making their metering fix times? How would aircraft using profile descents mix with aircraft not equipped for that kind of approach? Would airspace have to be redesigned to ensure the safety of the procedure? In addition, although the airborne system had proved itself capable of accuracies within seven seconds, the ground metering system at that time was only accurate within 30 seconds, so the system in practice could not operate as efficiently as it had in the test flights.[4]

The questions raised by the FAA were all valid and important issues. They also underscored the particularly wide gap between the research and operational environments with technology designed to improve not just one aircraft component, but an entire nationwide system. Furthermore, the profile descents tested in the TSRV 737 depended on an onboard flight management system, which, with the exception of a few Lockheed L-1011s, did not yet exist on any production airplanes. The Boeing 767 was the first new production airplane to include an FMS as standard equipment, and the first 767 did not go into service until three years after the Denver profile descent flight tests were completed.[5]

In an effort to resolve some of the issues surrounding the mix of aircraft with and without flight management systems, the Langley researchers conducted some additional profile descent experiments in 1984-85. Engineers used a hand held calculator to compute the necessary information for a profile descent on a T-39 Sabreliner jet and several United Airlines jet transports. Preliminary results showed the pilot workload was acceptable, but analysis showed the pilot had to fly the faster portion of the descent very precisely, which was difficult without a flight management system. In addition, the calculators needed to perform the computations cost around $400 each, and pilots would have to be trained in their use, creating additional costs for the airlines.[6]

Even if all the airliners used either an FMS or a hand held calculator, however, the issue of ensuring safety in a system where individual airplanes were controlling their own descent paths would remain. The controllers would be unable to predict the exact trajectory of the descending airplanes, and there was too much potential for unexpected maneuvers. In one example related to a Langley researcher by the FAA ARTCC staff at Denver, a pilot was asked if he could make a certain arrival time at the metering fix. He replied he could, and then proceeded to start a 360 degree turn, back into conflicting traffic, in order to delay his arrival until the correct time.[7]

The bottom line was that although the technology itself worked well, the ATC infrastructure was not equipped to incorporate it while still ensuring safe separation of air traffic. Even so, the United Airlines representatives who observed the test flights were impressed enough with the technology that they asked Boeing to look at the feasibility of incorporating 4-D capability into the flight management systems of the 767s they had on order. At that time, however, Boeing and its subcontractors had their hands full just developing a 3-D flight management system in time to meet the 767 production deadline, so a 4-D capability was out of the question.[8]

As flight management systems became more sophisticated, Boeing did start to incorporate a type of 4-D navigation capability into some of its airplanes. The Smith Industries flight management systems in the 737-300, 737-400, and 737-500 had the ability to compute 4-D flight paths. By 1993, Boeing was also planning to offer a kind of 4-D navigation, which it called Required Time of Arrival (RTA), for its 767 and 747-400 aircraft as part of a suite of advanced navigation and communication functions.[9]

Yet even in 1993, although Local Flow Management was in widespread use, the ATC infrastructure was still incapable of integrating full 4-D navigation. The FAA was finally developing a more automated system that would allow more advanced navigation and communication, however. The new technology, called the Center Tracon Automation System (CTAS), was a concept originally developed by a researcher named Heinz Erzberger at the NASA Ames Research Center. Unlike the profile descent concept tested by Langley and Boeing in 1979, CTAS was a ground-based system, but it gave the controller the same basic information the NASA pilots had derived from the airborne flight management system. Instead of just giving the controller a metering fix arrival time for each aircraft, the system also calculated an optimum, fuel-efficient descent path for each airplane that would not conflict with any other known traffic, based on current weather conditions and a database on each aircraft type's performance figures. The controller could then radio instructions for that descent profile to the pilot. The system achieved the same basic end as the 4-D profile descents tested by NASA's 737 in 1979, but through a ground-based system that required no airborne equipment and took other traffic into account, as well.[10]

In the fall of 1992, the TSRV 737 was again flown out to Denver to conduct preliminary tests using the CTAS concept. The flight tests produced arrival time accuracies within 11 seconds, although the results indicated that the wind modelling component of the system needed improvement. The FAA planned to implement CTAS at Denver and Dallas-Fort Worth by 1996 and then install it at 12 major airports across the United States.[11]

The profile descent concept tested with Langley's 737, which relied on a 4-D navigation capability in an airborne FMS to design and execute fuel-efficient profile descents, was never implemented. It was a good idea, but ahead of its time and perhaps untenable in the complex ATC system. Nevertheless, the research did eventually have an impact. The 737 experiments proved the potential fuel savings that could be gained from 4-D navigation and precision profile descents, lending support to the inclusion of 4-D navigation in some later model transport aircraft and to the eventual acceptance of the CTAS concept.

Cockpit Displayed Traffic Information (CDTI)

Soon after the profile descent experiments were completed in 1979, Langley researchers began work on another concept aimed at improving the efficiency of ATC system operations by giving pilots better navigation information and capabilities in the cockpit. The idea was Cockpit Displayed Traffic Information (CDTI), and the researchers in the TCV/ATOPS program were interested in it because they saw it as "an important step in the direction of 'electronic VFR' (visual flight rules)." If pilots could "see" the other traffic in the area, it might allow reduced separation between aircraft, which would increase the efficiency and capacity of terminal operations.[12]

The idea of giving pilots better information about potential conflicting traffic had been around since the mid-1940s, when researchers suggested that the new television and radar technologies might be combined to create a cockpit traffic display.[13] That idea never materialized, but in the early 1970s the Massachusetts Institute of Technology (MIT) received FAA sponsorship to conduct preliminary simulation studies of a more advanced cockpit display of traffic information. The MIT research indicated that the basic concept, at least, was well accepted by pilots.[14] Researchers in NASA's TCV/ATOPS program built on the MIT studies for a series of flight experiments in 1979 that tested both the basic CDTI concept and potential symbology for such a display, using the TSRV 737.

The CDTI flight tests, conducted in the fall of 1979, consisted of a total of 29 curved, decelerating approaches into the NASA Wallops Island Flight Facility in Virginia. The research pilots had to execute the approaches while they monitored the traffic situation and reacted to potential conflicts. The traffic displays were created by integrating traffic information into the electronic horizontal situation indicators (EHSI), or map displays, in the aft research cockpit. Since the focus of the NASA experiments was on the pilot's interface with a traffic display, the research flights used a pre-recorded data tape of simulated traffic to create the images on the cockpit display. The tapes presented a realistic scenario of numerous airplanes following different flightpaths into the Wallops Island airport, however. The tapes could also provide the research pilots with scenarios in which the other pilots made mistakes in addition to normal, error-free situations.

The format tested in the experiments was a "course-up" display, with two-thirds of the viewing area in front of the symbol representing the pilot's own airplane. The position of the 737 was updated almost continuously, while the other simulated traffic was updated every four seconds to replicate the speed with which an ATC radar could complete a sweep and update a display. The pilots could choose six different scales for the display, ranging from one to 32 miles, and could set the display to show or suppress data blocks with more detailed information about each airplane symbol on the screen.

The research flights also tested both "coded" and "uncoded" formats for the traffic symbology on the display. Both formats showed the past and current position of each aircraft and a trend vector indicating where it was headed, but the coded symbology also told pilots whether the traffic was above, at or below their own altitude, whether or not it was under ATC control, and if it had CDTI capability.

The results of the flight tests indicated that the display improved pilots' situation awareness and made them willing to use closer spacing with other aircraft during approaches. The pilots liked the coded symbology, although they indicated that they did not need to know whether other aircraft were CDTI equipped or under ATC control. There were some problems with use of the display, however. The EHSI could get extremely cluttered, especially if the data blocks on each airplane were displayed. The researchers also found that pilots had a tendency to fixate on the display, which could cause problems in an operational flight environment, where pilots needed to maintain an effective scan of the instrument panel and the airspace outside the aircraft.

In addition, the tests showed that the raw display data was not really adequate for use in approach sequencing. It was difficult to detect if an airplane ahead was slowing down until so much of the gap had closed that the pilot following the CDTI had to reduce speed sharply to maintain adequate spacing. The researchers also saw that trying to maintain the same spacing throughout an approach did not work, because all the airplanes stretched out along the approach path would have to slow down at the same time and to the same speed as the one closest to the airport to maintain the same spacing. That meant that airplanes would be slowing down to final approach speeds many miles from the airport.[15]

Langley engineers conducted some follow-on simulator studies to research enhanced display formats that would allow a CDTI to be used for more efficient sequencing. NASA managers finally decided, however, that concepts such as 4-D navigation could accomplish the same end as the CDTI technology with less difficulty. As a result, the CDTI technology was not pursued. The Traffic Alert Collision Avoidance System (TCAS) cockpit display the FAA later mandated for airliners did incorporate data on the location of potentially conflicting traffic, but the purpose of the information was for collision avoidance only, not for approach sequencing.[16]

Data Link

The data link research conducted by the ATOPS program was an effort to improve another aspect of ATC system operations. In addition to causing traffic delays, the growing congestion in terminal airspace was creating a radio frequency overload problem. So many pilots were trying to talk to controllers on the same frequency that it was often difficult for a pilot to squeeze in a transmission or request. In addition, the rapid pace at which controllers had to read off clearances and instructions in busy situations often led to miscommunications, errors, and the need to repeat transmissions. One possible solution the ATOPS program researchers saw for these problems was a two-way data link system.

A data link system would allow messages between pilots and controllers to be displayed on CRT screens in the cockpit and at the controller's station. The messages could be read and reread as necessary and stored for future reference. As a result, the system might be able to reduce not only the congestion of ATC frequencies, but also the number of miscommunications and errors and the need for repeated transmissions.[17] With the use of a satellite network, a data link could also allow pilots to communicate with controllers from remote locations, such as over the Pacific Ocean. In addition, data link offered the possibility of enhanced capabilities, such as displaying real-time weather reports and charts in the cockpit and direct communication between the airplane's flight computer and computers on the ground.

Engineers at the Langley Research Center began investigating the use of a two-way data link system for ATC communications in the early 1980s. Researchers working on a Single Pilot IFR (SPIFR) project conducted a flight test in a light twin engine airplane to evaluate whether a data link system would make ATC communications easier for pilots of small airplanes flying under instrument flight rules (IFR). During the SPIFR flight test, a pseudo-controller in the back of the airplane composed ATC messages for the pilot, which were then sent to the front of the plane and displayed on a screen in the cockpit.[18]

The flight test was followed by a series of real-time, piloted simulation studies that examined the use of various levels of data link capability in single pilot IFR flight operations. The simulation research showed that the data link system and cockpit display designed by the Langley engineers did, in fact, lessen the demands on the pilots' short term memory and reduce the number of transmissions needed between the pilots and air traffic controllers. The results also indicated that a data link system made it easier for the pilot to allocate time to critical cockpit tasks while receiving ATC messages.[19] Encouraged by the positive response they got from the single pilot flight and simulation studies, researchers began to look at data link technology for ATC communications in jet transports.

A commercial VHF data link system, called the ARINC Communications Addressing and Reporting System (ACARS) was already in use by the airlines. It allowed airline dispatchers to relay company messages, weather, and flight plan information to pilots. By 1989, Canadian air traffic controllers were also using an ACARS data link to transmit oceanic clearances to cockpit printers in aircraft preparing to cross the Atlantic Ocean, although pilots had to read back the clearances aloud over a conventional radio frequency. In 1991, the FAA began to provide pre-departure clearances via an ACARS data link to airliners while they were still parked at airport gates.[20] Using a two-way data link as the primary communication mode for tactical and strategic ATC information, however, would be a much more dramatic change from conventional procedures.

The initial NASA data link experiment with transport pilots consisted of a real-time simulation study that compared voice communications with data link messages for ATC communications and pre-recorded ATIS (Automatic Terminal Information Service) reports. The results indicated that pilots liked using a data link system for routine ATC communications, although they still preferred voice communications for urgent messages. Many of the test subjects also voiced some concern about the amount of "head-down" time required for reading and typing data link messages and the possibility of losing the situation awareness they obtained from listening to the communications between controllers and other pilots in the vicinity.[21]

In order to explore possible solutions to these concerns, the Langley researchers began another simulation study in 1990 that incorporated several additional features. In addition to the written messages printed on the CRT screen, the study used a digitized voice to annunciate data linked ATC messages to the flight crew. Preliminary results indicated that the addition of the digitized voice made the two-way data link system much more acceptable to pilots.[22]

Although the simulation results were promising, researchers felt it was also important to test the data link concept in a realistic ATC flight environment. Flight tests could validate the simulation results and point out potential operational problems with the technology that might not show up under simulated conditions. In addition, the ATOPS researchers had learned

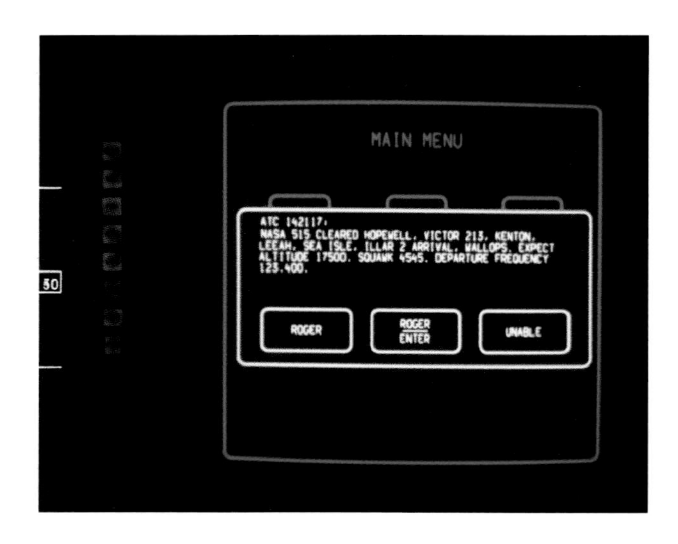

Data link displays with touch screen communication used to enhance traffic management around airports.
Left—A typical ATC message.
Center—Pilot touches roger button to acknowledge.
Right—Pilot touches speed button to formulate a speed change request.

that in the cost and risk-conscious world of airline operations, flying a new transport technology in an actual transport class airplane was often an important step toward winning acceptance for the concept among manufacturers, airlines and the FAA.

The main question the flight experiments were designed to answer was not whether the data link technology would work, but whether the system would be acceptable to pilots. Consequently, one of the most important features of the experimental equipment was the cockpit display the pilots would use to interact with the system. The data link information was displayed on a CRT screen, and the Langley engineers designed the display format to be as easy to use as possible. The screen was covered with a clear, touch-sensitive panel that allowed pilots to select choices simply by touching the appropriate place on the display screen, instead of having to use a separate alphanumeric key pad. The display also used a "windows" format similar to the type used in many personal computers, with three different layers.

The top layer, or window, was the smallest and always had visual priority over the other windows. It was used to display information sent from the ground to the airplane. The middle window was for the crew to compose messages to send to the ground, and the bottom, largest layer displayed the main menu page and the weather menu page. The top layer displayed was always the active window and had a white border and white print, while the inactive windows had blue colored windows and print. Each window had touch-sensitive areas that were drawn as buttons. The pilots would touch the button areas to make choices, scroll through a message, or select different menus or information. When the pilot touched the screen, magenta touch-target lines centered on the selection the computer thought the pilot was making would appear, and the button would turn from white to green. After the pilot lifted his finger, the button would then flash twice to indicate the command had been accepted.

The main menu contained six basic options, labelled ATC, Weather Menu, ATIS, NASA Ground, View Clearance, and View Messages. The bottom portion of the main menu was used to notify the pilots if they had non-time-critical messages from the ground waiting to be viewed. When the pilot touched a message waiting button, the message would be displayed in a small window. When the pilot had responded to the message, it would disappear. By touching the "Weather Menu" button, the pilots could access a wide variety of data linked weather information. Touching the "ATC" or "NASA Ground" button opened up the middle layer window, so the pilots could compose messages to data link to ATC or NASA facilities on the ground. The ATIS (Automatic Terminal Information Service) button opened up a menu that allowed the pilots to choose and receive the most current recorded weather, runway and other operational information for different airports. Selecting the "View Clearance" or "View Messages" buttons would present the

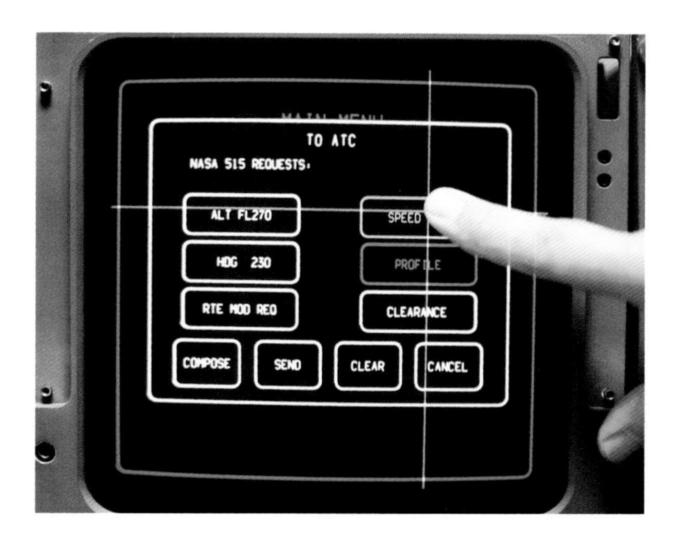

pilots with a printed record of the clearances or messages transmitted and received during the flight to that point.

If the pilot selected the ATC button, a second menu would appear with buttons for selecting various categories of ATC requests, such as "speed," "heading," "route modification," etc., each of which also read the current clearance or value. If the speed button read 250, for example, the pilot could touch the button, and a new window would open up with a heading that read "NASA 515 requests: Speed 250," and two scroll buttons, one with an up arrow and the other with a down arrow. By pushing the appropriate scroll button, the speed value would increase or decrease. When the desired number was reached, the pilot would touch an "OK" button in the lower right corner of the screen, and the display would return to the ATC menu page, with the new speed request printed at the top. The pilots could repeat this procedure for as many other request categories as they desired. To compose a route modification or a non-standard ATC request, the pilots could select a "compose" button on the ATC menu and type in whatever message they wanted, using the alphanumeric keys on the Control Display Unit (CDU) of the flight management system. When the message or request was complete, the pilot could touch a "Send" button on the main ATC menu page, and the message would be data linked down to a controller on the ground.

If a time-critical ATC message was received at any point, however, it would be displayed on top of whatever window was currently in use, and a digitized voice would repeat the message aloud to the crew. The flight crew had to respond to any time-critical messages before any other message could be composed or received. The flight crew had three possible options for responding to a time-critical ATC message. They could select a button that said "Unable," if they could not comply with the ATC instructions, or they could touch a "Roger" button to simply acknowledge the message and communicate their intention to follow the instructions. The third option was to select a "Roger/Enter" button. By touching that button, not only would a "Roger" message be data linked down to ATC personnel, but the ATC instructions would be automatically entered into the flight management system. With the touch of a single button, therefore, ATC-requested changes in routing, altitude, speed or heading could be acknowledged, accepted, and executed.

The ground equipment for the experiments consisted of a phone modem link to a digital, real time weather data base, a data link processor, two separate VHF data link sources that communicated with data link receiver/ transmitters on the airplane, and numerous voice frequencies. Since the point of the flight tests was to evaluate pilots' acceptance of a data link system for ATC communications, the flights were conducted in the vicinity of the Wallops Flight Facility, where actual communications with ATC were not required. For most of the flight tests, NASA researchers on the ground acted as air traffic controllers, composing instructions, clearances and route modifications to send to the flight crew. When weather conditions forced the crew to fly under actual instrument conditions one day, the research pilots were still able to use the data link system. Messages between the pilots and the FAA controllers were simply relayed through researchers in the NASA ground station, who data linked the controllers' instructions to the research crew and verbally relayed the crew's data linked responses and requests to the controllers.

The NASA researchers wanted to evaluate how operational flight crews would accept the use of a data link system, so they selected pilots from five different commercial airline companies to fly the research flights. A total of seven two-person crews were chosen and given one day of orientation in the TSRV 737 simulator before flying the data link experiments. Because the training was limited to one day, the researchers selected pilots who had previous experience using electronic flight displays and flight management systems. Each crew flew three different 250 mile circle routes that each included a takeoff, climb, cruise, descent, and approach to landing, so the flights could incorporate a range of typical airline/ATC communications. Each flight also included at least one route modification. In one of the circuits, the pilots used only voice communications with the ground controllers in order to establish a baseline against which the data link performance could be measured. The second and third circuits used data link as the primary communication source. Clearances for taxi, takeoff and landings, however, were always made with voice communications.

The errors, miscommunications and message repeats each crew experienced were tracked during the flights, and the crews were all debriefed after their flights were completed. The results were striking. There were five instances of confusion with voice communication, and none using data link. The pilots had to ask for messages to be repeated 46 times with voice communication. Messages only had to be repeated 12 times during the flights relying primarily on data link, and all of those repetitions were during portions of the flight where voice communications were being used. While there were seven errors with both voice and data link communications, all but one of the errors on flights using data link involved tuning the voice communication radio to the incorrect frequency. In other words, the ability to read, store and re-read the data link messages effectively eliminated errors due to miscommunications and the need for the repetition of ATC messages.

The airline pilots conducting the flights agreed that the use of data link reduced their workload and allowed them to distribute it better, especially if ATC commands could be acknowledged and put into the flight management computer with the touch of a single button. Six of the seven crews also thought that data link would make an acceptable primary ATC communication medium for most flight segments, as long as voice communication was available as a back-up. However, the crews all thought that communications in terminal areas should still be conducted primarily through voice radio to reduce the amount of "head-down" time in busy traffic areas. They also suggested that at least the time-critical ATC messages should be displayed in the pilot's forward field of view.[23]

The NASA experiments were the first flight tests using data link as a primary source for ATC communications. But the airlines already had a strong interest in the technology and were eager to get Langley's test results. The research flights using airline pilots were completed in early May 1990. Before a month had gone by, the human factors/data link group of the Air Transport Association had asked for a flight demonstration of the technology. Typical attendance for the group meetings was reportedly about 15 people, but 60 airline representatives showed up at Langley to see the data link system in operation.[24]

The Langley engineers also realized from the start that a data link system would require the support and involvement of the FAA as well as the airlines and airframe manufacturers. So although the flight tests did not evaluate the impact of data link on controller workload or ATC system safety, the researchers took several outside observers along on the flights, including an air traffic controller from the ATC data link design group. The controller's response to the data link system tested by Langley was extremely positive, and he thought that controllers would like to use data link for ATC airborne information with the exception of landing clearances.[25]

The FAA and the airlines were both interested in data link because they believed it could enable more efficient air traffic operations. The airlines, for example, saw data link as a way to enhance the efficiency of transoceanic flights. With only VHF and High Frequency (HF) radio communications, it was difficult for flights to maintain contact with ATC or the airline dispatchers far from shore. Consequently, it was difficult for flight paths to be changed en route, even if the pilots encountered different winds than were predicted. With a data link system, airline dispatchers could send updated wind information to their pilots via satellite, and the pilots could compute a more efficient flight path. The pilots could then send a re-routing request via satellite to a ground station in the U. S., and then through a VHF data link to air traffic controllers. If data link were combined with a global positioning system (GPS), the position of airplanes could be automatically sent to the oceanic ATC controllers so that they could view all the airplanes in their area as if they had radar. Armed with this information, controllers could allow more direct routing and closer spacing. Based on some preliminary trials, a data link system was estimated to have the potential of saving between 3,000 - 6,000 lbs. of fuel and eight minutes of flight time on a flight between Los Angeles, California, and Sydney, Australia.[26]

The FAA saw the use of data link primarily as a way of reducing frequency congestion and controller workload. However, a data link system might allow future enhancements to the planned CTAS procedures. Specifically, a VHF data link would enable the CTAS computer and each airplane's flight management computer to communicate directly. As a result, the computers could actually negotiate a safe descent profile optimized not only for that general type of aircraft, but for that particular airplane, taking into account its fuel, weight, and system performance.[27]

In 1993, FAA plans called for an ATC data link system for transoceanic flights by 1995 or 1996, with data link capability at key domestic en route, terminal and tower locations by late 1996. Although some questions still remained about what transmission format the data link system should use, the most likely option appeared to be a composite structure that used VHF frequencies, Mode S discrete code transponders and satellite links.[28]

As opposed to many kinds of new technology, data link did not have to be sold to the airlines. They wanted it as soon as possible and were even "pushing the FAA harder than the FAA could accommodate developing and implementing it."[29] As a result, manufacturers began incorporating data link capability in many new transport airplanes. Boeing, for example, included two-way data link in an updated suite of navigation and communication functions available for new or existing 747-400s and new production 767s. The company also planned to include two-way ATC data link capability in its new B-777 airplane.[30]

Data link technology clearly had potential for making flight operations in the ATC system more efficient. An equally important factor in the rapid transfer and acceptance of the research information by industry, however, was the timing of the Langley experiments. The NASA data link flights were done at a time when the airlines were already pushing the FAA to develop a data link capability for ATC communications. The successful flight tests lent the concept the exact kind of support and credibility the airlines were seeking, which is why they jumped at the technology so quickly. At the same time, the NASA research flights provided the FAA with a measure of confidence in the ability of a data link system to handle ATC communications as well as the acceptability of such a system to the pilots who would have to use it.

Precision Flare Laws

From the start, the researchers working on the TCV program believed that an important element in increasing the capacity of existing airports was the development of technology and procedures to allow less separation between aircraft. If airplanes could be spaced closer together, airports could handle a greater number of takeoffs and landings in any given time period. Closer aircraft spacing, however, required not only improved cockpit equipment and ATC communications, but more efficient landing and taxi operations, as well. Regardless of how efficient flight operations were, aircraft could not be spaced less than two minutes apart if it still took two minutes for an airplane to land, slow down, and taxi off the runway.

In an effort to allow aircraft to taxi off runways sooner, many airports were equipped with high-speed runway turnoffs by the late 1970s. The turnoffs were vastly underutilized, however, especially in low visibility conditions.[31] To make the most efficient use of the turnoffs, pilots had to plan their touchdowns for a point on the runway that would allow just enough time for the airplane to slow down to a safe speed before reaching one of the high-speed exits. Aircraft autoland systems only had to achieve a touchdown accuracy within 1500 feet in order to receive FAA certification, however.[32] This meant that airplanes took longer to touch down and often missed turnoffs, spending a greater amount of time on the runway. Engineers at the Langley Research Center and the Boeing Commercial Airplane Company reasoned that if autoland systems could be made more precise, they could plan the touchdown spot of airplanes to allow them to get off runways more quickly, increasing the potential capacity of airports. More precise autoland systems would also reduce the operational field length requirements for aircraft, opening up more airports as potential landing sites.

The part of the autoland systems that caused such wide dispersion rates was the control law that determined when the airplane began its landing flare. The most commonly used flare control law in the mid-1970s used the aircraft's altitude above the runway as the cue to begin the flare. The airplane's sink rate would be steadily decreased as the airplane got closer to the ground, until it landed. The problem with this approach was that depending on the winds, the aircraft would cover dramatically different amounts of ground between a given altitude and the point where it touched down on the runway. With a 40 knot headwind, for example, the groundspeed of the airplane would be slower, so it might cover little ground in the last 50 feet of a descent. If there was a 10 knot tailwind, on the other hand, the airplane could float far down the runway before it touched down.

The Boeing and NASA engineers researched and flight tested two possible improvements to this control law, using the TSRV 737 airplane. The first concept simply incorporated groundspeed as measured by the airplane's inertial navigation system (INS) into the flare law algorithms so the aircraft's sink rate would be arrested more quickly if the groundspeed was higher. The second approach was a more complex, but more precise, "path-in-space" flare trajectory law that aimed the aircraft toward a specific point on the runway. The path-in-space law essentially extended the glideslope all the way to landing and kept the airplane on the correct glideslope. The aircraft's altitude, sink rate and vertical acceleration were all commanded as a function of the plane's position along the runway.

The flight tests of the new control laws began in 1978, in conjunction with the microwave landing system (MLS) demonstration flights the NASA 737 was performing for the FAA. In 58 landings with the first "Variable Time Constant Flare" control law, all the touchdown points were within 641 feet, and 95 percent of them were within 548 feet. The path-in-space concept was then tested with three different landing guidance systems: an ILS (Instrument Landing System), a basic MLS, and an MLS with a secondary flare elevation signal. Ninety-five percent of the landings that used the basic MLS signal for guidance touched down within a 592 foot distance. Using the MLS signal with the secondary flare elevation signal, that distance dropped to 368 feet, and all of the ILS-guided landings touched down within 285 feet. Clearly, the new control laws could improve the performance of autoland systems far beyond the 1500 foot dispersion requirements set by the FAA.[33]

Nonetheless, convincing industry to adopt new flare control laws for the sole purpose of improving airport capacity would undoubtedly have been extremely difficult. More precise autoland systems would only increase capacity if every airplane was equipped with them, and then only if all the other separation issues could be resolved, as well. The precision flare laws offered another, more financially compelling advantage to manufacturers, however. A path in space or variable time constant flare law could make it easier for a manufacturer to meet the 1500 foot accuracy required for autoland certification, which translated to cost savings in the certification process. The Boeing 767/757 autoland system, for example, did not initially meet the FAA's 1500 foot requirement. In order to pass the FAA requirements, the design engineers ended up developing a path-in-space flare law for the airplane that was later adopted for the 747 aircraft, as well, although the production control law used different algorithms than those developed by the Boeing/NASA research engineers. In addition, the variable time constant flare law was incorporated into the Boeing 737-300 model aircraft, although it had to be modified slightly because the 737-300s did not have INS equipment.[34]

The flare law experiments also showed the researchers at NASA once again that having a transport airplane with which they could actually flight test and demonstrate new technology concepts could be extremely valuable. One of the NASA engineers who worked on the flare law research remembered getting a phone call during the experiments from a colleague who told him that, for a variety of reasons, a path-in-space flare law could never work. "Why don't you come down here next Tuesday and we'll fly it for you," the engineer replied, effectively ending the debate.[35] The fact that a path-in-space law had been successfully demonstrated on an airplane eliminated discussion about whether it was possible and substantially lowered the risk of incorporating it into a commercial airplane. The production engineers at Boeing merely had to decide how they wanted to design their own version.

Magnetic Cable Guidance

The underutilization of high-speed runway turnoffs in low visibility conditions was also due in part to the fact that pilots lacked the necessary guidance to help them find the exits and taxi safely off the runway. In an effort to overcome this obstacle, NASA researchers began investigating the possibility of using a buried magnetic cable to provide rollout, turnoff and taxi guidance for airplanes once they landed.

A magnetic cable system consisted of an electrical cable buried in the center of the runway, turnoffs and taxiways of an airport. An audio-frequency current was sent through the cable, setting up a magnetic field. By measuring the strength of the field, on-board airplane sensors could indicate how far away from the cable the airplane was, and the aircraft autopilot could use that information to follow the cable along the runway, turnoffs, and taxiways.

The idea of using a magnetic cable for aircraft guidance was first tested by the British in the 1950s and 1960s as a way to allow landing operations in extremely low visibility conditions. The British wanted to use the cable to provide guidance during an airplane's final approach to the airport as well as steering guidance on the ground, however, which proved to be beyond the capabilities of the technology.[36] Although the British never implemented the cable guidance system, researchers working with the TCV program in the late 1970s resurrected the idea as a way to improve the efficiency of ground operations at airports in poor weather conditions.

A couple of simulator studies evaluating the feasibility of a cable system for airplane ground navigation and guidance were conducted in the late 1970s and early 1980s at the Langley Research Center. The studies indicated that the idea might be both feasible and practical for commercial aircraft. At the same time, other researchers at Langley were working on possible designs for the cable system itself.[37]

The system was initially tested using a temporary cable and a van-mounted sensor at the Wallops Island Flight Facility in a series of experiments from 1979-1984. Then in 1988, both static and taxi tests were conducted with the cable system and the TSRV 737 airplane at Wallops Island to gather additional information on the performance of different signal gains and frequencies. Researchers were concerned that the large amounts of metal in an airplane might interfere with the signals, but the tests indicated that although the metal interfered with the system's ability to give accurate heading information, it could still reliably indicate the airplane's distance from the cable. There were some electromagnetic interference (EMI) problems caused by the airplane's power system and VHF radio communications, but it appeared that use of filtering techniques could reduce the EMI to an acceptable level.[38]

Using the data gathered in the 1988 tests, researchers fine-tuned the cable system and developed the necessary control laws to allow the 737's autopilot to process and use the magnetic cable signals. The entire system was then evaluated in high-speed taxi tests at Wallops Island in 1991. The tests used a combination of the Wallops Island microwave landing system/ distance measuring equipment (MLS/DME) and the magnetic leader cable to provide the guidance the TSRV 737's autopilot. The results of the tests indicated that the cable system could work, but it needed further development to smooth its operation to an acceptable level.

Additional research and tests with the magnetic leader cable system were put on hold at that point, however, because another potential solution to the same problem had appeared on the technology horizon. As research progressed with the satellite-based global positioning system (GPS), it appeared that the system might be able to provide guidance on the ground as well as in the air. In the spring of 1991, the TSRV 737 began ground tests using GPS to guide the airplane through its rollout and turnoff from the runway. Obviously, if the same GPS receiver that airliners were using for airborne navigation could also be used for ground guidance in low visibility conditions, it would save the cost of installing and maintaining the extra ground and airborne equipment the magnetic cable system would require.[39]

The research goal remained the same, however, even if the specific technology being evaluated had changed. In order to significantly reduce the amount of spacing between arriving aircraft, ground operations had to be made more efficient, especially in poor weather. The magnetic cable leader system and GPS navigation both held potential for providing better ground navigation guidance to pilots, and the TSRV 737 made it possible for the NASA researchers to evaluate their performance not only in theoretical or simulated conditions, but with a transport class airplane in a realistic airport environment.

Summary

Developing technology to improve the operation of the national airspace system offered potentially significant payoffs, but it was a far more complex process than simply inventing a more efficient airplane component. Operations-oriented technology had to win the support of the FAA as well as the airlines and airframe manufacturers, and it had to be not only cost-effective, but compatible with other air traffic and the ground-based infrastructure of the ATC system, as well. The 4-D profile descents researched by Langley engineers in the late 1970s worked extremely well on the 737 and showed potential for saving airlines significant amounts of money, but the ATC infrastructure could not support their use. The two-way data link research, on the other hand, received more support because the FAA was already planning infrastructure changes that could accommodate data link technology.

Improving the operations of the ATC system was also a difficult task because many of the components were inter-related. Developing technology to allow decreased spacing between aircraft in flight would have no benefit if the airports could not accommodate more closely spaced arrivals. Precision flare laws could help autoland systems deliver airplanes to a more optimum point on a runway, but that would only help increase airport capacity if additional technology could be developed to help pilots find the runway turnoffs and taxiways in low visibility conditions. Gaining support for technology that would improve individual components, therefore, could be difficult unless it could also provide a stand-alone benefit for the airlines or manufacturers. Even without being implemented system-wide, for example, data link could help airlines save fuel costs on transoceanic flights. The precision flare laws made it easier for manufacturers to pass certification testing for aircraft, even if the rest of the elements needed to improve airport capacity in poor visibility conditions were not available.

The flight experiments and demonstrations conducted by the TSRV 737 also played an important role in winning support for concepts like precision flare laws and data link communications. In addition to giving industry and the FAA valuable and convincing information about the performance of the technology in realistic flight conditions, successfully demonstrating concepts in a transport class airplane made it virtually impossible for anyone to argue that the technology would not work.

NASA

Chapter 8

A National Facility

The NASA Transport Systems Research Vehicle (TSRV) 737 was, without a doubt, a one-of-a-kind airplane. NASA had many other research aircraft, and the Federal Aviation Administration (FAA), the military, and the airframe manufacturers all had transport class test planes, but the NASA 737 possessed a unique combination of equipment and capabilities. In addition to having a complete second flight deck exclusively for research purposes, electronic flight displays, and a computerized flight control system, the airplane had extremely precise instrumentation and data gathering capabilities. The onboard research computers could record up to 540 pieces of data from various locations on the airplane at any given time.[1] Video equipment could record the screen displays in the aft cockpit as well as the view out the nose of the airplane. Since the research equipment and computers were installed in individual pallets in the back of the airplane, the airplane could be outfitted for different types of experiments fairly easily, and the large interior cabin of the 737 could accommodate up to 30 researchers and observers. The equipment on the TSRV 737 also allowed it to fly complex flight paths and perform extremely accurate navigation.

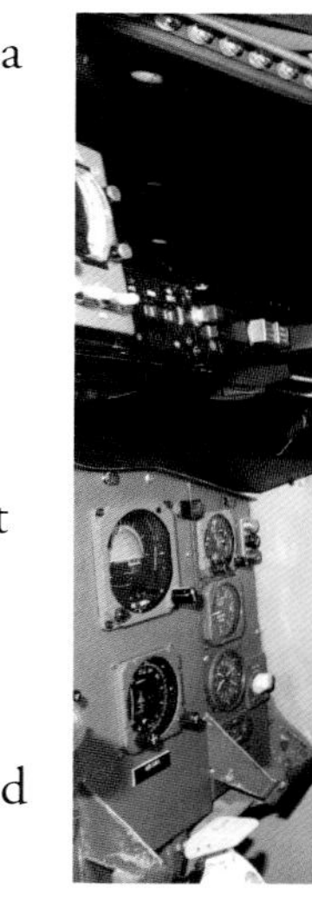

Left—The Langley 737 "flying laboratory" in flight.
Right—The helmet mounted display worn by research pilot Lee Person, being tested in 737 aircraft.

As a result, although NASA purchased the airplane specifically for the Terminal Configured Vehicle (TCV) program research, the airplane was also able to support a variety of other research projects over the years. Before the plane had been at the Langley Research Center a complete year, for example, the FAA requested its participation in the U.S. microwave landing system (MLS) demonstrations. Although the work was not part of the original TCV program agenda, the MLS managers in the FAA realized that the computerization and electronic flight displays in the 737 made it capable of providing a much more dramatic and convincing demonstration of the U.S. system than any airplane the FAA had available.

In the years that followed, the TSRV 737 was also used to flight test experimental wing surface coatings, evaluate the effect of poor weather conditions on runway surfaces and the ability of ground vehicles to measure those conditions accurately, and to gather data on air flow over fuselage and wing surfaces to help engineers improve the design of future transport aircraft. The McDonnell Douglas Corporation used the TSRV airplane to test a helmet-mounted display concept the company was developing for the X-30 National Aerospace Plane. Because the 737 could fly such complex and precise flight paths, the Department of Defense used it to determine if flight operations at the new proposed airport in Denver, Colorado would interfere with national defense satellites. The FAA also enlisted its help to model the Instrument Landing System (ILS) signal at the Los Angeles International Airport.

In short, the TSRV 737 had evolved from a support aircraft for a specific research program into a national airborne research facility. Whether the customer was a research directorate at Langley, another government agency, or an industry manufacturer, the 737 provided a flexible, highly capable platform that could gather valuable research data and flight test a wide variety of aeronautical and aerospace concepts.

Wing Surface Coatings

As fuel prices rose in the late 1970s, the air transport industry became increasingly interested in technology and procedures that could make airline operations more efficient. One area manufacturers focused on was airframe drag reduction, because even a small reduction in drag could have a tremendous impact on operating costs. A one percent drag reduction on a Boeing 727 airliner, for example, was estimated to save 20,000 gallons of fuel per year.[2]

Preliminary experiments in the low turbulence wind tunnel at the Langley Research Center showed that smoothing a wing surface area by applying an adhesive film coating could reduce its drag by as much as 12%, which translated to a 2-3% reduction in the overall drag of the airplane.[3] In 1977, the Boeing Commercial Airplane Company began investigating the potential of specific coating materials, running a total of 15 liquid coatings and 60 film adhesives through a series of 17 laboratory tests to determine which of the different materials could best withstand the rigors of airline use. The materials were first evaluated for their resistance to erosion from rain or various aircraft fluids such as fuel, deicing solutions, or hydraulic fluid. Out of all the materials, four adhesive films and three liquid coatings proved the most resistant to erosion and were recommended for further testing.

Since the adhesive films had a lower resistance level than the liquid coatings, however, they were not recommended for high-erosion areas of the airplane, such as the leading edges of the wings. The films showed potential for areas like the forward body of the airplane, but installing adhesive film on large, curved surfaces would have been an expensive and time-consuming effort. As a result, the rest of the evaluations focused primarily on the liquid coating materials.

The liquid coatings, which went by the names CAAPCO, Chemglaze, and Astrocoat, were run through another series of laboratory tests to further evaluate their resistance to erosion and their compatibility with aircraft systems. The CAAPCO and Chemglaze coatings were then applied to two operational airliners for flight service evaluation.[4] Continental Airlines applied the coatings to the wing and horizontal tail leading edges of a Boeing 727 and tested their resistance to erosion in two different environments. The aircraft was flown for 14 months in the Air Micronesia route system, where an annual rainfall of over 90 inches and the fact that some airports used coral runways caused significant erosion problems with paint on aircraft leading edges. Continental then conducted a second, 11-month evaluation of the coatings with the same B-727 on domestic routes in the United States. Although the coatings suffered significant erosion in both cases, an outboard horizontal tail section with the coatings applied by Boeing Laboratory technicians was then installed on the 727 and flown for an additional 18 months,

A Langley technician works on the wing of the model Boeing 737 in the 14 by 22 foot subsonic wind tunnel.

accumulating 3800 flight hours with almost no erosion of the coatings. The two coatings were also tested by Delta Airlines on a B-727 to evaluate the impact of different colors and primers on the effectiveness of the coatings. After 16 months and 4348 flight hours, some coated areas had peeled or eroded, but others were still holding up fairly well.

The next question was whether or not this kind of liquid, elastomeric polyurethane coating could reduce aircraft drag. Since any reductions in drag were expected to be small, results from wind tunnel models or smaller aircraft would not necessarily apply to transport class airplanes. Consequently, drag measuring flight tests had to be conducted on a full-scale, transport class airplane that could record precise data through instrumentation on the surface of the wing. This was obviously beyond the capabilities of operational airliners, but the NASA TSRV 737 was perfectly suited for the task.

The test substances were applied to the upper inboard surface of the left wing and compared against the performance of the same section on the right wing, which was kept as a bare metal surface. The flight tests compared the performance of the CAAPCO substance against the Corogard corrosion-protective paint that was a popular aircraft surface coating at that time, as well as a gritty strip that was installed on the leading edge of the wing section to represent a coating that was somewhat eroded. The results showed that compared to the bare metal surface, the CAAPCO substance reduced the total drag of the airplane by about .2% in cruise conditions, whereas the Corogard coating increased aircraft drag by about the same amount.

The Boeing and NASA experiments showed that the CAAPCO coating could be resistant to erosion and could reduce drag on the wing of an aircraft, but more research was needed to determine if a CAAPCO or Chemglaze substance would provide as much protection against corrosion as the coatings already in use. The coatings also might not be as effective in actual airline operations, because the quality of the application process clearly affected their lifespan and effectiveness. Although the laboratory coated wing tested by Continental held up extremely well, laboratory-quality work would be difficult, if not impossible, to achieve in a busy airline maintenance environment. But while there were issues that might affect the commercial use of the substances, the TSRV 737 flight tests showed Boeing that elastomeric polyurethane coatings at least had the potential for reducing drag on transport aircraft.[5]

LEBU/High Lift

The TSRV 737's precise data gathering capability also led it to be chosen for NASA research projects that were not within the original parameters of the TCV/ATOPS program. Two different flight experiments, for example, focused on measuring and analyzing air flow over sections of the aircraft wing and fuselage in an effort to help engineers design more efficient transport aircraft in the future. A full-scale aircraft was an important tool in research areas involving air flow and drag analysis, because some of the measurements were sensitive to "scale effects." In other words, some of the flow characteristics observed on small wind tunnel models would not hold true for a full-scale aircraft in flight. The TSRV 737 allowed researchers to obtain accurate flight data that then could be used to update computer models and provide more accurate data to aircraft design engineers.

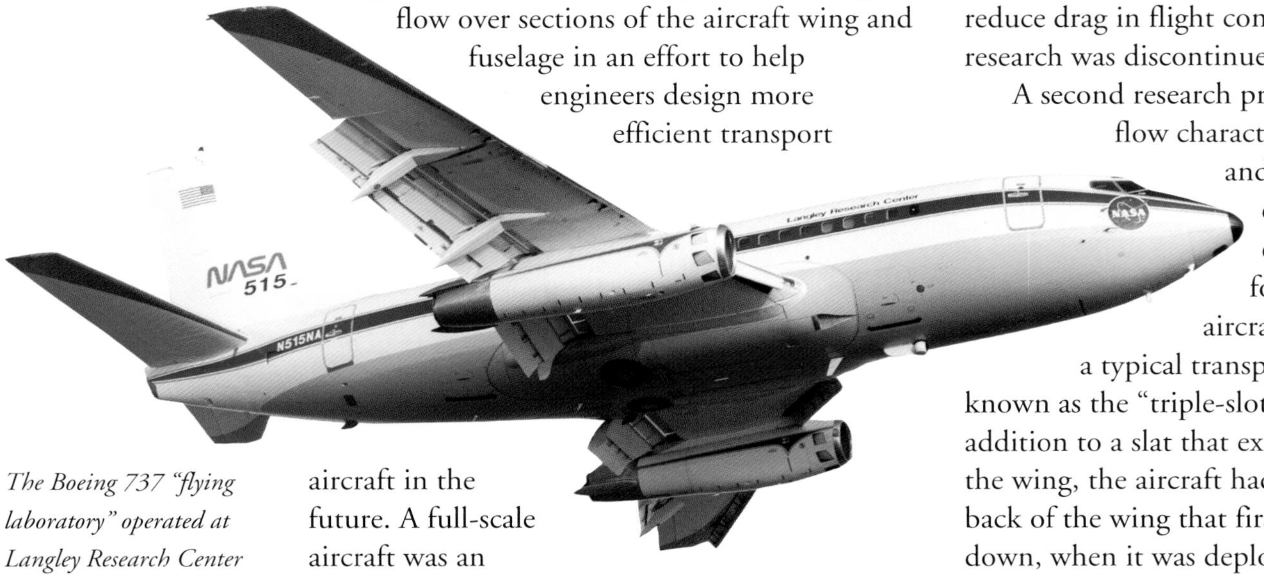

The Boeing 737 "flying laboratory" operated at Langley Research Center with flaps deployed during high-lift research.

In 1988, researchers used the 737 to measure the air flow around its fuselage as a first step toward evaluating the effectiveness of Large Eddy Break-Up (LEBU) devices. The LEBU concept involved mounting small airfoils on the airframe to help reduce skin friction drag. In order to determine the effect of the LEBU devices, however, researchers first had to have precise information about the standard airflows around a transport airframe. So the upper portion of the 737 fuselage was outfitted with numerous data gathering instruments including pressure belts, pitot rakes, hot wire rakes, hot films, and piezoelectric foil to measure the pressure, speed, flow, and turbulence characteristics of the airflow over the airframe. Data was gathered throughout a range of speeds, attitudes and altitudes from 10,000 feet to 25,000 feet and from Mach .5 to Mach .8.[6] A second set of flight experiments had been planned with LEBU devices installed on the 737 airframe. Further ground testing of the LEBU concept indicated that it would not actually reduce drag in flight conditions, however, so the research was discontinued.[7]

A second research project measured the air flow characteristics of the 737's wing and flap system to help engineers create more efficient high-lift designs for future transport aircraft. The TSRV 737 had a typical transport aircraft flap system, known as the "triple-slotted Fowler flap." In addition to a slat that extended from the front of the wing, the aircraft had a three-part flap at the back of the wing that first slid back, and then down, when it was deployed. As the flap slid back and the slat slid forward, the area of the wing, and therefore the lift it could produce, increased. This was critical when the aircraft was flying slowly, such as on approach to landing or immediately after takeoff.

The triple-slotted flap system worked well. When Airbus Industries came out with a simpler, single piece flap for its A-310 and A-320 aircraft that had the same performance as the three-part design, however, NASA and the U.S. manufacturers realized that the European consortium had edged ahead of the U.S. in high lift technology. To try to correct this perceived lag in U.S. technology, NASA began a multi-phased program in subsonic transport high-lift research.[8]

One of the first steps in the program was to learn more about the flow characteristics of current transport high-lift systems. This data could then be used to create more accurate and precise math and computational fluid dynamics models which, in turn, could be used by engineers to design better systems. In order for the models to be accurate, however, the data had to be obtained from a full-scale transport aircraft

The Boeing 737 testbed during runway friction tests at Brunswick Naval Air Station, Maine, in 1985.

in actual flight conditions. Since the TSRV 737 was already set up for extensive and precise data gathering and it was kept at the Langley Research Center, where the high-lift research was being conducted, it was the logical choice for the experiments.

For the initial flight tests in 1990, the 737's right wing and flap system were "tufted" with short pieces of string to help researchers visualize the basic air flow patterns across them in various flight configurations. In 1991, a second set of flight tests was conducted with more elaborate instrumentation on the three elements of one right wing flap section. Pressure belts recorded the surface pressure distribution over the flap segments, and instruments called Preston tubes measured the skin friction levels at various locations on the flap surfaces. A third set of flight tests in February 1992 used the same instrumentation, but expanded the test area to a full-chord strip that started at the front of the leading edge slat and ran back across the wing to the trailing edge of the flap. Another set of flights with even more precise instrumentation, including infrared imaging systems, hot-film sensors and micro vortex generators, was scheduled for the end of 1993.[9]

The large gaps in between the flight tests were one of the main drawbacks to using the TSRV for flight experiments. So many research projects wanted flight time on the airplane that it was difficult to get a place on the schedule. Nevertheless, the data obtained from the 737 flights was very useful to the on-going high-lift research at NASA. The flight test data corroborated some wind tunnel test results, corrected the predictions of others, and gave research engineers additional information about the dynamics of high-lift flow physics. That information could help manufacturers design more efficient aircraft and, at the same time, restore the United States' competitive edge in the field of high-lift technology.

Runway Friction

In January 1982, two airline accidents within a matter of weeks suddenly focused national attention on the hazards of winter flying. On January 13, 1982, an Air Florida 737 crashed into the 14th Street Bridge after departing Washington National Airport, killing 78 people on board the airplane. Ten days later, a World Airways DC-10 landing at Logan Airport in Boston, Massachusetts ran off the end of the icy runway and into the bay, killing two passengers and injuring four others.[10] Spurred by those two accidents, the House subcommittee on aviation recommended that the FAA conduct a focused research and development program in runway friction measurement in an effort to improve safety in one of the critical areas of winter flight operations. The recommendation led to an appropriations bill for the FAA and NASA to "study the correlation between aircraft stopping performance and runway friction measurements on wet and contaminated surfaces." The bill also specified that the research would focus on "determining if it is possible to predict aircraft stopping performance based on runway friction measurements using new technology friction measuring devices."[11]

The FAA, NASA and other groups had actually been studying runway friction and the effects of wet, snow-covered, icy, or otherwise "contaminated" runway surfaces on aircraft performance for some time. Engineers at the Langley Research Center, for example, had been investigating the impact of different runway surfaces on braking performance since 1968. Yet by 1982, pilots still had to rely solely on the subjective reports of other pilots landing or departing ahead of them for information on runway conditions. These reports were imprecise and often of limited value, because what was "adequate" for a Northwest Airlines pilot accustomed to flying in winter conditions might be considered "severe" by an Air Florida pilot. Ground-based friction-measuring vehicles were in existence in 1982, but they were only used to tell airport operators when repairs needed to be made to runway surfaces. The research recommended by the House subcommittee was an effort to provide pilots and airport operators with more precise and reliable information about runway conditions in bad weather. Pilots could then either modify their landing technique to accommodate the conditions or, if performance was degraded beyond a minimum safety level, operations could be suspended until the runway conditions improved.[12]

Researchers wanted data from more than one kind of transport aircraft, so both NASA's TSRV 737 and a Boeing 727 owned by the FAA were used for the tests, although the FAA airplane did not have the extensive research equipment or capabilities of the 737. NASA technicians installed a special instrumentation packet on the 727 to enable it to collect the necessary friction data for the research experiments, but the 737 was still able to collect more detailed information, such as how hard the pilots were braking during the test runs. The tests, which ran from June 1983 through March 1986, took place at NASA's Wallops Island Flight Facility and the Langley Air Force Base in Virginia, the FAA Technical Center in New Jersey, and at the Brunswick Naval Air Station in Maine. The tests were conducted at numerous sites so data could be collected in a variety of weather conditions, and researchers could evaluate the impact of different runway surfaces on braking friction as well as the quality of the ground vehicle measurements.

The Boeing 737 and ATOPS researchers working on the runway friction tests in 1989 at Wallops Flight Facility.

The research effort evaluated a number of different ground friction measuring devices. A diagonal-braked vehicle (DBV), for example, was a car with a specially modified braking system that allowed only two diagonally opposed tires to lock up when the brakes were applied sharply. The DBV measured the speed, acceleration and stopping distance from the point of braked-wheel lockup to determine the friction level of the runway. Another ground device called a Mu-Meter consisted of a 540 lb. trailer towed behind a truck that determined surface friction by measuring the side-forces imposed on the trailer wheels. A third ground vehicle, called a BV-11 Skiddometer, measured the speed of the vehicle, the torque applied during braking, and the slip ratio of an instrumented wheel to determine the runway friction level. Over the course of the tests, half a dozen different ground vehicles were evaluated at different locations.

The tests were conducted by having a ground vehicle make a pass down the runway first, followed by one of the two test airplanes. The measurements of the ground device and the airplane would then be compared. Braking performance was measured over a range of speeds, ranging from 40 mph to over 100 mph. For the slower runs, the aircraft would accelerate to the required speed and then apply maximum braking, but for the faster runs, the aircraft would take off, land, and then test the braking performance as it slowed down to a stop. The research also looked at the impact of engine reversers on aircraft braking performance in contaminated runway conditions, and the effectiveness of different kinds of runway deicing substances.[13]

Measurements were taken on a wide variety of runway surfaces and conditions. Dry runway measurements were taken to establish the standard against which degraded performance could be measured. Tests were then conducted on wet, flooded, slush-covered, snow covered and icy runways. In some cases, natural rainfall allowed researchers to measure the impact of both surface water levels and the intensity of rainfall on runway friction levels. If it was not raining, wet runway conditions could be created by flooding surfaces with water trucks. Some of the winter conditions would have been harder to simulate but, fortunately, that was not necessary.

The TSRV 737 and its research crew travelled to the Brunswick Naval Air Station in March 1985 to test runway friction levels in snow and icy conditions. The researchers wanted to test snow levels up to eight inches, and immediately after the plane arrived, eight inches of snow fell. A 2,000 foot test section of snow was prepared, with a long cleared strip at either end to allow the airplane to stop and turn around. The first thing the researchers discovered was that eight inches of snow increased the friction level so much that although the 737 finally reached the 90 knot speed the test required, the snow caused so much drag that the aircraft could never have reached its takeoff speed. The snow was progressively reduced for additional tests with six, four and two inches of snow, by which time the conditions had deteriorated into the precise kind of slush conditions the researchers wanted to test next. After the snow measurements were completed, the temperature at New Brunswick fell, allowing the runway to be frozen for the icing tests. The lack of friction on ice-covered runways became very clear when the 737 accelerated to 90 knots as it entered the ice-covered section and, despite maximum braking efforts by the pilot, exited the section at 92 knots.[14]

The runway friction tests showed researchers that the ground vehicle measurements correlated extremely well with aircraft performance, meaning that they could be used to give pilots and airport operators reliable information about runway friction conditions in bad weather. The results also indicated that grooved runway surfaces were an extremely effective method of maintaining safe friction levels in poor weather conditions. Braking performance on transversely grooved runway surfaces was almost as good in wet and slippery conditions as it was on dry runways. These results played a significant role in expanding the use of grooved surfaces in the transportation industry. By 1993, over 800 commercial runways in the world were

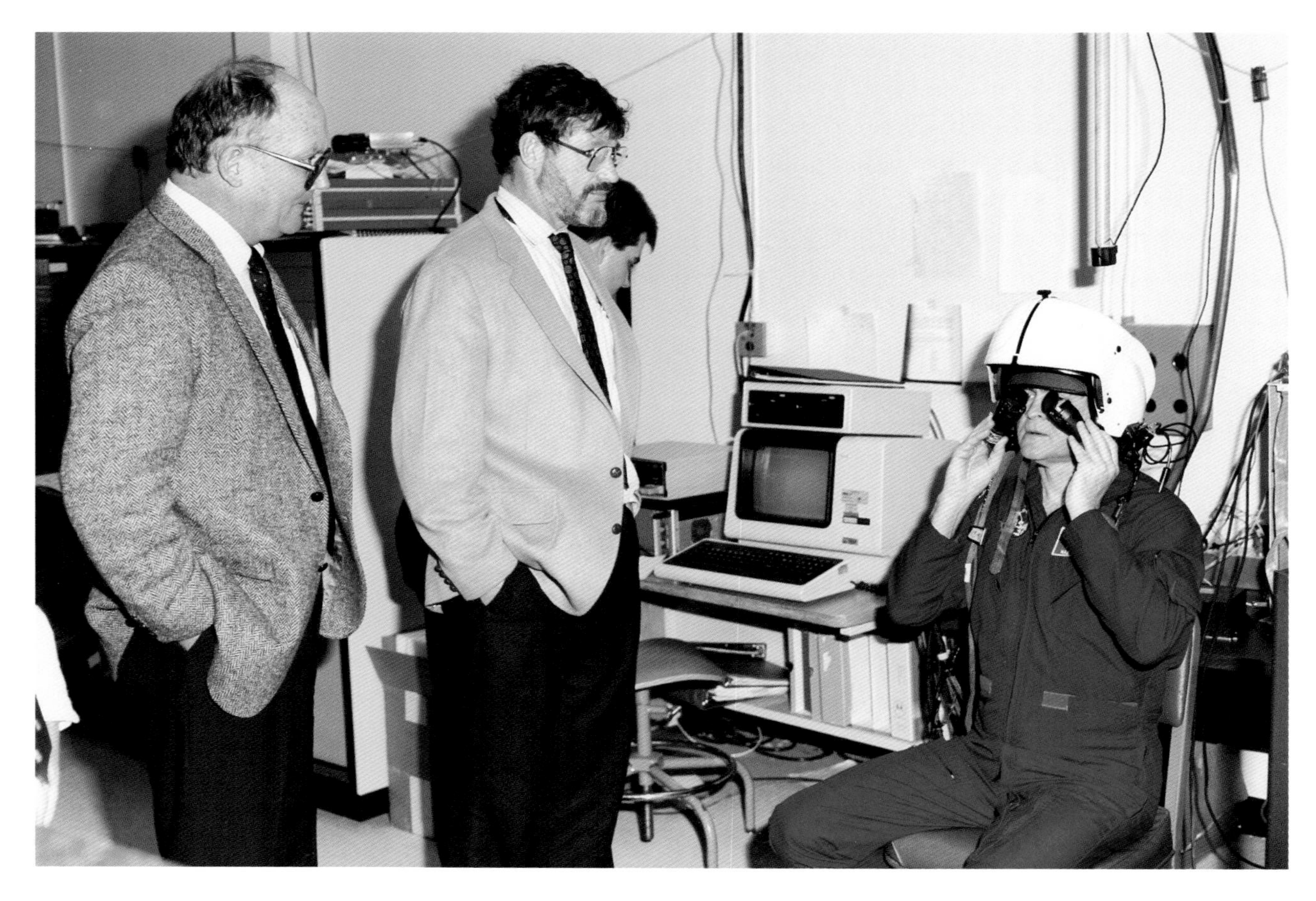

The helmet-mounted display being tested on the ground at Langley Research Center in 1989. Dr. Jeremiah F. Creedon, director for Flight Systems at Langley, in the middle, looks on.

constructed with grooved surfaces. In addition, sections of highway in all 50 states within the U.S. were using grooved surfaces to improve traction in poor weather. While most of the highway applications used longitudinal grooving for ease of installation, transverse grooving was also being installed at an increasing number of intersections to improve braking performance.[15]

The use of ground vehicles for friction-measuring also increased dramatically as a result of the NASA/FAA tests. Before the runway friction research, fewer than a dozen airports had the machinery, and there were no guidelines to tell operators how to use the devices to judge friction levels in poor weather. By the early 1990s, between 80 and 100 airports had purchased ground friction-measuring devices. In addition, the FAA issued advisory circulars that spelled out what the minimum friction measurements should be for each different vehicle in various conditions to ensure safe aircraft braking performance. Airport operators now had a much more reliable method for judging the safety of runway conditions and knowing when operations should be suspended.[16]

Helmet Mounted Display

The helmet mounted display research with the TSRV 737 stemmed from research the McDonnell Douglas Corporation was conducting on the X-30 National Aerospace Plane (NASP). Engineers working on the X-30 faced a number of formidable design challenges. The plane was supposed to take off from a conventional runway, go into space and travel at hypersonic speeds, and then re-enter the earth's atmosphere and land once again on a runway. The performance requirements of such an vehicle required the design to be as light, streamlined and as simple as possible. One potential strategy for saving significant amounts of weight and drag was to design the aircraft without any cockpit windows. Under normal conditions, it was argued, automatic landing systems and advanced flight displays could safely guide the aircraft without any direct outside visibility for the pilots. In order for such a revolutionary design to be acceptable or even considered, however, it still had to afford the pilots some way of flying and landing the aircraft visually in case of an emergency.

McDonnell Douglas researchers who were working on the X-30 cockpit design came up with an idea for a helmet-mounted display that would use television cameras or sensors in the nose of the airplane to provide the necessary visual display of the outside world for the pilots. A helmet mounted display would be more flexible than a fixed cockpit display, because it could track the pilot's head movements and show him the specific portion of the outside scene where his eyes were "looking." Helmet mounted displays were already being used in military helicopters, but they had never been tested for basic control of a transport aircraft in a cockpit that had absolutely no outside visibility.

The TSRV 737 was a far cry from the X-30. But the McDonnell Douglas engineers knew the 737 was involved with state-of-the-art cockpit displays, and the windowless aft flight deck on the airplane seemed like the ideal place to test the viability of a synthetic vision system. The research systems on the aircraft were also set up to incorporate new experiments with a minimum of effort. So the McDonnell Douglas researchers approached NASA with a proposal to test a helmet mounted display system on the airplane, and the managers at Langley agreed. McDonnell Douglas would provide the experimental technology, and NASA would provide the testbed and flight time.

Since the purpose of the flight experiments was simply to test the basic viability of the helmet display concept, the test system was constructed from crude, off-the-shelf components. Two television cameras were mounted in the nose of the 737, giving the pilot a total field of regard 80 degrees across and 30 degrees high. Within that area, the pilot's field of view at any given moment was 40 degrees wide and 30 degrees high. The images conveyed by the cameras were displayed on two eyepieces in the pilot's helmet. Because the display was to be used for basic aircraft control, critical flight data including altitude, airspeed, flight path angle and flight path acceleration were superimposed on the televised image.[17]

Although the McDonnell Douglas engineers had initially envisioned using the aft cockpit of the 737 for the test flights, they wanted to be able to compare the results of the helmet mounted display landings with conventional landings using outside visual references. Visual landings had to be made from the 737's forward cockpit, and the controls and displays in the aft flight deck were dramatically different from those in the front. In order to make a valid comparison of landing accuracies with and without the helmet display, therefore, all the landings had to be done from the forward cockpit. Since safety considerations precluded the front cockpit windows from being covered, the visor of the helmet used for the synthetic vision display was painted a flat black color and kept down over the pilot's eyes during the helmet-guided landings.

The helmet mounted display system was tested by two NASA research pilots and two pilots from McDonnell Douglas. In addition to practice time in a ground simulator, each pilot made a minimum of 14 visual landings to NASA's Wallops Island Flight Facility and observed an additional 14 landings through the

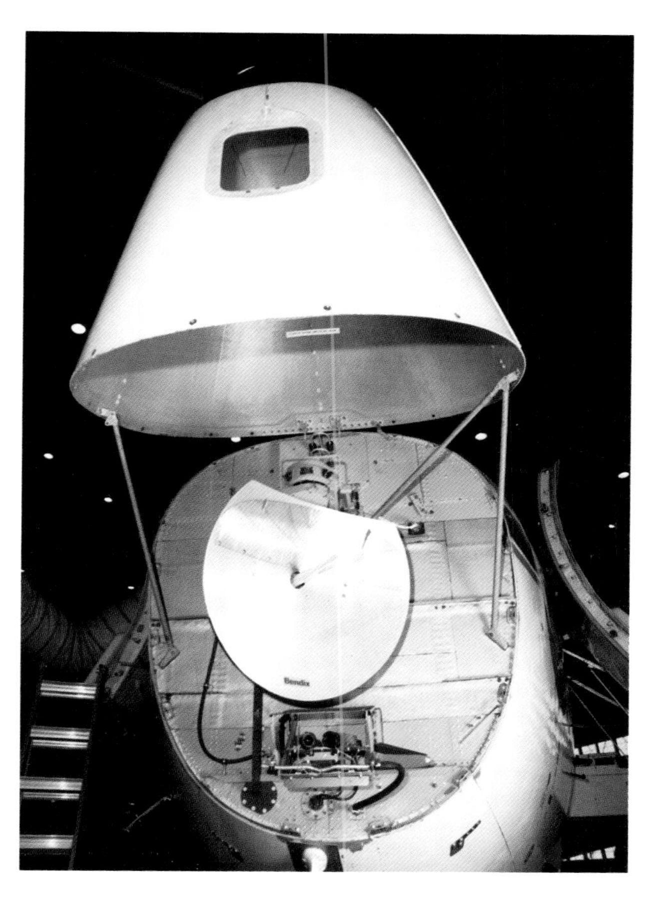

Radome of the Boeing 737 testbed aircraft, used to provide information to the helmet mounted display.

Measuring aircraft skids during the runway friction tests.

helmet mounted display before attempting any landings with the synthetic vision system. In evaluating the system, the McDonnell Douglas engineers wanted to compare both the pilots' perceived workload and the accuracy of the landings with and without the helmet display. While the Wallops Island airport was equipped with laser tracker that could provide data on the accuracy of the landings, the researchers wanted to give the pilots immediate feedback on how close they had gotten to the target landing spot. To obtain that information, ground personnel ran out onto the runway immediately after each landing and found the sticky rubber patches that marked where the 737's tires had just touched the runway. The distance between those marks and the target point was then quickly measured and radioed to the flight crew on the airplane.

The test flights were conducted throughout May and June of 1989. A total of 67 landings were completed using the helmet display system, with very favorable results. The accuracy of the landings with and without the helmet display were almost identical, although pilots reported that their workload was higher for the landings using the synthetic vision system. There were also some difficulties caused by the limitations of the test equipment, such as an image processing time lag that made pilots reluctant to move their head once they were on a short final approach. Still, the flights showed that a helmet mounted synthetic vision system could be used to land a transport airplane.[18]

Although the helmet mounted display tests had been very successful, the X-30 manned vehicle program was abandoned in 1992. McDonnell Douglas continued funding some helmet display research for military applications, since windowless cockpits could potentially help shield aircraft from both radar detection and laser weapons. The McDonnell Douglas engineers also believed the concept might one day find its way into another advanced transport aircraft design.[19] But while the future of the helmet mounted display system was still uncertain, there was no question that the TSRV 737 had been useful in its initial development. The 737 allowed the McDonnell Douglas engineers to test the basic viability of the concept, economically and in actual flight conditions, before investing large amounts of company funds and staff time in fully developing the technology.

Airport '85

Perhaps the most unusual experiment ever conducted with the TSRV 737 was a flight test program for the Air Force in 1985. Air Force officials were apparently concerned that aircraft operating out of the new airport planned for Denver, Colorado would block critical communications between orbiting satellites and receiver antennas at Buckley Air National Guard Base, which was located just west of the airport site. The best way to determine if the airliners would really cause a problem was simply to fly a transport aircraft through the signal beam and see if it interfered with the transmission. The difficulty with this approach was that to intersect the beam, an aircraft had to navigate through a constantly moving three-foot square hole in the sky. The Air Force also wanted the tests completed in only three or four months.

After an unsuccessful search for an Air Force aircraft that could perform that kind of demanding precision navigation and could conduct the flight test in that short a period of time, the Air Force finally approached NASA about using the TSRV 737. The 737 had an extremely precise guidance system that could be programmed to indicate course deviations as small as a few feet, and its velocity vector electronic flight displays allowed the pilot to see not only the attitude of the aircraft, but the exact flight path it was following. NASA agreed to support the Air Force effort, and Langley engineers began work on the project in the spring of 1985.

In order for the 737 to achieve the precise accuracy the Air Force tests required, the research flights were designed to use guidance from two different sources. The initial flight path for each run was designed on board the aircraft and put into the navigation computers, which then generated a magnetic course for the pilot to follow. The flight path had to be designed on board the airplane because the target was constantly moving. Each new test run required a different flight path. The second source of guidance came from an extremely precise Marine Corps fire control radar on the ground. The Marine personnel called small course corrections over a radio frequency to the research pilot, as well a countdown to the intersection point with the target. The countdown was important because at the precise moment the airplane intersected the target, the Air Force wanted the 737 to pitch up to a 30 degree nose-high attitude. Although the approach to the target had to be flown from the aft cockpit to control the flight path with the precision the tests required, the aft cockpit flight controls could only command half deflection of the 737's control surfaces. To get an rapid pitch-up of 30 degrees, command of the airplane had to be handed over to the front cockpit. The countdown helped the research pilots execute the transfer of command and the pitch-up maneuver at the exact moment the plane intersected the target.

To add to the challenge of the flight tests, all the electronic displays in the 737's aft cockpit malfunctioned just before the Denver flights. In 1985, the airplane was still equipped with the original experimental, monochrome General Electric flight displays, and they had a history of maintenance difficulties. Unfortunately, there was not enough time to repair the displays and still get the Air Force tests done on time. So NASA research pilot Lee Person had to fly the tests with only an electromechanical Course Deviation Indicator (CDI) in the aft cockpit for course guidance. The CDI was a standard navigation instrument that indicated the aircraft's relative position to a selected course. If the needle on the CDI was centered, the plane was on course. If the needle was left or right of center, it indicated that the airplane needed to turn left or right to get back on the correct path. Since the CDI NASA used for the Air Force

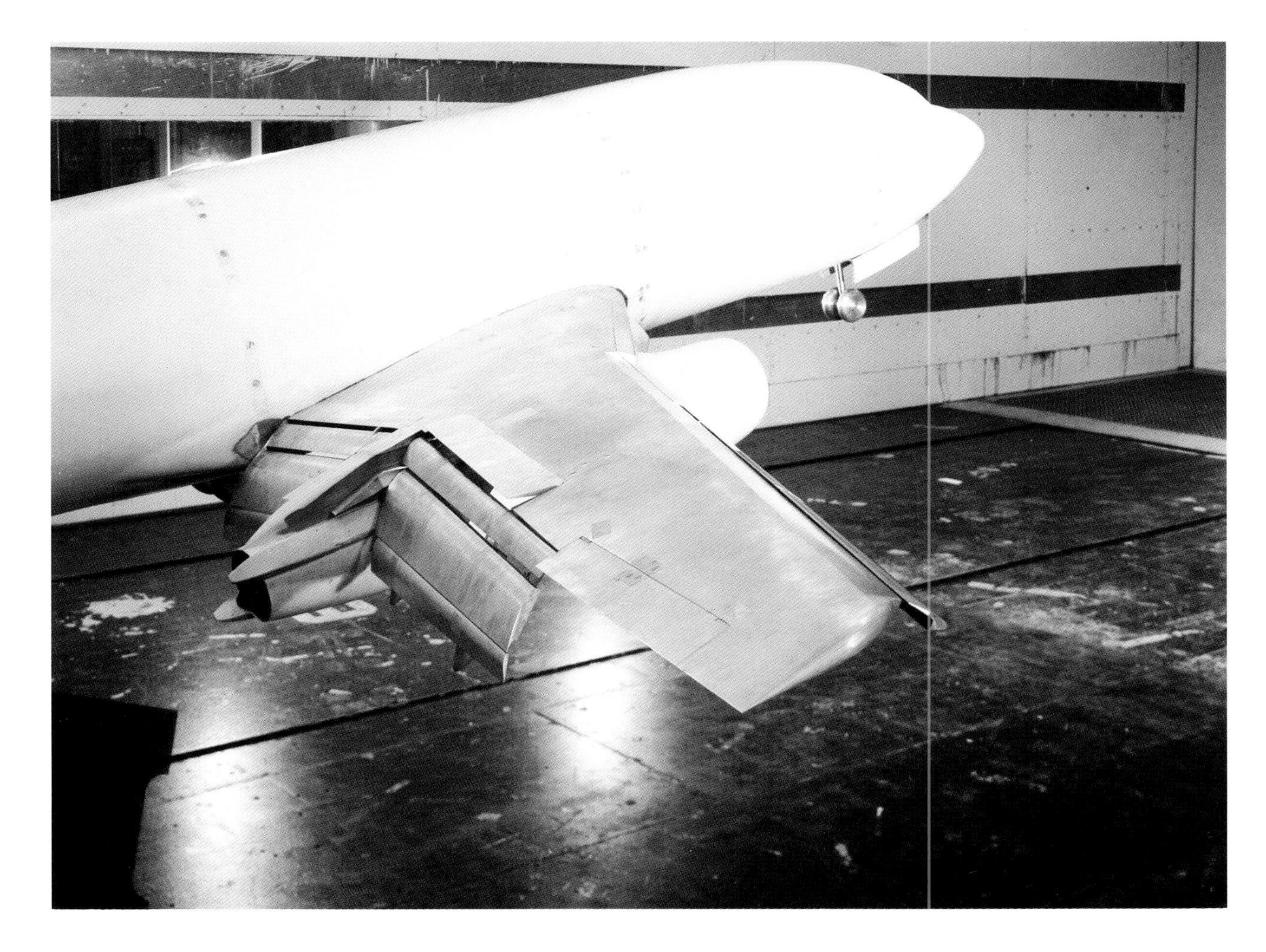

A 1/8th scale model of the Boeing 737 undergoing wing tests in the Langley Research Center wind tunnel. This research tested flow physics over the aircraft wing. Over 700 pressure ports were placed on the right-hand wing to measure airflow.

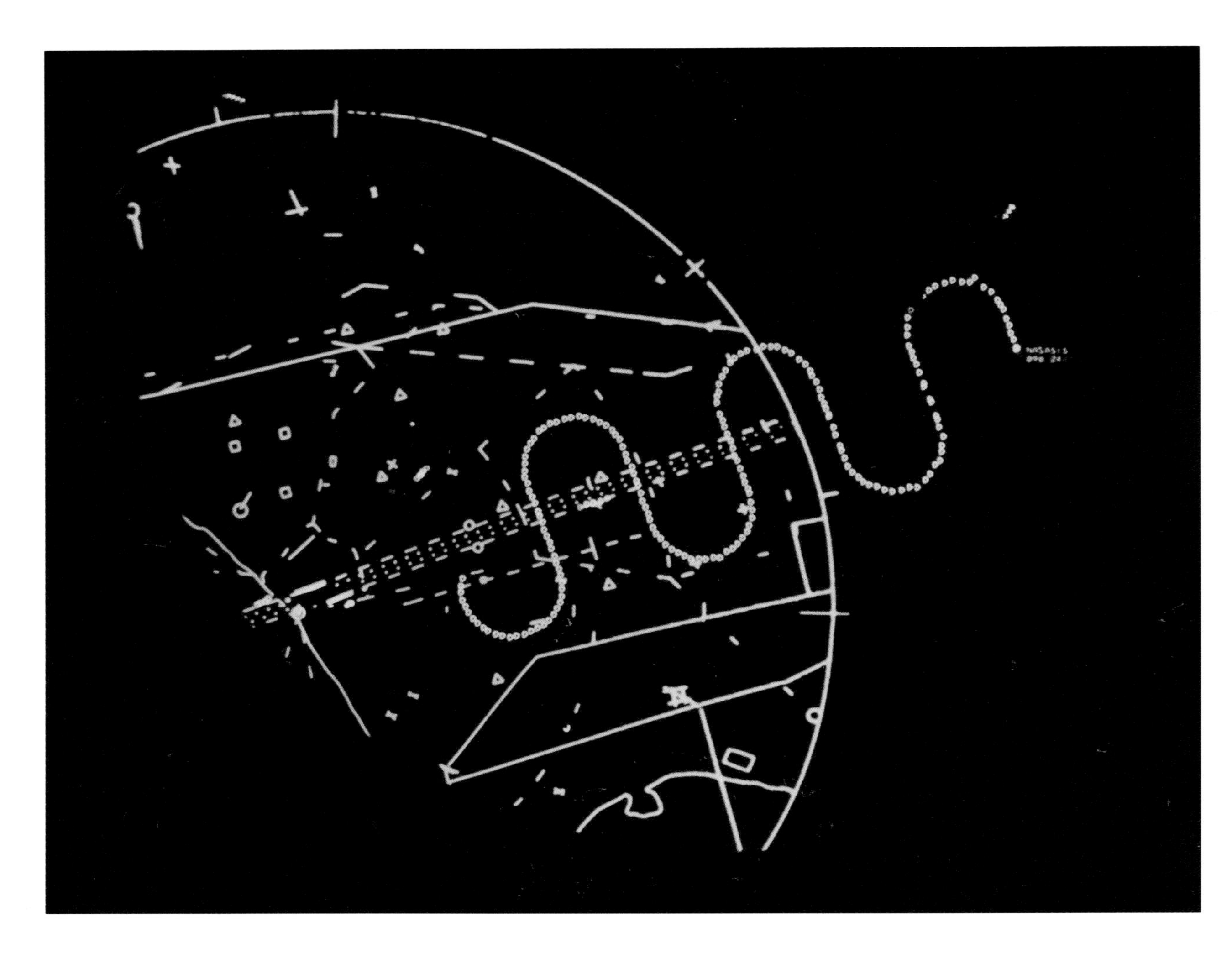

An electronic display of a "boustrophedonic" flight path the 737 created and followed to map the ILS signal at the Los Angeles International Airport.

flight tests received its guidance from the Marine Corps fire control radar, however, it indicated much smaller course deviations than a standard instrument would. The autopilot control knobs were also modified to allow much more precise corrections in the flight path. Instead of the usual configuration, in which each click of a knob altered the airplane's track angle by one degree, the controls were altered so that each click changed the track angle only one-tenth of a degree. As a result, Person was able to make corrections as small as one or two feet. [20]

Between the computer-generated flight paths on board the airplane, the course corrections radioed from the Marine fire control radar and the precision autopilot control of the airplane, the NASA research pilots were able to repeatedly find and intersect the moving, one-meter cube in space they were seeking. The Air Force was extremely satisfied with the results, and the NASA personnel who worked on the project were justifiably proud of what they had done. The task they had undertaken had been so difficult that not even military aircraft had been able to accomplish it. Yet the 20-year old 737 at Langley and its crew of researchers had not only completed the mission successfully, but they had done it on budget, and on time. The 737 was proving itself a much more flexible and capable resource the early TCV program researchers had ever imagined it could be.

ILS Signal Modelling

In 1992, the FAA began investigating whether it would be possible to decrease the distance between the long, parallel runways at the Los Angeles International Airport (LAX) and still maintain safe separation between aircraft on approach to the airport. If the space between the runways could be reduced, it would allow the construction of more runways on the airport, which would boost the airport's capacity. Since LAX controllers typically assigned airliners long, straight-in approaches from 30 or 40 miles away, however, analysts needed information on how accurate the standard Instrument Landing System (ILS) signal was at those distances in order to determine whether more closely spaced approach courses would be safe.

In order to gather that information, the FAA enlisted the assistance of the TSRV 737. The NASA 737 had the ability to gather extensive data on the ILS signal characteristics, and its computers could also design and fly precise, complex navigation routes that could cover the entire signal range. Specifically, the FAA wanted the airplane to fly evenly spaced, descending "S" turns across the ILS signal, starting from a point 30 miles away from the airport. One of the NASA researchers dubbed the back-and-forth navigation course a "boustrophedonic" flight path, which sounded very impressive and technical. It was not until some time later that the other engineers looked the term up in the dictionary and discovered that it meant simply, "as the ox plows."[21]

The Los Angeles ILS modelling research took place on April 1-3, 1992. The flights had to be conducted in the middle of the night so the experiment would not interfere with the normal airport traffic, but they were uneventful and obtained the ILS data the FAA analysts needed to explore expansion options at LAX. The experiments also allowed NASA researchers to compare the accuracy of a differential global positioning system (GPS) signal against that of the ILS, so both the FAA and NASA obtained some valuable information from the research.

The ILS modelling work at LAX was not a large or complex research project. Nevertheless, it involved a task that would have been difficult or impossible for any airplane without the TSRV's unique equipment and capabilities to perform. The NASA airplane, on the other hand, was able to complete the research relatively easily and in a timely manner. The LAX flights demonstrated once again that the TSRV 737 could support not only ATOPS program-related research, but a variety of other tasks and research efforts for NASA, industry, and other government agencies.[22]

Summary

When NASA purchased the prototype Boeing 737, it was to be used as a support system for a specific research program. The engineers who designed the TCV program did not expect the airplane to be used to test helmet mounted synthetic vision systems, to gather data on flow physics, or to find three-foot wide holes in the sky for the United States Air Force. But in designing a research tool to flight test advanced transport concepts, the NASA and Boeing engineers ended up creating an ideal testbed for a much broader range of technologies and research projects. The TSRV 737 may have begun as a test plane for a single research program, but it evolved into a national resource for airborne research. Like the many wind tunnels at the Langley Research Center, the NASA 737 provided both government and industry with a fully instrumented research facility for gathering data, testing new designs and demonstrating concepts to further aeronautical technology.

Conclusion

The Boeing 737 "flying laboratory" in flight on another research mission as part of the Advanced Transport Operating Systems Program conducted at NASA's Langley Research Center.

Research supported by the United States government has played an important role in the advancement of aeronautics and the U.S. aviation industry since the formation of the National Advisory Council for Aeronautics (NACA) in 1915. Government involvement in research has allowed industry to pursue concepts that would otherwise have been too high-risk, long-term, or expensive to research and develop. It has also encouraged the development of technologies that benefit society but do not offer manufacturers or users enough of an economic incentive for industry to sponsor the research itself. As a result, government research institutions like NACA and its successor, the National Aeronautics and Space Administration (NASA), have contributed greatly to both the welfare of society and the economic health of the aeronautics industry and, consequently, the country as a whole.

Although NACA and then NASA have always had to balance their aeronautics research efforts between near-term projects that have a more immediate benefit for industry and long-term endeavors that help build the nation's technology base for future aircraft design, the organizations have always focused on finding pragmatic, technological solutions to the nation's aeronautical problems. The original NACA charter called for the agency to "supervise and direct the scientific study of the problems of flight, with a view to their practical solution."[1] The mission statement of NASA's Langley Research Center, one of the main government facilities for aeronautics research since 1918, specifically calls for it to "perform innovative aerospace research relevant to national needs; transfer technology to users in a timely manner; and support U.S. government agencies, U.S. industry, NASA Centers, the educational community, and the local community." The mission statement also notes that "Our success will be measured by the extent to which our research results and technologies contribute to the design, development, and operation of future aerospace vehicles and missions."[2]

By these standards, the research conducted with Langley's Boeing 737 Transport Systems Research Vehicle (TSRV), as part of the Terminal Configured Vehicle (TCV)/Advanced Transport Operating Systems (ATOPS) program, was extraordinarily successful. The program was created in 1973 specifically to research innovative technologies that could help solve some of the problems facing the national air transportation system. In the twenty years that followed, the airplane supported a wide variety of research projects with other NASA centers, the Federal Aviation Administration, the Department of Defense, industry manufacturers, and a number of universities. In addition, the transfer of technological information from the TCV/ATOPS program research was creative, timely and surprisingly effective, with the end result that the program and its research airplane had a significant impact on the development and application of a number of aeronautical technologies.

The TSRV 737 was instrumental in the development and acceptance of electronic flight displays for transport aircraft, which led to the creation of "glass cockpits." Its demonstrations of complex, curved path approaches using the Time Reference Scanning Beam (TRSB) microwave landing system (MLS) gave the U.S. candidate technology an unassailable edge in the international competition for a new instrument landing system. Years later, its research with global positioning system (GPS) approaches and autolands changed the nature of the entire debate about GPS and helped solidify the technology's position as a serious contender to be a partial or total replacement for MLS.

The windshear research conducted with the airplane led to the development of forward-looking detection systems that gave airliners the ability to survive or avoid potentially lethal microbursts. The Digital Autonomous Terminal Access Communication (DATAC) data bus developed installed and tested on the TSRV 737 became the basis for a new national design standard for transport aircraft data bus systems. The Total Energy Control System (TECS) was incorporated into an unmanned, high-altitude, long-range reconnaissance vehicle by the Boeing Commercial Airplane Company. The electronic Engine Monitoring and Control System (EMACS) display format developed by a Langley engineer and flown on the 737 was adopted almost immediately by a general aviation avionics manufacturer and was included in the tentative cockpit design for the McDonnell Douglas Corporation's MD-XX airliner.

Although the computer-driven, fuel-efficient profile descents the NASA engineers evaluated with the TSRV 737 were not supported by the air traffic control (ATC) system, the NASA experiments proved the potential value of the technique, and the capability for time-based navigation eventually began to be implemented into some new airliners. The ATC data link experiments with the 737 gave the concept a critical measure of credibility and support, accelerating the acceptance and use of data link communication within the ATC system. The airplane also tested precision flare laws that helped Boeing engineers improve the autoland performance for several of Boeing's transport aircraft.

In addition, the TSRV 737 provided a highly capable testbed for numerous other successful research projects. The airplane helped conduct runway friction tests that proved the accuracy of ground friction measuring vehicles and the value of grooved runway and highway surfaces. As a result, airport operators gained access to reliable information about the safety of runway conditions, and the use of grooved surfaces increased at airports and on the nation's highways. A joint flight test project with McDonnell Douglas proved that a pilot could use a helmet-mounted synthetic vision display to land a windowless transport aircraft. Because it was able to navigate successfully through a moving, meter-square spot in the sky, the TSRV 737 was able to obtain critical information for the United States Air Force. The airplane's flight research to model the instrument landing system (ILS) beam at the Los Angeles International airport gave the FAA valuable information about whether the runways could be spaced any closer together.

Although the airplane was still flying and conducting additional research 20 years after it was purchased by NASA, it had already had a tremendous impact on the "design, development and operation" of new aircraft. Achieving those results was neither simple nor easy, however. The world of aeronautics had changed dramatically from the early days of NACA, when a simple cowling design could revolutionize aircraft design and aircraft companies were clamoring to absorb whatever new knowledge or technology NACA could discover. The big problems facing the airlines in the 1970s were no longer ones of basic structures and aerodynamics. They were complex problems of getting aircraft to operate more efficiently and safely within an increasingly congested air traffic environment, and they required systems-oriented solutions.

Systems solutions are themselves complex, however. They typically need input from numerous research disciplines and involve many more elements and people. Systems-oriented research looks not only at individual aircraft components, but also the interactions between those components and the rest of the aircraft systems, the pilots, the operation of the aircraft within the ATC system, and the aircraft's compatibility with other air traffic in the vicinity.

The TCV program was created to research this kind of system-oriented technology, and the program organization reflected the complexity of the kind of research it set out to conduct. The matrix structure that caused so many management difficulties with the program was used precisely because the TCV research required input from numerous technical disciplines. The program also began with a joint agreement with the FAA and included an on-site contingent of Boeing engineers for the first five years. Few of its research projects, in fact, were conducted without the involvement of more than one research discipline, one or more other government agencies, or industry.

In addition to these kinds of challenges, the TCV/ATOPS program had to contend with the basic complexity of the technology development and transfer process. Both the selection of research projects and the eventual application of new technologies developed by the program were affected by political, social, economic and regulatory forces. The MLS demonstrations, for example, were initiated and then expanded because of the heated political controversy surrounding the international landing system decision. The windshear research was organized because of the political and social pressure following the 1985 crash of a Delta L-1011 jumbo jet in Dallas Texas. The runway friction tests were funded after several airline accidents highlighted some of the dangers of winter flight operations. Even the basic funding for the TCV/ATOPS program itself fluctuated widely depending on the administrative and political pressures at play throughout its 20-year history.

Forces that had little to do with the intrinsic worth of the concepts researched through the TCV/ATOPS program also had a tremendous impact on the eventual application of those technologies in commercial products. New ideas faced a human and organizational tendency to resist change, and as companies grew in size, effectively communicating information about new innovations to all the necessary players became more difficult. More importantly, the airline industry had changed dramatically since the days when pilots and aeronautical engineers ran the companies. As new technology became more expensive to produce and incorporate into aircraft designs, it had to "earn its way" onto airplanes more than it had in the past. In other words, technological innovations had to offer significant economic or other tangible benefits to be incorporated into new airliners; a trend that became even more pronounced after 1978, when deregulation made the airline industry more competitive and cost conscious.

Because pilots typically flew more than one aircraft, airlines also tried to keep cockpits of different aircraft relatively similar, both for safety and for training considerations. Dramatically new equipment could require retraining for all of an airline's pilots, not to mention re-certification of an airplane design, both of which involved significant additional costs. As a result, even when new technologies were adopted, their full capabilities were often not used. The electronic attitude directional indicator (EADI) displays incorporated by Boeing in the 767/757s, for example, were formatted to duplicate an electromechanical instrument. Technologies such as MLS, profile descents or ATC data link communications faced even greater barriers to application, because they required changes in the ATC system, and airlines would not invest in equipment if the ATC system could not support its use.

In view of all this, the achievements of the TSRV 737 and the TCV/ATOPS program in researching, developing and transferring aeronautics technology are even more striking. There were several factors that enabled the program to have such an impact, however. First, the program was focused on solving problems that were both relevant and important to the air transport industry. Second, industry engineers were involved in the program from the very beginning, and the TCV/ATOPS research was characterized by a high level of communication between NASA engineers and industry representatives. As a result, the NASA researchers were more aware of industry concerns and problems, and they were able to obtain valuable feedback and suggestions about their research while it was still in process. Furthermore, the on-site involvement of a contingent of Boeing engineers for the first five years of the program and the numerous cooperative research efforts between NASA and industry in the years that followed allowed groups of industry engineers to become extremely knowledgeable about the technologies the NASA program was evaluating. Those engineers, in turn, played an important role in convincing other company decision-makers to invest in further development and application of the concepts.

The most influential factor in the successful transfer of so many technologies from the TCV/ATOPS program to practical applications, however, was the TSRV 737 airplane. The unique Boeing aircraft, with its two cockpits, computerized and highly capable systems, and easily reconfigured research equipment, allowed a wide variety of new technologies to be flown in an actual transport class aircraft and often in realistic flight conditions. This capability was important, because as technology became more complex and expensive, industry became less able or willing to invest in innovations that had been tested only in laboratories or simulators. The gap between that level of development and a commercial application was often too broad, and the risks involved were too high. Research and demonstration flights, however, gave technology a level of credibility that no amount of laboratory or simulation testing could achieve and allowed researchers to demonstrate its potential capabilities and operational benefits in a vivid, visual manner to government and industry leaders. The impressive, curved-path automatic landing demonstrations performed by the TSRV 737 airplane, for example, played a critical role in the selection of the U.S. candidate MLS system by the International Civil Aviation Organization (ICAO). Flight demonstrations of the electronic map display in the 737 helped convince airline operators to support the inclusion of a similar display in Boeing's new 767/757 aircraft.

Furthermore, a concept had to be developed further if it was going to be flight tested than if it was only going to be evaluated in simulations. Details and problems that wouldn't come into play in a laboratory had to be resolved before a technology would work on an airplane. Consequently, developing commercial applications for flight tested concepts entailed fewer risks for industry, which was an important consideration. Industry decision-makers also had more confidence in a technological innovation that had been successfully flight tested. Boeing, for example, knew that the DATAC data bus worked in theory. What gave the company the confidence to include the technology in its next transport aircraft design, however, was the fact that the TSRV 737 had used DATAC without difficulty throughout hundreds of flight hours.

Most importantly, flight testing a new concept on the TSRV 737 provided essentially unassailable proof that the technology would work. The technique or innovation still might not prove economically viable, but a successful flight test ended the discussion about whether it could be done. The TSRV's research flights with path-in-space flare laws, for example, ended the engineers' debate about whether the theory was valid. And what made the airplane's GPS-guided autoland flights so significant was not the technical performance of the system, but the fact that the airplane had actually completed automatic landings using GPS technology. The fact that the system still had to use a radar altimeter and the accuracy of the landings was not good enough to meet a Category II or III certification standard was secondary. The NASA flight tests abruptly ended the debate about whether a GPS autoland was possible, and refocused the discussion and further research on what level of accuracy the technology could attain.

Of course, not all of the concepts flight tested with the TSRV 737 were picked up by industry or the FAA for practical application. Some did not prove viable, and logistical or economic issues overrode the technical worth of others. Nevertheless, the Boeing 737 TSRV proved immeasurably valuable in successfully researching and transferring advanced technologies and concepts from NASA to other government agencies and industry. It provided persuasive, visual evidence of a new technology's potential advantages and often gave decision-makers the necessary confidence in experimental concepts to support the development of practical applications.

The value of NASA's 737 research airplane, however, went beyond its ability to transfer technology to industry. The airplane also had a significant influence on the Langley Research Center itself. The fact that the TCV/ATOPS program research included flight tests in a transport airplane kept its engineers focused on feasible technology and real-world air transportation problems. Since those researchers and engineers were drawn from various directorates around the center, that "real-world" anchor impacted attitudes throughout the facility. In addition, the Boeing 737 Transport Systems Research Vehicle provided the Langley center, already famous for its wind tunnels, with another kind of national research facility. The TSRV 737 offered government and industry a flexible, capable research platform that could test a wide variety of complex, systems-oriented technologies in a realistic flight environment. And as aeronautical problems became more complex, that kind of research facility was proving to be as important a national resource as the wind tunnels had been in the early days of flight.

Without question, NASA's Boeing 737 was a unique airplane. But the Terminal Configured Vehicle/Advanced Transport Operating Systems program was also a remarkable research effort. From the beginning, the TCV/ATOPS program involved complex relationships and organizational challenges, and both its research and the application of its findings were influenced heavily by political, business and economic factors. One of the managers who came to the TCV/ATOPS program from the Apollo space program concluded that the challenge of putting a man on the moon was relatively easy compared with trying to research and transfer technology to improve the air transportation system.[3]

One of the reasons the program was able to succeed in spite of its complex internal and external challenges was because the people involved with the TSRV airplane and the TCV/ATOPS program were as unusual as the research effort itself. The program never even would have existed if it were not for the vision of the Langley engineers who saw the need for a systems-oriented, subsonic air transport research program and argued successfully for the purchase of the prototype Boeing 737-100 airplane. Throughout its history, the engineers, researchers, and technicians who worked with the airplane and the program gained a reputation for having a enthusiastic, "can do" attitude that made many difficult research projects possible. The nature of the program attracted engineers who liked solving practical, real-world problems, and the resourcefulness and dedication of the technicians who worked on the plane was inspiring and contagious. Although it sometimes meant laboring all night in a freezing hangar to repair research systems, warming a computer component with a borrowed hair dryer, working by flashlights and generator power in order to finish a new data bus design, or pulling together a superhuman effort to repair and outfit the airplane in a few weeks instead of the months it should have taken, the people who worked with the TSRV 737 made sure that the plane successfully completed every single research project it was scheduled to conduct.

The reason the engineers, technicians and staff worked so hard on the TCV/ATOPS research projects was that they believed what they were doing was extremely important, not only to NASA, but to the aerospace industry and the country itself. They knew the research they did with the TSRV airplane was going to do more than generate technical reports. If they succeeded, their work could impact the landing system used around the world, revolutionize the information available to a new generation of airline pilots, and save lives.

In retrospect, the TCV/ATOPS program and the TSRV 737 did all of that and more. The prototype Boeing 737-100 was originally purchased to support a single research program, which was expected to last only 5-6 years. Twenty years later, it was still performing an important role, not only for the TCV/ATOPS program, but for the Langley Research Center and the aerospace industry, as well. It had made significant contributions to the research and development of new aeronautical technologies that could help U.S. industry maintain a competitive edge in the global market, improve the operation of the national airspace system, and help save lives. The airplane might once have been an unwanted hulk on the ramp of the Boeing aircraft factory in Seattle, but the prototype 737-100 had become a national asset. The stubby transport airplane was not as glamorous as NASA's X-series research vehicles or as well known as the Space Shuttle, but the contributions it made were every bit as important.

Chapter Notes

Chapter 1: NASA, Industry, and Technology: The Complex Nature of Progress

[1] Executive Office of the President, Office of Science and Technology Policy, *Aeronautical Research and Technology Policy, Vol. I: Summary Report*,, (Washington, D.C., November 1982), 13.

[2] Hans Mark and Arnold Levine, *The Management of Research Institutions: A Look at Government Laboratories*, NASA SP-481, (Washington, D.C., 1984), 265.

[3] The Denver Research Institute, "NASA Partnership with Industry: Enhancing Technology Transfer," , NASA-CR-180-163, July 1983, x.

[4] Daniel P. Kaplan, *Using Federal R&D to Promote Commercial Innovation*, (Washington, D.C.: Congress of the United States Congressional Budget Office, 1988), 22-23.

[5] *Aeronautical Research and Technology Policy*, 1-11.

[6] The phrase "technology development" has a number of different connotations for professionals involved in aeronautical research. In this chapter, and throughout the book unless otherwise specified, I use it only to describe the process of researching a concept to the point where a workable, test-ready piece of technology exists. I do not mean the process of developing a piece of technology to a point where it is ready for commercial application, which is a different matter.

[7] Office of Science and Technology Policy, Executive Office of the President, "Report of the White House Science Council, Federal Laboratory Review Panel," (Washington, D.C., May 1983), 11.

[8] Herbert J. Coleman, "National Research Policy Aimed to Bolster Aviation," *Aviation Week & Space Technology*, 15 November 1982, 22; same idea also contained in: *Aeronautical Research and Technology Policy*, 9.

[9] Kaplan, *Using Federal R&D*, 10; Delmar Fadden, Boeing Commercial Airplane Company, interview with author, Seattle, Washington, 27 April 1993; William E. Howell, interview with author, Hampton, Virginia, 6 April 1993.

[10] Executive Office of the President, Office of Science and Technology Policy, *National Aeronautical R&D Goals: Agenda for Achievement*, report of the Aeronautical Policy Review Committee, (Washington, D.C. February 1987), 2.

[11] Testimony before a House subcommittee on technology and competitiveness, as quoted in: Christopher P. Fotos, "Industry Experts Say NASA Must Devote More Resources to Civil Aeronautics," *Aviation Week & Space Technology*, 24 February 1992, 42; Robert S. Ames, "U.S. Must Understand the Link Between R&D and the Economy," *Aviation Week & Space Technology*, 12 October 1987, 149-50; *Aeronautical Research and Technology Policy*, 15.

[12] Office of Science and Technology Policy, *National Aeronautical R&D Goals*, 3; Denver Research Institute, "NASA Partnership with Industry," Appendix A-1, A-3, C-1; Ames, "R&D and the Economy," 149-150; "First Steps Toward Competitiveness," editorial, *Aviation Week & Space Technology*, 16 September 1991, 9; David F. Bond and Patricia A. Gilmartin, "Industry Collaboration Grows for Technology Development," *Aviation Week & Space Technology*, 16 September, 1991, 20-23; Christopher P. Fotos, "Industry Experts Say NASA Must Devote More Resources to Civil Aeronautics," *Aviation Week & Space Technology*, 24 February, 1992, 42.

[13] Thomas S. Kuhn, *The Structure of Scientific Revolutions*, 2nd ed., Foundations of the Unity of Science Series: Vol. 2, No. 2, (Chicago: University of Chicago Press, 1970), Chapter 11; Thomas P. Hughes, *American*

Genesis: A Century of Invention and Technological Enthusiasm, 1870-1970, (New York: Viking Penguin, 1989), 446-472; Derek J. de S. Price, *Little Science, Big Science*, (New York: Columbia University Press, 1963, 10, 29, as quoted in: Arnold Pacey, *The Culture of Technology*, (Cambridge, MIT Press, 1983), 13, also 3-18.

[14] Mark and Levine, *Research Institutions*, 3-4; Hughes, *American Genesis*, 446-472; Pacey, *Culture of Technology*, 13-34.

[15] Mark and Levine, *Research Institutions*, 5.

[16] Hughes, *American Genesis*, 71-74.

[17] Samuel A. Morello, interview with author, Hampton, Virginia, 8 April 1993; David Hughes, "Glass Cockpit Study Reveals Human Factors Problems," *Aviation Week & Space Technology*, 7 August 1989, 32-36; David Hughes, "Pilots, Research Studies Give Mixed Reviews to Glass Cockpits," *Aviation Week & Space Technology*, 23 March 1992, 50-51; Breck W. Henderson, "NASA Ames Pushes Automation Toward Human-Centered Design," *Aviation Week & Space Technology*, 23 March 1992, 69-70.

[18] The National Aeronautics and Space Act of 1958, as quoted in the Denver Research Institute, "NASA Partnership with Industry," Appendix, B-1.

[19] "The NASA Program of Industrial Applications," (Address by Louis B. C. Fong, Director, Office of Technology Utilization, NASA, at the Third National Conference on the Peaceful Uses of Space, Chicago, Illinois, 8 May 1963), from NASA Historical Archive files.

[20] *TRW Electronics & Defense/Quest*, Winter, 1982-1983, p. 65, as quoted in: the Denver Research Institute, "NASA Partnership with Industry," xx.

[21] Kuhn, *Scientific Revolutions*; Joel Arthur Barker, *Future Edge: Discovering the New Paradigms of Success*, (New York: William Morrow & Company, 1992).

[22] Hughes, *American Genesis*, 456-61; Barker, *Future Edge*, 140-149.

[23] Al Ries and Jack Trout, *Marketing Warfare*, (New York: Penguin Books USA Inc., 1986) 83-99; Kuhn, *Scientific Revolutions*; Barker, *Future Edge*, 55-70; R.P. Schmitt, et al., "Technology Transfer Primer," Wisconsin University-Milwaukee, Center for Urban Transportation Studies, FHWA/TS-84/226, July 1985, 3; Howell, interview, 6 April 1993.

[24] Discussed in numerous interviews, but at length in: Howell, interview, 6 April 1993.

[25] Denver Research Institute, "NASA Partnership with Industry," Appendix, D-3; William D. Mace and William E. Howell, "Integrated Controls for a New Aircraft Generation, *Astronautics & Aeronautics*, Vol. 16, No. 3, March 1978, 48-53; R.P. Schmitt, et al., "Technology Transfer Primer," 4.

[26] James Ott, "White House Calls for Changes in Procurement Procedures," *Aviation Week & Space Technology*, 25 November 1985, 28; Robert Dunn and H.W. Withington, Boeing Commercial Airplane Company (retired), interview with author, Seattle, Washington, 27 April 1993; Alan Mulally, Boeing Commercial Airplane Company, interview with author, Seattle, Washington, 28 April 1993; John Warner, Boeing Commercial Airplane Company, interview with author, Seattle, Washington, 27 April 1993; Thomas Walsh, interview with author, Hampton, Virginia, 6 April 1993.

[27] Dr. Jeremiah F. Creedon, et al., "NASA Technology Transfer," report of the Technology Transfer Team, 21 December 1992.

[28] Creedon, et al., "NASA Technology," 14a; Leo S. Packer, "Proposal for Enhancing NASA Technology Transfer to Civil Systems," 26 September 1969, (unpublished document, from NASA Historical Archives), 20; Denver Research Institute, "NASA Partnership with Industry," x - xix, Appendix D-5; Schmitt, et al., "Technology Transfer Primer," introduction, 1, 5; "Government Focus on Data Transfer to Industry Urged," *Aviation Week & Space Technology*, 23 July 1984, 131; Kaplan, *Using Federal R&D*, 49; Warner, interview, 27 April 1993; Howell, interview, 6 April 1993; Fadden, interview, 27 April 1993; Anthony A. Lambregts, Boeing Commercial Airplane Company, interview with author, Seattle, Washington, 26 April 1993.

[29] Howell, interview, 6 April 1993; Jeremiah F. Creedon, interview with author, Hampton, Virginia, 5 April 1993; Warner, interview, 27 April 1993; Fadden, interview, 27 April 1993.

[30] H.W. Withington to John P. Reeder, Letter, 6 June 1979 (from the ATOPS office files)

[31] Daniel S. Goldin, comments upon the release of the Special Initiatives Team on Technology Transfer report, from NASA News press release dated 8 January 1993.

Chapter 2: Addressing the New Challenges of Air Transportation: The TCV/ATOPS Program

[1] Oran Nicks, phone interview with author, Hampton, Virginia, 5 May 1993.

[2] Senate Committee on Aeronautical and Space Sciences, *Aeronautical Research and Development Policy Report*, 90th Congress, 2nd sess., 1968, S. Rept. 957.

[3] Barry Graves, phone interview with author, Minneapolis,

Minnesota, 20 April 1993; Thomas M. Walsh, interview with author, Hampton, Virginia, 6 April 1993; Robert Taylor, interview with author, Hampton, Virginia, 7 April 1993; Seymour Salmirs, personal notes, 1969-1974 and phone interview with author, Minneapolis, Minnesota, 20 April 1993; Samuel A. Morello, interview with author, Hampton, Virginia, 8 April 1993; Jack Reeder, personal files, 1969-1971.

[4] Department of Transportation and National Aeronautics and Space Administration, *Civil Aviation Research and Development Policy Study*, DOT TST-10-4, NASA SP-265, (Washington, D.C., March, 1971), 2-3 2-6.

[5] Roland L. Bowles, interview with author, Hampton, Virginia, 5 April 1993; ATOPS program presentation viewgraphs, from Flight Systems directorate files.

[6] *Civil Aviation Research and Development Policy Study*, 2-4 2-6.

[7] Thomas M. Walsh, interview, 6 April 1993; Seymour Salmirs, presentation materials for briefing to NASA Associate Administrator Lovelace, 1974; Heinz Erzberger, phone interview with author, Hampton, Virginia, 5 May, 1993.

[8] Jack Reeder, *Proposal for Systems Research Approach to Integrating Vehicle-Instrument-Display-Pilot Capability for Total Flight Missions*, draft, 1969, annotated with additional personal notes, 1971; Oran Nicks, interview, 5 May 1993; Thomas M. Walsh, interview, 6 April 1993; Robert Taylor, interview, 7 April 1993; Draft RTOP 133-61-, *Advanced Operating Systems for Conventional Takeoff and Landing Aircraft*, prepared by Jack Reeder and Bob Taylor January 14-24, 1972, and annotated with personal notes by Jack Reeder.

[9] NASA Langley Research Center, *Terminal Configured Vehicle Program Plan*, (Hamton, VA, December 1, 1973), 2.

[10] Ibid, 4-24.

[11] Langley Research Center Central Correspondence Files, Ed Cortright memo to NASA Headquarters requesting permission for sole source procurement of the Boeing 737-100, 16 October 1972; Jack Reeder presentation notes, *Reasons for 737 Choice*, 12 July 1972.

[12] Bernard Hainline, retired, Boeing Commercial Airplane Company, interview with author, Seattle, Washington, 26 April 1993; H.W. Withington and Robert Dunn, retired, Boeing Commercial Airplane Company, interview with author, Seattle Washington, 27 April 1993; Richard A. Peal, Boeing Commercial Airplane Company, interview with author, Seattle, Washington, 28 April 1993.

[13] Richard A. Peal, interview, 28 April 1993; Samuel A. Morello, interview, 8 April 1993; David C.E. Holmes and Wesley C. Easley, interview with author, Hampton, Virginia, 9 April 1993; Memorandum to Research Aircraft Flight Division files from Seymour Salmirs, Aero-Space Technologist, Flight Programs Branch, RAFD, 13 July 1972, summarizing visit to Boeing Company in Seattle, Washington, to take first look at the company's prototype 737, PA-099.

[14] Numerous books have been published about the United States SST program controversy. For example, see: Mel Horwitch, Clipped Wings: The American SST Conflict, (Cambridge, Mass: MIT Press, 1982).

[15] "Supersonic Transport Advanced Electronic Display Proposal," summary of program objectives and criteria, with trip report (dated 20 September 1971) by Seymour Salmirs, Aero-Space Technologist, Flight Programs Branch, Research Aircraft Flight Division to Director for Aeronautics, summarizing 14 September 1971 meeting at Boeing Company for review of the program (from private files of S. Salmirs); Bernard Hainline, viewgraph of NASA TCV Program Evolution, personal work notes collection and interview with author, Seattle, WA, 26 April 1993; H.W. Withington and Robert Dunn, interview, 27 April 1993; *Year By Year: 75 Years of Boeing History 1916-1991*, Boeing Historical Archives, (Seattle, Washington, November 1991), 101-113; Agenda, "DOT/SST Phase II Technology Follow-On Advanced Electronic Display System)ADEDS) — Task VI, Inter-Agency Council Review," The Boeing Company, Seattle, Washington, 27-28 September 1972; Attendance Lists, "DOT/SST Follow-On Technology — Phase II, Inter-Agency Council Review No. 2," 21-22 March 1973, "Inter-Agency Council Review, Flight Control Development," 11 September 1973 and "Inter-Agency Council Review, Advanced Electronic Displays System (ADEDS) — Task VI," 12 September 1973 (from private files of S. Salmirs).

[16] Seymour Salmirs job order, under Research and Technology Resume No. 133-, All-Weather Airborne Systems Study, 1 October 1971.

[17] Siegbert Poritsky, interview with author, Washington, D.C., 13 April 1993; Thomas M. Walsh, interview with author, Hampton, Virginia, 6 April 1993; Jeremiah F. Creedon, interview with author, Hampton, Virginia, 5 April 1993; Samuel A. Morello, interview, 8 April 1993; William E. Howell, interview with author, Hampton, Virginia, 6 April 1993.

[18] *Agreement Between the Federal Aviation Administration and National Aeronautics and Space Administration Concerning Cooperation to Achieve Improved Terminal Area Operations*, 3 May, 1973.

[19] D. H. Cosley and R.A. Peal, "Advanced Electronic Display System (ADEDS) Flight Test Report, Vol III — Flight Test Results," FAA-SS-22-3, technical report, July 1974.

[20] Richard A. Peal, interview, 28 April 1993; Richard A. Peal, personal notes; TSRV 737 flight records, from ATOPS office files.

Note: The Boeing 737 airplane purchased by NASA was actually referred to by several different names. It was called the Research Support Flight System (RSFS), the Terminal Configured Vehicle (TCV), and the Transport Systems Research Vehicle (TSRV). Since the TSRV label outlasted the other two, the airplane is referred to by that title throughout the book to help avoid confusion.

[21] During the TCV program research, the primary flight display was usually referred to as the Electronic Attitude Directional Indicator (EADI) and the map display was called the Electronic Horizontal Situation Indicator (EHSI), but these terms are no longer used. The accepted terms for these displays are now the Primary Flight Display and the Map, or Navigation, display.

[22] David C.E. Holmes and Wesley C. Easley, interview, 9 April 1993; TSRV flight logs, (from ATOPS office files).

[23] Seymour Salmirs and Harold N. Tobie, "Electronic Displays and Digital Automatic Control in Advanced Terminal Area Operations," AIAA Paper No. 74-27, presented at the AIAA 12th Aerospace Sciences Meeting, Washington, D.C., January 30-February 1, 1974.; Samuel A. Morello, et al, "Flight-Test handling Qualities Documentation of the Research Support Flight System," NASA-TM-X-72618, October 1974.

[24] Jeremiah F. Creedon, interview with author, Hampton, Virginia, 7 May 1993.

[25] David C.E. Holmes and Wesley C. Easley, interview , 9 April 1993; Roland L. Bowles, interview, 5 April 1993.

[26] The organizational structure of the Langley Research Center was essentially a vertical one. Under the director of the center were half a dozen or so "Directorates" (the number varied slightly over the years). The next level beneath a Directorate was a Division. The next step down from a division was a branch, and underneath that was a section.

[27] Langley Research Center Announcement No. 54-73, "Establishment of Terminal Configured Vehicles Program Office," (from ATOPS office files).

[28] James R. Hansen, *Engineer in Charge: A History of the Langley Aeronautical Laboratory, 1917-1958*, (Washington, D.C.: National Aeronautics and Space Administration, 1987), 24-32, 58.

[29] Barry Graves, interview, 20 April 1993; Jeremiah F. Creedon, interviews, 5 April 1993 and 4 May 1993; William E. Howell, interview, 6 April 1993; Samuel A. Morello, interview, 8 April 1993; William F. White, interview with author, Washington, D.C. 13 April 1993.

[30] Jeremiah F. Creedon, interview, 4 May 1993.

[31] Attendance list, "Terminal Configured Vehicle Flight Experiments Working Group (FEWG) meeting," 18 July 1973 (from personal files of S. Salmirs); Organizational chart listing committee attached with Langley Research Center Announcement to all organizational units from Edgar M. Cortright, Langley Research Center director, *Assignments for Terminal Configured Vehicle Program*, 11 April 1973 (from ATOPS office files).

[32] John Warner, Boeing Commercial Airplane Company, interview with author, Seattle, Washington, 27 April 1993; Delmar M. Fadden, Boeing Commercial Airplane Company, interview with author, Seattle, Washington, 27 April 1993; Richard A. Peal, interview, 28 April, 1993; Anthony A. Lambregts, Boeing Commercial Airplane Company, interview with author, Seattle, Washington, 26 April 1993; H.W. Withington and Robert Dunn, interview, 27 April 1993.

[33] Jeremiah F. Creedon, interviews, 5 May 1993 and 7 May 1993; Langley Research Center organizational charts; Langley Research Center Announcement, *Assignments for Terminal Configured Vehicle Program*, 11 April 1973; Walsh, interview, 6 April 1993; John Warner, interview, 27 April 1993; Samuel A. Morello, interview, 8 April 1993.

[34] William D. Mace, phone interview with author, Minneapolis, Minnesota, 19 May 1993; Jeremiah F. Creedon, interview, 5 April 1993; TSRV 737 flight logs (from ATOPS program office files).

[35] Jeremiah F. Creedon, interviews, 5 April 1993, 5 May 1993 and 7 May 1993; Langley Research Center, *Terminal Area Productivity Level III Plan*, May 1993.

Chapter 3: Revolution in the Cockpit: Computerization and Electronic Flight Displays

[1] Benjamin M. Elson, "Digital Technology Gaining Acceptance," *Aviation Week & Space Technology*, 7 November 1977, 131-134, and "767 Digital Avionics Stress Flexibility," *Aviation Week & Space Technology*, 4 September 1978, 181-188, and "Analog to Digital Systems Switch Seen," *Aviation Week & Space Technology*, 23 October 1978, 115-121; Barry Miller, "Wider Use of Digital Techniques Seen," *Aviation Week & Space Technology*, 10 November 1975, 90-95.

[2] Earl L. Wiener and Renwick E. Curry, *Flight Deck Automation: Promises and Problems*, NASA-TM-81206, June 1980.

[3] Walter B. Gartner and Larry L. Jenney, *Display*

Requirements and Concepts for Space Shuttle Recovery and Landing, NASA CR-123151, July 1971.

[4] *Report of the Department of Transportation Air Traffic Control Advisory Committee,* Vol. 1 (Washington D.C., December 1969), 3-6; D.K. Graham, *Transport Airplane Flight Deck Development Survey and Analysis: Report and Recommendations,* NASA CR-145121, January 1977, 9-10; John P. Reeder, Robert T. Taylor, and Thomas M. Walsh, *New Design and Operating Techniques for Improved Terminal Area Compatibility,* SAE Paper 740454, (presented to the Society of Automotive Engineers Air Transportation Meeting, Dallas, Texas, 30 April - 2 May 1974); Robert Dunn, *Flight Displays for the Next Generation Aircraft,* SAE Paper 760930, (presented at the Society of Automotive Engineers Aerospace Engineering and Manufacturing Meeting, San Diego, California, 29 November - 2 December 1976).

[5] J. Wyall and D. Eastman, *Flight Test Demonstration of Selected Curved-Segmented Approach Paths Based on Microwave Landing System Guidance,* AFFDL-TR-76-43, January 1976; and D. Eastman, MLS Project Engineer, AFFDL FGR: "MLS Simulation Results," unpublished memorandum.

[6] Peter R. Kurzhals, "New Directions in Civil Avionics," *Astronautics & Aeronautics,* March 1978, 40.

[7] Duncan McIver and Jack J. Hatfield, "Coming Cockpit Avionics," *Astronautics & Aeronautics,* March 1978, 54-63; Graham, *Flight Deck Survey,* 8-10; Gartner and Jenney, *Display Requirements for Shuttle*; John P. Reeder, "Flight Experiments with Electronic Displays Having Predictive Information," (paper, presented at Radio Technical Commission for Aeronautics (RTCA) conference, Washington, D.C., November 18-19, 1976); Samuel A. Morello, *Recent Flight Test Results Using an Electronic Display on the NASA B-737,* AGARD-CP-240, August 1978.

[8] Samuel A. Morello, interview with author, 8 April 1993; ATOPS office flight records.

[9] Reeder, "Experiments with Electronic Displays."

[10] Lee H. Person, Jr. and George G. Steinmetz, "The Integration of Control and Display Concepts For Improved Pilot Situational Awareness," (paper, presented at a Flight Safety Foundation seminar, Acapulco, Mexico, 9 - 12 November 1981); G.G. Steinmetz, L.H. Person and S.A. Morello, *Have We Overlooked the Pilot's Role in an Automated Flight Deck?* AIAA Paper No. 81-2262, (presented in St. Louis, Missouri, November 17-19, 1981); Wiener and Curry, *Flight Deck Automation.*

[11] Steinmetz, Person, and Morello, *Have We Overlooked the Pilot's Role.*

[12] Lee H. Person and Kenneth R. Yenni, interview with author, Hampton, Virginia, 7 April 1993.

[13] A Category II landing is one performed with a 100-foot ceiling and only a quarter mile of forward visibility.

[14] George G. Steinmetz, et al., *A Piloted-Simulation Evaluation of Two Electronic Display Formats for Approach and Landing,*" NASA-TN-D-8183, April 1976; Samuel A. Morello, Charles E. Knox, and George G. Steinmetz, *Flight-Test Evaluation of Two Electronic Display Formats for Approach to Landing Under Instrument Conditions,* NASA-TP-1085, December 1977; Reeder, "Flight Experience with Electronic Displays," 1976; Person and Yenni, interview, 7 April 1993.

[15] Although the electronic flight display research went on throughout the life of the program, 1978 is considered the end of the initial research phase for CRT displays for several reasons. In addition to the fact that the basic technology had been proven and several technical papers were published on the subject, 1978 was the year Boeing made the decision to apply the technology into its next commercial airplane.

[16] Lee H. Person, Jr. and Kenneth R. Yenni, "Flying NASA's Terminal Configured Vehicle Against the Microwave Landing System," Society of Experimental Test Pilots, *Technical Review,* Vol. 14, No. 2, 1978, 110-123; Morello, interview, 8 April 1993; Person and Yenni, interview, 7 April 1993.

[17] John Whitfield, Lockheed L-1011 program manager, phone interview with author, 6 October 1993.

[18] Elson, "Technology Gaining Acceptance," 131-134; Society of Engineering Test Pilots, *Technical Review,* Vol. 14, No. 2, 1978, 124+; John Whitfield, Lockheed L-1011 program manager and Don Moore, Lockheed L-1011 chief pilot, phone interview with author, 15 June 1993.

[19] "Airline Experiments Mini-Symposium" Held at the Hilton "1776" Inn, Williamsburg, Virginia, 24 - 26 January 1975. Letter of Invitation from John P. Reeder, chief, Terminal Configured Vehicle Program, to Mr. J. Wyld, Director Flight Technical, Air Canada, with schedule of events and partial list of antendees (from personal files of S. Salmirs).

[20] H. W. Withington, former vice president of engineering and Robert Dunn, former chief engineer of systems technology for the Boeing Commercial Airplane Company, interview with author, Seattle, Washington, 27 April 1993.

[21] Delmar Fadden, chief engineer, avionics/flight systems, Renton Division, Boeing Commercial Airplane Company, interview with author, Seattle, Washington, 27 April

1993; John Warner, vice president of Boeing Computer Services, interview with author, Seattle, Washington, 28 April 1993; Dunn and Withington, interview with author, 27 April 1993; Richard A. Peal, director of systems engineering, Boeing Commercial Airplane Company, interview with author, Seattle, Washington, 28 April 1993.

[22] This evolution was related to the author in more than 20 separate interviews with managers at the NASA Langley Research Center in Hampton, Virginia and the Boeing Commercial Airplane Company in Seattle, Washington.

[23] The prevalent nature of these kinds of concerns about new flight deck technology is also supported in Graham, *Flight Deck Survey*.

[24] Air Transport Association, Flight Systems Integration Committee Memorandum No. 77-22, "Report of the Thirteenth Meeting of the Committee," 7-8 September, 1977 (from personal files of S. Salmirs).

[25] Peal, interview, 28 April 1993; Jerry Moore, Honeywell, Inc., phone interview with author, 18 June 1993; David Nakamura, Boeing Commercial Airplane Company, phone interview with author, 18 June 1993; Arvind J. Dandekar, director of international marketing and business, Collins Commercial Avionics, phone interview with author, 10 June 1993; Fadden, interview, 27 April 1993; Morello, interview, 8 April 1993.

[26] Elson, "767 Digital Avionics," 181.

[27] "Coordination Sheet," on cost of ownership comparison of CRT displays and electromechanical instruments, Boeing internal document, 1978; Peal, interview, 28 April 1993; Dandekar, phone interview, 10 June 1993; Nakamura, phone interview, 18 June 1993; Moore, phone interview , 18 June 1993.

[28] Fadden, interview, 27 April 1993; Bernard Hainline, interview with author, Seattle, Washington, 26 April 1993; Morello, interview, 8 April 1993; Flight manifests and records from the ATOPS office, Langley Research Center, Hampton, Virginia.

[29] Hainline, interview, 26 April 1993; Peal, interview , 28 April 1993; Elson, "767 Digital Avionics," 181-188.

[30] Dandekar, phone interview, 10 June, 1993; Peal, interview, 28 April 1993; Dan Martinec, Chairman, Airlines Electronic Engineering Committee, ARINC, phone interview with author, 16 June 1993; Moore, phone interview, 18 June 1993; Nakamura, phone interview, 18 June 1993.

[31] Thomas S. Kuhn, *The Structure of Scientific Revolutions*, 2nd ed., Foundations of the Unity of Science Series: Vol. 2, No. 2 (Chicago: University of Chicago Press, 1970); Joel Arthur Barker, *Future Edge: Discovering the New Paradigms of Success* (New York: William Morrow & Company, 1992).

[32] Warner, interview, 27 April 1993; Fadden, interview, 27 April 1993; Morello, interview, 8 April 1993.

[33] Elson, "Spaciousness Key to 767 Flight Deck," *Aviation Week & Space Technology*, 16 April 1979, 57-63; Morello, interview, 8 April 1993; Fadden, interview, 27 April 1993.

[34] Several people from the Langley Research Center served on this task force, including researchers who had worked with the ATOPS program.

[35] "IFALPA To Boycott Two-Man-Cockpit Aircraft," *Aviation Week & Space Technology*, 26 March 1979, 32; "German Pilot Association Opposes Two-Man Crew" and "ALPA Crew Position," *Aviation Week & Space Technology*, 20 July 1981, 36; Richard G. O'Lone, "767 Program Altered for Two-Man Crew," *Aviation Week & Space Technology*, 7 December 1981, 26-27.

[36] Wiener and Curry, *Flight Deck Automation*; Steinmetz, Person and Morello, *Have We Overlooked the Pilot's Role*; Graham, *Flight Deck Survey*; Morello, interview, 8 April 1993; Fadden, interview, 27 April 1993; Warner, interview, 27 April 1993.

[37] David Hughes, "Glass Cockpit Study Reveals Human Factors Problems," *Aviation Week & Space Technology*, 7 August 1989, 32-36; Hughes, "Pilots, Research Studies Give Mixed Reviews to Glass Cockpits," *Aviation Week & Space Technology*, 23 March 1992, 50-51.

[38] Bruce A. Smith, "Flight Management System Adds Roles," *Aviation Week & Space Technology*, 16 April 1979, 64-65.

[39] Graham, *Flight Deck Survey*.

[40] Graham, *Flight Deck Survey*; Morello, interview, 8 April 1993; Thomas M. Walsh, interview with author, Hampton, Virginia, 6 April 1993.

[41] Fadden, interview, 27 April 1993; Morello, interview, 8 April 1993; Walsh, interview, 6 April 1993; Hughes, "Glass Cockpit Study," 32-36; Hughes, "Pilots Give Mixed Reviews," 50-51.

[42] Morello, interview, 8 April 1993.

[43] Walsh, interview, 6 April 1993; Morello, interview, 8 April 1993; Breck W. Henderson, "NASA Ames Pushes Automation Toward Human-Centered Design," and Edward H. Phillips, "Pilots, Human Factors Specialists Urge Better Man-Machine Cockpit Interface," *Aviation Week & Space Technology*, 23 March 1992, 67-70.

[44] NTSB accident records, 1982-1993; Hughes, "Glass Cockpit Study," 32-36.

[45] H.W. Withington, vice president - engineering, Boeing Commercial Airplane Company, letter to Mr. John P. Reeder, Chief, Terminal Configured Vehicle Program Office, NASA Langley Research Center, 6 June 1979.

Chapter 4: A Technology Eclipsed: The Microwave Landing System and the Dawn of GPS

[1] Performed by a DC-3. John P. Reeder, "NASA-JMLS-TRSB Flight Demonstration," (presentation viewgraphs, Montreal, Canada March/April 1978, from ATOPS office files).

[2] Department of Transportation and National Aeronautics and Space Administration, *Civil Aviation Research and Development Policy Study*, DOT TST-10-4, NASA SP-265, (Washington, D.C., March, 1971).

[3] Jack Reeder, *Proposal for Systems Research Approach to Integrating Vehicle-Instrument-Display-Pilot Capability for Total Flight Missions*, draft, 1969, annotated with additional personal notes, 1971; "Report of Department of Transportation Air Traffic Control Advisory Committee, Vol. 1," December 1969 (from Federal Aviation Administration history records).

[4] By the 1990s, the organization was called only "RTCA, Inc." The full title was dropped.

[5] Philip J. Klass, "Future Landing Aid Needs Study Launched," *Aviation Week & Space Technology*, 11 March 1968, 31-32; *Time Reference Scanning Beam Microwave Landing System*, Department of Transportation/Federal Aviation Administration public information publication, 1977, 5.

[6] Memo with attachments from John P. Reeder, chief, Terminal Configured Vehicle Program Office, to distribution, regarding MLS flight demonstrations in Montreal, Canada, 4 April 1978 (from ATOPS office files); *Time Reference Scanning Beam*, 5.

[7] Frank L. Frisbie, Former FAA microwave landing system program office manager, interview with author, Washington, D.C., 13 April, 1993; Vincent L. Bencivenga, senior electronic engineer, microwave landing system program office staff, FAA, interview with author, Washington, D.C., 12 April 1993; Philip J. Klass, "Scanning Beam MLS Seen U.S. Choice," *Aviation Week & Space Technology*, 6 January 1975, 47-49; *Time Reference Scanning Beam*, 5.

[8] *Time Reference Scanning Beam*, 6-10; Thomas M. Walsh, Samuel A. Morello, and John P. Reeder, "Review of Operational Aspects of Initial Experiments Utilizing the U.S. MLS," SP-416, (paper, presented at Aircraft Safety and Operating Problems Conference, 18 - 20 October 1976), 9.

[9] Frisbie, interview, 13 April 1993; International Microwave Landing System Symposium Program, 30 November - 4 December 1973 (from private files of S. Salmirs).

[10] The FAA had installed MLS systems at Wallops Island and at the FAA National Aviation Flight Evaluation Center (NAFEC) in Atlantic City, New Jersey for development and evaluation purposes.

[11] Thomas M. Walsh, interview with author, Hampton, Virginia, 6 April 1993; William F. White, former researcher, Flight Instrument Division, Langley Research Center, interview with author, Washington, D.C., 13 April 1993.

[12] Walsh, interview, 6 April 1993; ATOPS office photograph files, Langley Research Center.

[13] John P. Reeder memo to staff, 7 March 1975 (from the personal files of B. White).

[14] Meeting notes, including outline of effects of MLS demonstration on TCV program projects, (from personal files of S. Salmirs); Thomas M. Walsh, "Terminal Configured Vehicle Program Research Having Potential for Fuel Savings," (paper, presented at the Flight International Conference on Fuel Economy in the Airlines, Royal Aeronautical Society, London, England, 1-2 April 1980, 6; White, interview, 13 April 1993; Frisbie, interview, 13 April 1993; Walsh, Morello, and Reeder, "Review of Initial Experiments," 9.

[15] Walsh, "Research Having Potential for Fuel Savings," 7; William F. White, comp., *Flight Demonstrations of Curved, Descending Approaches and Automatic Landings Using Time Reference Scanning Beam Guidance*, NASA-TM-78745, May 1978, 35-36; Hueschen, interview, 4 May 1993; Bencivenga, interview, 12 April 1993.

[16] Walsh, Morello, and Reeder, "Review of Experiments Utilizing the MLS," 11-13; White, comp. *Flight Demonstrations of Approaches and Landings*, 1, 3; also, Charles W. Meissner, Jr., "System Description," in White, comp.,*Flight Demonstrations of Approaches and Landings*, 47-50; Walsh, "Research Having Potential for Fuel Savings," 8; Hueschen, interview, 4 May 1993.

[17] Memorandum to TCV program office staff, from James E. Stitt, director for Electronics, 24 May 1976, acknowledging staff effort for demonstration.

[18] Richard M. Hueschen, interview with author, Hampton, Virginia, 4 May 1993; Walsh, interview, 6 April 1993; White, comp., *Flight Demonstrations of Approaches and Landings*, 1; ATOPS office flight records.

[19] Thomas M. Walsh, interview with author, Hampton, Virginia, 4 May 1993; Hueschen, interview, 4 May 1993; Delmar Fadden, Boeing Commercial Airplane Company, interview with author, Seattle, Washington, 27 April

1993; Wes Easley and David Holmes, interview with author, Hampton, Virginia, 9 April 1993.

[20] Walsh, Morello, and Reeder, "Review of Experiments Utilizing the MLS," 10, 14, 15, 18; White, comp., *Flight Demonstrations of Approaches and Landings*, 1-2, 36, 39.

[21] Walsh, Morello, and Reeder, "Review of Experiments Utilizing the MLS," 16; Walsh, "Research Having Potential for Fuel Savings," 11; Bencivenga, interview, 12 April 1993.

[22] Walsh, Morello, and Reeder, "Review of Experiments Utilizing the MLS," 17; Walsh, "Research Having Potential for Fuel Savings," 12; ATOPS office flight records; Hueschen, interview, 4 May 1993.

[23] The progression of the U.S.-British MLS controversy was covered in: Philip J. Klass, "Competing MLS Techniques Scrutinized," *Aviation Week & Space Technology*, 9 August 1976, 48-51; Klass, "MLS Faces Key Decision in Montreal," *Aviation Week & Space Technology*, 10 January 1977, 19-21; Kenneth J. Stein, "U.S.-Sponsored MLS Tested at Kennedy," *Aviation Week & Space Technology*, 12 December 1977, 34-35; Klass, "Landing System Battle Detailed," *Aviation Week & Space Technology*, 13 February 1978, 12-14; Klass, "Landing System Hearings Spur Charges," *Aviation Week & Space Technology*, 20 February, 1978, 65-72; Klass, "'Secrecy' Issue Aired at MLS Hearings," *Aviation Week & Space Technology*, 27 February 1978, 54-55; Kenneth J. Stein, "British Test Landing System in U.S.," *Aviation Week & Space Technology*, 27 March 1978, 29-30; Frisbie, interview, 13 April 1993; Bencivenga, interview, 12 April 1993.

[24] Letter from G.T. Connors to John P. Reeder, with "Supplemental Agreement No. DOT-FA77WAI-883 to memorandum of Agreement of May 3, 1973," outlining the MLS demonstration work requested by the FAA, dated 29 November 1977 (from ATOPS office files); Walsh, "Research Having Potential for Fuel Savings," 7.

[25] John P. Reeder, "NASA-MLS-TRSB Flight Demonstrations," (presentation notes, December 1977, from ATOPS office files).

[26] Walsh, "Research Having Potential for Fuel Savings," 9; John P. Reeder, Robert A. Schmitz, and Leonard V. Clark, *Operational Benefits from the Terminal Configured Vehicle*, NASA-TM-80046, 15-17.

[27] Reeder, Schmitz, and Clark, *Operational Benefits*, 17-18; Walsh, "Research Having Potential for Fuel Savings," 9-10.

[28] Easley and Holmes, interview, 9 April 1993; Dr. Jeremiah Creedon, interview with author, Hampton, Virginia, 7 May 1993.

[29] Lee H. Person, Jr. and Kenneth R. Yenni, "Flying NASA's Terminal Configured Vehicle Against the Microwave Landing System," Society of Experimental Test Pilots, *Technical Review*, Vol. 14, No. 2, 1978, 113; Walsh, "Research Having Potential for Fuel Savings," 9-10; Reeder, Schmitz, and Clark, *Operational Benefits*, 17-19.

[30] Walsh, "Research Having Potential for Fuel Savings," 10-11.

[31] Frisbie, interview, 13 April 1993; Bencivenga, interview, 13 April 1993; Hueschen, interview, 4 May 1993.

[32] Reeder, Schmitz, and Clark, *Operational Benefits*, 12, 20.

[33] Walsh, interview, 6 April 1993.

[34] Bencivenga, interview, 12 April 1993; Frisbie, interview, 13 April 1993; James T. McKenna, "FAA's Assertions of MLS Benefits Fail to Sway Airline Operations Personnel," *Aviation Week & Space Technology*, 1 August 1988, 86-87; "U.S. Airlines Reassess Position Against MLS," *Aviation Week & Space Technology*, 19 September 1988, 122.

[35] Frisbie, interview, 13 April 1993; Dr. Jeremiah Creedon, interview with author, Hampton, Virginia, 5 April 1993; Walsh, interview, 6 April 1993; "FAA Schedules Briefings On Deployment of MLS," *Aviation Week & Space Technology*, 1 December 1980, 31; Paul Proctor, "Flight Departments Request Revised MLS Installation List," *Aviation Week & Space Technology*, 12 May 1986, 77-78; "FAA Continues to Support MLS Installation Plan," *Aviation Week & Space Technology*, 13 October 1986, 47; Kenneth J. Stein, "FAA Initiates Two-Phase Effort To Speed Acceptance of MLS," *Aviation Week & Space Technology*, 23 March 1987, 36-38; Philip J. Klass, "Cost and Schedule Questions Threaten MLS Installation," *Aviation Week & Space Technology*, 4 January 1988, 68-69.

[36] James K. Gordon, "FAA Projects Nine-Month Delay in Production MLS Deliveries," *Aviation Week & Space Technology*, 25 March 1985, 32-33; Klass, "Cost Questions Threaten MLS," 68; James T. McKenna, "ATA Will Establish Task Force To Critique MLS Programs," *Aviation Week & Space Technology*, 6 March 1989, 68; Philip J. Klass, "FAA Alters Microwave Landing System Deployment Plan to Ease ILS Transition," *Aviation Week & Space Technology*, 8 January 1990, 31; Bencivenga, interview, 12 April 1993; Frisbie, interview, 13 April 1993.

[37] "MLS Transition Undergoes Scrutiny," *Aviation Week & Space Technology*, 18 April 1988, 86; Philip J. Klass, "GAO Recommends Postponing MLS Purchases Until

Benefits Are Clear," *Aviation Week & Space Technology*, 13 June 1988, 23; Philip J. Klass, "Airlines Back Microwave System to Replace Some ILS," *Aviation Week & Space Technology*, 2 December 1991, 26.

[38] *RTCA Task Force Report on the Global Navigation Satellite System (GNSS) Transition and Implementation Strategy*, (Washington, D.C.: RTCA, Inc., September 1992), 1.

[39] Bruce D. Nordwall, "GPS Applications, Production Grow as System Gains Acceptance," *Aviation Week & Space Technology*, 31 October 1988, 83-84; Hueschen, interview, 4 May 1993.

[40] Hueschen, interview, 4 May 1993; Philip J. Klass, "MLS Simulations Show Curved Approaches Can Boost Traffic Flow," *Aviation Week & Space Technology*, 20 August 1990, 94; Poritsky, interview, 13 April 1993; Creedon, interview, 7 May 1993; Philip J. Klass, "Integrated GPS/MLS System Could Be Useful for Terminal Area Operations," *Aviation Week & Space Technology*, 18 February 1991, 57.

[41] Hueschen, interview, 4 May 1993; Cary R. Spitzer, interview with author, Hampton, Virginia, 13 May 1993.

[42] Creedon, interview, 5 April 1993.

[43] Hueschen, interview, 4 May 1993, and phone interview with author, 29 June 1993; Spitzer, interview, 13 May 1993; Creedon, interview, 7 May 1993; Richard M. Hueschen and Cary R. Spitzer, "Analysis of DGPS/INS and MLS/INS Final Approach Navigation Errors and Control Performance Data," (paper, presented at ION conference, San Diego, California, 27-29 January 1992), 6-11.

[44] Creedon, interviews, 5 April 1993 and 7 May 1993; Hueschen, interview, 4 May 1993.

[45] Hueschen, interview, 4 May 1993.

[46] Bencivenga, interview, 12 April 1993; David Hughes, "ICAO Delegates Back FANS Concept, Set Stage for Global Satellite Systems," *Aviation Week & Space Technology*, 14 October 1991, 36, 43; "Europeans Favor Satellite Navigation But Raise Concerns About GPS' Reliability," *Aviation Week & Space Technology*, 6 April 1992, 60.

[47] *Special Committee on Future Air Navigation Systems, 4th Meeting*, report, ICAO Document 9524, 2-20 May 1988.

[48] "ICAO Remains Dubious About GNSS Role," *Flight International*, 31 March - 6 April 1993, 6; "1995 Set For FAA GNSS Decision," *Flight International*, 31 March - 6 April 1993, 5.

[49] "BA Drives to Retain MLS as Main System," *Flight International*, 31 March - 6 April 1993, 6; "Final Approach," *Flight International*, 31 March - 6 April 1993, 34-36.

[50] Bencivenga, interview, 12 April 1993; Hueschen, interview, 4 May 1993; Walsh, interview, 6 April 1993; Siegbert Poritsky, interview with author, Washington, D.C., 13 April 1993; Philip J. Klass, "FAA Steps Up Program to Introduce GPS as Instrument Approach Aid," *Aviation Week & Space Technology*, 17 August 1992, 35-36.

Chapter 5: "The Best That We Can Do"
Taming the Microburst Windshear

[1] AAC/ARTS Evaluation of NASA Wind Shear Program, 1992, document from files of Roland Bowles, manager, NASA Wind Shear Program.

[2] *Low Altitude Wind Shear and Its Hazard to Aviation*, Report of the Committee on Low-Altitude Wind Shear and Its Hazard to Aviation, (Washington: National Academy Press, 1983), 14-15; Roland L. Bowles, "Windshear Detection and Avoidance: Airborne Systems Survey," IEEE, (Proceedings of the 29th Conference on Decision and Control, Honolulu Hawaii, December 1990), 708; Michael S. Lewis, et al., "Design and Conduct of a Windshear Detection Flight Experiment," AIAA Paper 92-4092, 1992, 2.

[3] James Ott, "Inquiry Focuses on Wind Shear As Cause of Delta L-1011 Crash," *Aviation Week & Space Technology*, 12 August 1985, 16-19; "Delta Accident Report Focuses On Wind Shear Research," reprint of NTSB accident report on the 2 August 1985 Delta Flight 191 crash, part 4, *Aviation Week & Space Technology*, 24 November 1986, 73-75; "Safety Board Analyzes Responses to Weather Data," reprint of NTSB accident report on the 2 August 1985 Delta Flight 191 crash, part 7, *Aviation Week & Space Technology*, 15 December 1986, 103-107.

[4] *Low-Altitude Wind Shear*, ix, 1; Eugene Kozicharow, "NTSB Cites Wind Shear In New Orleans Accident," *Aviation Week & Space Technology*, 28 March, 1983, 32.

[5] William H. Gregory, "Too Little and Too Late," editorial, *Aviation Week & Space Technology*, 12 August 1985, 11; Herbert J. Coleman, "Administration Criticized for Delay In Wind Shear Research, Terminal Radar Buy," *Aviation Week & Space Technology*, 23 September 1985, 29; "Engen Defends Air Transport System in Senate Testimony," *Aviation Week & Space Technology*, 7 October 1985, 30; A. Gary Price, interview with author, Hampton, Virginia, 13 May 1993; Roland L. Bowles, manager, Wind Shear Program Office, interview with author, Hampton, Virginia, 12 May 1993.

[6] *Low-Altitude Wind Shear*, 11-12, 14-16.

[7] T. Theodore Fujita, "Spearhead Echo and Downburst Near the Approach End of a John F. Kennedy Airport Runway, New York City," Satellite and Mesometeorology Research Project, SMRP Paper 137, University of Chicago, March 1976; *Low-Altitude Wind Shear*, 11-12, 20-21.

[8] Viewgraphs and public information on microburst wind shear from NASA Wind Shear Program Office files; *Low-Altitude Wind Shear*, 19-32.

[9] *Low Altitude Wind Shear*, 33-37; "Wind-Shear Detection Technology Examined in 727 Accident Report, reprint of NTSB report on the 31 May 1984 United Airlines Flight 663 accident, part 4, *Aviation Week & Space Technology*, 7 October 1985, 89-91. NTSB Report reprint, "Delta Accident Report," 73.

[10] *Low Altitude Wind Shear*, 16-18.

[11] Bowles, interview, 12 May 1993; Bowles, "Windshear Detection," 719.

[12] *Low-Altitude Wind Shear*, 1; Bowles, "Windshear Detection," 710.

[13] Kozicharow, "NTSB Cites Wind Shear," 32.

[14] *Low-Altitude Wind Shear*, ix; "Wind Shear Study," *Aviation Week & Space Technology, 28 March 1983*, 32.

[15] Low-Altitude Wind Shear, 1, 81-82.

[16] Department of Transportation, Federal Aviation Administration, 14 CFR Parts 121 and 135, "Airborne Low-Altitude Windshear Equipment and Training Requirements; Notice of Proposed Rulemaking," *Federal Register*, Vol 52, No. 1041 June 1987, Docket No. 19110; Notice No. 79-11A, 20564.

[17] Bowles, "Windshear Detection," 710; Ott, "Inquiry Focuses on Wind Shear," 16; "Safety Board Analyzes Responses," NTSB Report Reprint, 103.

[18] Price, interview, 13 May 1993; Dr. Jeremiah F. Creedon, interview with author, Hampton, Virginia, 7 May 1993; George C. "Cliff" Hay, manager, FAA Wind Shear program office, phone interview with author, 13 July 1993; Bowles, interview, 12 May 1993.

[19] "NTSB Recommends Upgraded Training, Reporting to Avoid Wind Shear," reprint of NTSB report on 2 August 1985 Delta Airlines Flight 191 accident, *Aviation Week & Space Technology*, 2 February 1987, 96; Hay, interview, 13 July 1993.

[20] Hay, interview, 13 July 1993, George C. "Cliff" Hay, "Overview of the Integrated Federal Aviation Administration (FAA) Wind Shear Program Plan," SAE Technical Paper 861702, (paper, presented at the Aerospace Technology Conference and Exposition, Long Beach, California, 13-16 October 1986).

[21] Hay, "Overview of Integrated Program," 62-64.

[22] Bowles, interview, 12 May 1993; "Memorandum of Agreement Between Federal Aviation Administration (FAA) and National Aeronautics and Space Administration (NASA) Concerning Airborne Windshear Detection and Avoidance Program," DTFA01-86-Z-02018, 24 July 1986, (from ATOPS office files).

[23] Michael S. Lewis, deputy manager, NASA wind shear program office, interview with author, Hampton, Virginia, 7 May 1993; Bowles, interview, 12 May 1993; Bowles, "Windshear Detection," 708.

[24] FAA, "Airborne Windshear Equipment" NPRM, 20564-20565, 20570; "Airborne Infrared System Provides Advance Warning of Turbulence," *Aviation Week & Space Technology*, 19 June 1989, 130; Hay, interview, 13 July 1993; Bowles, interview, 12 May 1993;

[25] *Low-Altitude Wind Shear*," 1.

[26] Kozicharow, "NTSB Cites Wind Shear," 32.

[27] Bowles, "Windshear Detection," 710.

[28] Bowles, interview, 12 May 1993; Bowles, "Windshear Detection," 724.

[29] Bowles, interview, 12 May 1993; Lewis, interview, 7 May 1993; Bowles, "Windshear Detection," 712-715, 724; "'F-Factor' to Warn Pilots of Wind Shear Severity," *Aviation Week & Space Technology*, 7 September 1992, 147.

[30] Bowles, "Windshear Detection," 711.

[31] "Safety Board Analyzes Responses," NTSB report reprint, 103.

[32] *Low-Altitude Wind Shear*, 44-45.

[33] "Memorandum of Agreement," 24 July 1986.

[34] Information on all three forward-looking candidate systems was gathered from: *Low-Altitude Wind Shear*, 43-46; Bowles, "Windshear Detection," 716-724; Bowles, interview, 12 May 1993; Lewis, interview, 7 May 1993; Nasa Facts 176, "Making the Skies Safe From Windshear, June 1992; Viewgraphs from the wind shear program office files, Langley Research Center.

[35] Lewis, et al., "Design and Conduct of an Experiment," 3; William B. Scott, "NASA Flies 737 Through Microbursts in Wind Shear Flight Research Effort," *Aviation Week & Space Technology*, 16/23 December 1991, 46; Bowles, interview, 12 May 1993; Lewis, interview, 7

May 1993.

[36] Bowles, "Windshear Detection," 719.

[37] Lewis, et al., "Design and Conduct of an Experiment," 3.

[38] Memorandum of Agreement, "For Airborne Windshear Advanced Technology Operational Program," FAA/NASA Interagency Agreement No. DTFA01-90-Z-02021, 31 May 1990.

[39] Lewis, et al., "Design and Conduct of an Experiment," 4-6.

[40] Lewis, interview, 7 May 1993.

[41] Lewis et al., "Design and Conduct of an Experiment," 4-6; Lewis, interview, 7 May 1993; Michael S. Lewis, phone interview with author, 15 July 1993; Viewgraphs from NASA Wind Shear Program Office files.

[42] Lewis, et al., "Design and Conduct of an Experiment," 3, 6-8; Lewis, interview, 7 May 1993; Lee H. Person, interview with author, Hampton, Virginia, 14 May 1993; Scott, "NASA 737 Flies Through Microbursts," 46-47; video footage and photographic records of 1991 Orlando and Denver flight tests, from NASA Wind Shear Program Office files.

[43] Creedon, interview, 7 May 1993; Bowles, interview, 12 May 1993;

[44] Artie D. Jessup, phone interview with author, 16 July 1993; Creedon, interview, 7 May 1993; Bowles, interview, 12 May 1993.

[45] Bruce D. Nordwall, "Modified Doppler Detects Wind Shear More Reliably," Aviation Week & Space Technology, 7 September 1992, 143-151; Michael Finneran, "Burst-Busters," NASA Magazine, Winter 1993, 18-22; Bowles, interview, 12 May 1993; Lewis, interview, 7 May 1993; Creedon, interview, 7 May 1993.

[46] Michael S. Lewis, phone interview with author, 16 July 1993; Bowles, interview, 12 May 1993; Hay, interview, 13 July 1993; Lewis, interview, 7 May 1993; Philip J. Klass, "New Airborne Radar Shows Promise of Detecting Dangerous Microbursts," *Aviation Week & Space Technology*, 10 February 1992, 44-45; Nordwall, "Modified Doppler," 143-151.

[47] AAC/ARTS Evaluation of NASA Wind Shear Program, 1992.

[48] Creedon, interview, 7 May 1993.

Chapter 6: Improving Aircraft Systems

[1] "Terminal Configured Vehicle Program Plan," Langley Research Center, 1 December 1973, 1-3; "Advanced Transport Operating Systems Program Review," Langley Research Center, 20 October 1982 (presentation viewgraphs, from Flight Systems Directorate office files).

[2] David C.E. Holmes and Wes C. Easley, interview with author, Hampton, Virginia, 9 April 1993; more detailed information on DATAC operation can be found in: David C.E. Holmes, "Global System Data Bus Using the Digital Autonomous Terminal Access Communication Protocol," (paper, presented at the IEEE/AIAA 7th Digital Avionics Systems Conference and Technical Display, Fort Worth, Texas, 13-16 October 1986; Also in: W.C. Easley and J.S. Tanguy, "Interface of the Transport Systems Research Vehicle Monochrome Display System to the Digital Autonomous Terminal Access Communication Data Bus," NASA TM 87728, May 1986.

[3] Holmes and Easley, interview, 9 April 1993; William E. Howell, interview with author, Hampton, Virginia, 6 April 1993.

[4] Holmes and Easley, interview, 9 April 1993.

[5] Howell, interview, 6 April 1993; Boeing demonstration conducted 16 September 1985 (from B-737 flight records in ATOPS program office files); Simone Pottenger, Boeing Commercial Airplane Company, phone interview with author, 22 July 1993.

[6] Holmes and Easley, interview, 9 April 1993; Daniel Martinec, Airlines Electronic Engineering Committee, Aeronautical Radio, Inc., phone interview with author, 22 July 1993.

[7] Artie D. Jessup and Cary R. Spitzer, interview with author, Hampton, Virginia, 7 May 1993.

[8] James R. Kelly, Lee H. Person, and Kevin R. Bruce, "Flight Testing TECS — The Total Energy Control System," SAE TP-861803 (presented at the Aerospace Technology Conference and Exposition, Long Beach, California, 13-16 October 1986; James R. Kelly, interview with author, Hampton, Virginia, 5 May 1993; Anthony A. Lambregts, Boeing Commercial Airplane Company, interview with author, Seattle, Washington, 26 April 1993; Delmar Fadden, chief engineer, avionics/flight systems, Renton Division, Boeing Commercial Airplane Company, interview with author, Seattle, Washington, 27 April 1993; Lee H. Person, interview with author, Hampton, Virginia, 14 May 1993; TSRV B-737 flight logs, from ATOPS office files.

[9] Terence S. Abbott, interview with author, Hampton, Virginia, 14 May 1993; Terence S. Abbott, "Task-Oriented Display Design: Concept and Example," SAE Technical Paper 892230, (presented at Aerospace Technology Conference and Exposition, Anaheim, California, 25-28 September 1989.

[10] D.L. Mahaffey, Richard L. Horst, and Robert C.

Munson, "Behavioral Comparison of the Efficacy of Bar Graphs and Polar Graphics for Displays of System Status," *Proceedings of the 1986 IEEE International Conference on Systems, Man and Cybernetics*, IEEE Catalog No. 86CH2364-8, Institute of Electrical and Electronics Engineers, Inc., 1986, 1514-1519; Robert C. Munson and Richard L. Horst, "Evidence for Global Processing of Complex Visual Displays," *Proceedings of the Human Factors Society 30th Annual Meeting*, Vol. 2, Human Factors Society, Inc., 1986, 776-780.

[11] Terence S. Abbott, "A Simulation Evaluation of the Engine Monitoring and Control System Display," NASA TP-2960, February 1990; Abbott, interview, 14 May 1993.

[12] Robert H. Kinder, General Manager, Engineering Technology and Advanced Aircraft Programs, McDonnell Douglas Corporation letter to Dr. J.F. Creedon, NASA Langley Research Center, 15 August 1991.

[13] Abbott, interview with author, 14 May 1993; Robert Brooks, ARNAV Systems, Inc., phone interview with author, 22 July 1993.

[14] Thomas S. Kuhn, *The Structure of Scientific Revolutions*, 2nd ed., Foundations of the Unity of Science Series: Vol. 2, No. 2, (Chicago: University of Chicago Press, 1970); Joel Arthur Barker, *Future Edge: Discovering the New Paradigms of Success*, (New York: William Morrow & Company, Inc., 1992), 55-92.

[15] David B. Middleton, interview with author, Hampton, Virginia, 14 May 1993; David B. Middleton, Raghavachari Srivatsan, Lee H. Person, "Simulator Evaluation of Displays for a Takeoff Performance Monitoring System," NASA TP-2908, May 1989; James T. McKenna, "NASA Develops System to Monitor Aircraft Performance on Takeoff," *Aviation Week & Space Technology*, 13 November 1989, 43-50.

[16] David B. Middleton, Raghavachari Srivatsan, Lee H. Person, "Simulator Evaluation of Displays for a Revised Takeoff Performance Monitoring System," NASA TP-3270, December 1992, 1.

[17] Middleton, interview, 14 May 1993; NASA 515 Vehicle flight records, ATOPS program office files.

[18] Middleton, interview, 14 May 1993; Richard A. Peal, director of systems engineering, Boeing Commercial Airplane Company, interview with author, Seattle, Washington, 28 April 1993.

[19] Middleton, interview, 14 May 1993.

[20] Fadden, interview, 27 April 1993.

[21] Dr. Jeremiah F. Creedon, interview with author, Hampton, Virginia, 5 April 1993.

[22] Stephanie, Public Affairs, Everett Division, Boeing Commercial Airplane Company, phone interview with author, 20 July 1993.

[23] Kinder to Creedon, letter, 15 August 1991.

Chapter 7: Improving Aircraft Operations

[1] LFM was not the same thing as a "slot time," which assigned each inbound aircraft a specific, reserved arrival time. LFM matched the number of arrivals with the actual, real-time capabilities of the airport. This number often differed from the slot time reservations, due to delays or poor weather conditions.

[2] Charles E. Knox, interviews with author, Hampton, Virginia, 7 April 1993 and 7 May 1993; Charles E. Knox, "Denver Local Flow Management Flight Tests," summary with viewgraph, 11 October 1979 (from ATOPS office files); John P. Reeder, "Participation in Flight Tests at Denver Stapleton Airport," memo with attachments, to distribution, 20 August 1979 (from ATOPS office files).

[3] Knox, "Denver Flight Tests," 11 October 1979; Charles E. Knox and Dennis G. Cannon, "Development and Test Results of a Flight Management Algorithm for Fuel-Conservative Descents in a Time-Based Metered Traffic Environment," NASA-TP-1717, October 1980, 1-2, 25-31; Knox, interviews, 7 April 1993, 7 May 1993, and 13 May 1993.

[4] "Comments From Onboard Observers, TCV Denver Time-Based Metering/Local Flow Management Flight Tests, June 19 through June 28, 1979," typed summary, (from ATOPS office files); Ralph Kiss, Chief, Denver ARTC, "NASA TCV Flight Tests With Denver ARTC," with additional comments on NASA/Denver ARTCC Time-Based Metering and Agenda Item Responses, undated typed report (from ATOPS office files).

[5] Knox, interview, 13 May 1993; John Whitfield, Lockheed L-1011 program manager and Don Moore, Lockheed L-1011 chief pilot, phone interview with author, 15 June 1993; Boeing Commercial Airplane Company press materials on aircraft production, flight and delivery dates.

[6] Charles E. Knox, "Flight Planning For Time-Constrained/Fuel Efficient Descents," typed summary report of research experiments, 9 September 1981 (from ATOPS office files); Charles E. Knox, "Planning Fuel-Conservative Descents With or Without Time Constraints Using a Small Programmable Calculator," NASA TP-2085, February 1983; C.E. Knox, D.D. Vicroy and D.A. Simmon, "Planning Fuel-Conservative Descents in an Airline Environment Using a Small Programmable Calculator," NASA TP-2393, May 1985; Knox, interview, 13 May 1993.

[7] Knox, interview, 7 May 1993.

[8] "767 FMCS — Initial 4D Guidance Alternatives," 767 Study Engineering Work Authorization, SEWA No. 39, undated, referencing United Airlines Letter, J. Goodwine to F. Copes Van Hesselt, "B-767 Flight Management System — 4-D Nav," 6 July 1979 and United Airlines, "4-D Navigation Capability," CRWS No. 34-189; Knox, interview, 13 May 1993; David Allen, Boeing Commercial Airplane Company, Everett Division, phone interview with author, 2 August 1993.

[9] Allen, interview, 2 August 1993.

[10] Heinz Erzberger, Thomas J. Davis, Steven Green, "Design of Center-Tracon Automation System," (paper, presented at the AGARD Guidance and Control Symposium on Machine Intelligence in Air Traffic Management, 11-14 May 1993, Berlin, Germany.

[11] "CTAS/TSRV Trajectory Prediction Flight Experiment," Plan of Test No. V92135, 2 October 1992 (from David H. Williams office files); David H. Williams, phone interview with author, 4 August 1993.

[12] John Garren and John P. Reeder, "Cockpit Display of Traffic Information (CDTI), A Perspective," memo, undated (from ATOPS office files).

[13] D. H. Ewing and R. W. K. Smith, "Teleran-Air Navigation and Traffic Control by Means of Television and Radar," RCA Review, Vol VII, No. 4, December 1946, 601-621.

[14] Mark E. Connelly, "Simulation Studies of Airborne Traffic Situation Display Applications, Final Report," Report ESL-R-751, May 1977.

[15] Terence S. Abbott, et al., "Early Flight Test Experience With Cockpit Displayed Traffic Information," NASA TM-80221, February 1980; Terence S. Abbott, et al., "Flight Investigation of Cockpit-Displayed Traffic Information Utilizing Coded Symbology in an Advanced Operational Environment," NASA TP-1684, 1980; Knox, interview, 13 May 1993; David H. Williams, phone interview with author, 16 August 1993.

[16] David H. Williams, phone interviews with author, 4 August 1993 and 16 August 1993.

[17] Charles E. Knox and Charles H. Scanlon, "Flight Tests Using Data Link for Air Traffic Control and Weather Information Exchange," SAE Paper 901888, *SAE 1990 Transactions*, Section 1, Vol. 99, Part 2, 1683.

[18] Knox, interview, 7 May 1993.

[19] Charles E. Knox and Charles H. Scanlon, "Flight Tests With a Data Link Used for Air Traffic Control Information Exchange," NASA TP-3135, September 1991, 1; David A Hinton and Gary W. Lohr, "Simulator Investigation of Digital Data-Link ATC Communications in a Single-Pilot Operation," NASA TP-2837, December 1988; Knox, interview, 7 May 1993.

[20] Philip J. Klass, "Predeparture Clearance to Be Sent Via Data Link at Major Airports," *Aviation Week & Space Technology*, 25 June 1990, 43.

[21] Knox and Scanlon, "Flight Tests Using Data Link," 1684; Marvin C. Waller and Gary W. Lohr, "A Piloted Simulation Study of Data Link ATC Message Exchange," NASA TP-2859, February 1989; Knox, interview, 7 May 1993.

[22] Knox and Scanlon, "Flight Tests Using Data Link," 1683-1684.

[23] Knox and Scanlon, "Flight Tests With a Data Link;" Knox, interviews, 7 April 1993, 7 May 1993; Edward H. Phillips, "Langley Data Link System Provides ATC Communications, Weather Depiction," *Aviation Week & Space Technology*, 6 January 1992, 52-53.

[24] Knox, interview 7 May 1993; TSRV 737 flight log records from ATOPS office files.

[25] Knox and Scanlon, "Flight Tests Using Data Link," 1692.

[26] Knox, interview, 13 May 1993; Allen, interview, 2 August 1993.

[27] David H. Williams and Steven M. Green, "Piloted Simulation of an Air-Ground Profile Negotiation Process in a Time-Based Air Traffic Control Environment," NASA TM-107748; Williams, interview, 4 August 1993.

[28] Hugh McLaurin, Federal Aviation Administration, phone interview with author, 2 August 1993. Note: a transponder is a transmitter in an airplane that sends out a coded signal to air traffic controllers to help them locate the position of aircraft on their radar scopes. Mode "A" transponders report only a selectable numerical code and the lateral position of the airplane, while Mode "C" transponders report altitude, as well. Mode "S" transponders send out a discrete code that applies only to that particular aircraft and always remains the same.

[29] Knox, interview, 7 May 1993.

[30] Allen, interview, 2 August 1993; Barbara Murphy, Boeing Commercial Airplane Company, Everett Division, phone interview with author, 10 August 1993.

[31] Kenneth E. Hodge, "Aircraft Developments that Hold Promise for Increased Compatibility with an Advanced ATC System," *Proceedings*, Air Traffic Control Association, 22nd Annual Meeting, Law Vegas, Nevada, 10-13 October 1977, 185.

[32] Anthony A. Lambregts, Boeing Commercial Airplane

Company, interview with author, Seattle, Washington, 26 April 1993.

[33] Anthony A. Lambregts and Jeremiah F. Creedon, "Development and Flight Evaluation of Automatic Flare Laws with Improved Touchdown Dispersion," AIAA Paper 80-1757, (printed in collection of papers from the AIAA Guidance and Control Conference, Danvers, Massachusetts, 11-13 August 1980); Lambregts, interview, 26 April 1993; Jeremiah F. Creedon, interview with author, Hampton, Virginia, 7 May 1993.

[34] Lambregts, interview, 26 April 1993; Dwight Schaeffer, Boeing Commercial Airplane Company, phone interview with author, 2 August 1993.

[35] Dr. Jeremiah Creedon, interview with author, Hampton, Virginia, 7 May 1993.

[36] W. Thomas Bundick, David B. Middleton, and William L. Poole, "Results of Aircraft Open-Loop Tests of an Experimental Magnetic Leader Cable System for Guidance During Roll-Out and Turnoff," NASA TM-4135, February 1990, 2; A.F. Hammond, "Guidance and Control of Aircraft Ground Movement at Airports During Restricted Visibility — A survey of Requirements and Possible Systems," Technical Report No. 65071, British Royal Aircraft Establishment, March 1965; H.C. Morgan and P. England, "A Taxi-Guidance System for Aircraft Using a Single Magnetic Leader Cable," Technical Report No. 66065, British Royal Aircraft Establishment, February 1966.

[37] S. Pines and Richard M. Hueschen, "Guidance and Navigation for Automatic Landing, Rollout, and Turnoff Using MLS and Magnetic Cable Sensors," Contractor Report under Contract No. NAS1-14311, catalog no. 78-1296, 1978.

[38] Bundick, Middleton and Poole, "Results of Aircraft Open-Loop Tests;" W. Thomas Bundick, phone interview with author, 19 August 1993.

[39] David B. Middleton, phone interview with author, 18 August 1993.

Chapter 8: A National Facility

[1] John White, Operations Manager, ATOPS program, interview with author, Hampton, Virginia, 5 April 1993.

[2] Richard L. Kreitinger and David B. Middleton, "Aircraft Surface Coatings for Drag Reduction/Erosion Protection," SAE Paper 811070 (presented at the Aerospace Congress & Exposition, Anaheim, California, 5-8 October 1981), 1.

[3] William D. Beasley and Robert J. McGhee, "An Exploratory Investigation of the Effects of a Thin Plastic Film Cover on the Profile Drag of an Aircraft Wing Panel," NASA TM-74073, October 1977.

[4] Continental Airlines also tested a third coating, called Astrocoat, on its 727, but the Astrocoat performance was below that of the Chemglaze and the CAAPCO substances, and it was not included in the subsequent Delta tests or the NASA flight evaluations.

[5] Richard L. Kreitinger and David B. Middleton, "Aircraft Surface Coatings for Drag Reduction/Erosion Protection," SAE Paper 811070, (presented at the Aerospace Congress & Exposition, Anaheim, California, 5-8 October 1981); David B. Middleton, phone interviews with author, 23 August 1993 and 26 August 1993.

[6] A. Bertelrud, R.D. Watson and C.B. McGinley, "Flow Measurements on the Fuselage of a Boeing 737 Airplane," AIAA Paper 89-0209, (presented at the 27th Aerospace Sciences Meeting, Reno, Nevada, 9-12 January 1989).

[7] Ralph D. Watson, phone interview with author, 27 August 1993.

[8] Long P. Yip, interview with author, Hampton, Virginia, 7 May 1993; Edward H. Phillips, "NASA/Langley Using Varied Approach to Develop Subsonic High-Lift Devices," *Aviation Week & Space Technology*, 10 February 1992, 49.

[9] Long P. Yip, et al., "Subsonic High-Lift Flight Research on the NASA Transport Systems Research Vehicle (TSRV)," AIAA Paper 92-4103, (presented at the AIAA 6th Biennial Flight Test Conference, Hilton Head, South Carolina, 24-26 August 1992); Long P. Yip, et al., "In-Flight Pressure Distributions and Skin-Friction Measurements on a Subsonic Transport High-Lift Wing Section," AGARD Conference Proceeding CP-415, Paper 21 (presented at the Symposium on High-Lift System Aerodynamics, Banff, Alberta, Canada, 5-8 October 1992); Yip, interview, 7 May 1993.

[10] From National Transportation Safety Board accident records.

[11] Bill wording as quoted in Thomas J. Yager, William A. Vogler and Paul Baldasare, "Evaluation of Two Transport Aircraft and Several Ground Test Vehicle Friction Measurements Obtained for Various Runway Surface Types and Conditions," NASA TP-2917, February 1990, 1.

[12] Thomas J. Yager, phone interview with author, 23 August 1993.

[13] Yager, Vogler and Baldasare, "Friction Measurements," 3-11, 16-22; Yager, interview, 23 August 1993.

[14] Lee H. Person, interview with author, Hampton, Virginia, 14 May 1993.

[15] Yager, interview, 23 August 1993.

[16] Yager, Vogler, and Baldasare, "Friction Measurements," 20-22; Yager, interview, 23 August 1993.

[17] Kenneth R. Yenni and William E. Howell, "Flight Tests of a Helmet-Mounted Display Synthetic Visibility System," NASA Document, apparently unpublished (from ATOPS office files); Mark S. Rolwes, McDonnell Douglas Corporation, phone interview with author, 22 August 1993; Mark S. Rolwes, "An Alternative Approach to Providing External Vision to Pilots of Future Air Vehicles," IEEE Paper, CH2929-8/90/0000-0540, 1990, 540-544.

[18] Rolwes, interview, 22 August 1993; Yenni and Howell, "Helmet-Mounted Display," 2-3; Person, interview, 14 May 1993; TSRV 737 flight log records (from ATOPS office files).

[19] Rolwes, interview, 22 August 1993.

[20] James Kelly, interview with author, Hampton, Virginia, 5 May 1993; James Hall, interview with author, Hampton, Virginia, 7 April 1993; Person, interview, 14 May 1993; "Examples of Advanced Technologies that have been Transferred to Industry Applications after Initial Flight Test on Langley ATOPS B-737 Aircraft," ATOPS office summary document; TSRV 737 flight log records (from ATOPS office files).

[21] Webster's New Twentieth Century Dictionary of the English Language, Unabridged, 2nd ed., (New York: Simon & Schuster, 1983), 215.

[22] Charles E. Knox, interview with author, Hampton, Virginia, 13 May 1993; Person, interview, 14 May 1993; TSRV 737 flight logs (from ATOPS office files).

Conclusion

[1] Hans Mark and Arnole Levine, *The Management of Research Institutions: A Look at Government Laboratories*, NASA SP-481, (Washington, D.C., 1984), 265.

[2] Langley Research Center Mission Statement summary, viewgraph, from Flight Systems Directorate files, NASA Langley Research Center, 1993.

[3] Thomas M. Walsh, former deputy chief, TCV/ATOPS program, interview with author, Hampton, Virginia, 6 April 1993.

Bibliographic Essay

The majority of the material for this book came from five different sources. The primary source of information was 60 individual interviews with engineers and managers from NASA, the Federal Aviation Administration, and industry who were involved with NASA's Boeing 737 or the technology the airplane helped to research. Information pertaining to the specific research projects conducted with the airplane was also obtained from NASA technical reports, technical papers, technical memoranda, and contractor reports. Some of these technical publications were located through the University of Minnesota Walter Library, in Minneapolis, Minnesota. The remainder were found through the Floyd L. Thompson Technical Library at the Langley Research Center in Hampton, Virginia, or in the Advanced Transport Operating Systems (ATOPS) program office, also at Langley.

A third important source, especially with regard to the early days of the Terminal Configured Vehicle (TCV) program, was specific correspondence, memos, proposals, and notes from the ATOPS office files. The ATOPS office files also contained extensive information about the 737, including flight logs, passenger manifests, detailed reports of each research flight, and summaries of the 737's flight time by year and by research project. In addition, several managers at NASA and at the Boeing Commercial Airplane Company provided copies of their personal notes that they had saved since the time they had worked with the TCV program. Information about congressional action related to the program, political forces that impacted the airplane's research, and material on the history of technology transfer in NASA came from the historical archives at NASA Headquarters in Washington, D.C.

The fifth source for the material in this book was popular literature and industry publications. *Aviation Week & Space Technology*, a weekly aerospace news magazine, provided good background information on relevant developments in the aviation industry and the incorporation of new technologies into commercial products. Valuable information on the theories of technology transfer and change came from a variety of publicly available books, ranging from Thomas S. Kuhn's *The Structure of Scientific Revolutions* to *Marketing Warfare* by Al Ries and Jack Trout.

Illustration Credits

Pages	Credits
Cover	NASA Art Program, artist John Clark, NASA photo number 93-HC-409.
End paper	NASA photo.
iv	NASA photo.
vi	Courtesy Boeing Commercial Aircraft Corporation Archives.
vi	Courtesy Boeing Commercial Aircraft Corporation Archives.
vii	Courtesy Boeing Commercial Aircraft Corporation Archives.
viii-ix	NASA photo number L-80-2960.
x-1	(Left) NASA photo number LAL 3412. (Right) NASA photo number L-76-6225.
2-3	Original art by NASA Langley Research Center artist William B. Kluge.
4-5	Original art by NASA Langley Research Center artist William B. Kluge.
6-7	Original art by NASA Langley Research Center artist William B. Kluge.
8-9	(Left) NASA photo number 88-11728 L-89-12410. (Right) NASA photo number L-81-4715.
10	NASA photo number L-73-5357.
11	NASA photo number L-87-10,498.
12-13	Courtesy Boeing Commercial Aircraft Corporation Archives.
14	NASA photo number L-82-5,226.
15	NASA photo number L-87-01078.
16-17	NASA photo number 92-09653.
19	NASA photo number L-85-10,992.
20	NASA photo number 89-13,503.
22-23	NASA photo number 76-H-70.
24	(Left) NASA photo number L-89-328. (Right) NASA photo number WI89-44-3.
26	NASA photo number L-74-7810.
27	NASA photo number L-74-5183.
28	NASA photo number L-86-2784.
29	NASA photo number L-87-3645.
30	NASA photo number L-90-8321.
31	NASA photo number L-90-13735.
32	NASA photo number L-80-2871.
33	NASA photo number L-74-5187.
34	NASA photo number L-75-3195.
35	NASA photo number L-86-10,859.
36	NASA photo number L-87-9199.
37	NASA photo number L-90-8322.
38-39	NASA photo number 92-09978.
40-41	(Left) NASA photo number 92-09637. (Right) NASA photo number L-87-7703.

Pages	Credits
42	NASA artist's conception.
44	NASA photo number L-85-7219.
45	NASA photo number L-74-7896.
48	NASA photo number.
49	NASA photo number L-78-4715.
52	NASA photo number 89-6358.
54-55	(Left) NASA photo number L-92-8374. (Right) NASA photo number 92-09647.
56-57	(Left) NASA photo number 91-18889. (Right) NASA photo number 92-09638.
58	NASA photo.
59	NASA photo number 92-09631.
60	NASA photo number L-88-89717.
62	(Top) NASA photo number 91-01645. (Bottom) NASA photo number L-92-1814.
63	(Top) NASA photo number 91-01645. (Bottom) NASA photo number L-92-1814.
64	NASA photo number 92-09652.
65	NASA photo number 92-10002.
66	NASA photo number L-92-6965.
67	NASA photo number L-92-6965.
69	NASA photo number 92-09629.
70	NASA photo number 92-09510.
71	NASA photo number 91-12297.
72	NASA photo number 92-12352.
74-75	(Left) NASA photo number L-91-15885. (Right) NASA photo number 92-10532.
76	NASA photo number L-87-09642.
79	NASA photo number 92-10540.
80-81	NASA photo numbers (L-R) L-91-16689, 91-16694, and 91-16704.
84	NASA photo number L-89-11171.
85	NASA photo number L-89-11170.
88	NASA photo number 92-09988.
96-97	NASA photo numbers (L-R) L-90-6326, 90-06592, and 90-06609.
104-105	(Left) NASA photo number 92-10541. (Right) NASA photo number 89-04534.
107	NASA photo number L-93-8172.
108	NASA photo number L-92-1805.
109	(Top) NASA photo number L-85-2995.
110	NASA photo number 89-06012.
112	NASA photo number 89-03671.
113	NASA photo number L-89-4514.
114	NASA photo number 89-06014.
115	NASA photo number L-76-6226.
116	NASA photo number L-92-4166.
118	NASA photo number L-89-13502.

Glossary of Acronyms

ACARS	ARINC Communications Addressing and Reporting System
ACFS	Advanced Concepts Flight Simulator
ADEDS	Advanced Digital Electronic Displays
AFD	Aft Flight Deck
AGCS	Automatic Guidance and Control System
ARINC	Aeronautical Radio, Inc.
ARTCC	Air Route Traffic Control Center
ATA	Air Transport Association
ATC	Air Traffic Control
ATIS	Automatic Terminal Information Service
ATOPS	Advanced Transport Operating Systems
AWOP	All-Weather Operations Panel (of ICAO)
CARD	Civil Aviation Research and Development (study)
CDI	Course Deviation Indicator
CDTI	Cockpit Displayed Traffic Information
CDU	Control and Display Unit
C/O	Check Out
CRT	Cathode Ray Tube
CTAS	Center Tracon Automation System
CTOL	Conventional Take-Off and Landing (aircraft)
CWS	Control Wheel Steering
DATAC	Digital Autonomous Terminal Access Communication (data bus)
DME	Distance Measuring Equipment
DOT	Department of Transportation
EADI	Electronic Attitude Director Indicator
EASILY	Experimental Avionics Simulation and Integration Laboratory
EFSS	Experimental Flight Systems Section (at Langley)
EHSI	Electronic Horizontal Situation Indicator
EICAS	Engine Indication and Crew Advisory System
EMACS	Engine Monitoring and Control System
EPR	Engine Pressure Ratio
FAA	Federal Aviation Administration
FID	Flight Instrumentation Division (at Langley)
FLTCTL	Flight Control
FMC	Flight Management Computer
FMS	Flight Management System
GNSS	Global Navigation Satellite System
GPS	Global Positioning System
HDD	Heads-down Display
HUD	Heads-up Display
ICAO	International Civil Aviation Organization
IFR	Instrument Flight Rules
ILS	Instrument Landing System
INS	Inertial Navigation System
IRU	Inertial Reference Unit (same as INS)
JAWS	Joint Airport Weather Studies
LEBU	Large Eddy Break-Up (devices)
LFM/PD	Local Flow Management/Profile Descent
LIDAR	Light Detecting and Ranging
LLWAS	Low Level Windshear Alert System
MLS	Microwave Landing System
NACA	National Advisory Committee for Aeronautics
NAFEC	National Aviation Facilities Experimental Center
NAS	National Academy of Sciences
NASA	National Aeronautics and Space Administration
NASP	National Aerospace Plane
NCAR	National Center for Atmospheric Research
NTSB	National Transportation Safety Board
OAS	Organization of American States
OPMIS	Optical Propulsion Management Interface System
OST	Office of Science and Technology (developed into OSTP)
OSTP	Office of Science and Technology Policy
PFD	Primary Flight Display
RNAV	Area Navigation
R&D	Research & Development
RTCA	Radio Technical Commission for Aeronautics
SBIR	Small Business Innovative Research (program)
SPIFR	Single Pilot Instrument Flight Rules (program)
SSFD	Flight Director System
SST	Supersonic Transport
STEP	Service Test and Evaluation Program
TAP	Terminal Area Productivity
TCAS	Traffic Alert and Collision Avoidance System
TCV	Terminal Configured Vehicle
TDWR	Terminal Doppler Weather Radar
TECS	Total Energy Control System
TOPMS	Take-Off Performance Monitoring System
TRSB	Time Reference Scanning Beam (MLS)
TSRV	Transport Systems Research Vehicle
UHF	Ultra High Frequency
VCWS	Velocity Vector Control Wheel Steering
VFR	Visual Flight Rules
VHF	Very High Frequency
WFF	Wallops Flight Facility

NASA Boeing 737 Transport Systems Research Vehicle Specifications

MODEL:	Boeing 737-130* Serial No. 19437 Boeing Designation: PA-099 (Prototype Boeing 737) *(Aircraft was a 737-100, given customer designation of 737-130 when modified to NASA specifications)
DATE OF MANUFACTURE:	1967
FIRST FLIGHT:	April 9, 1967
DESCRIPTION:	Twin-jet, short-range transport
TOTAL FLIGHT HOURS:	
Upon arrival at Langley	978
At end of FY 1993	2,936
SPECIFICATIONS:	
Engines (2)	Pratt & Whitney JT8D-7 14,000 lbs thrust each
Wing Span	93 ft.
Length	94 ft.
Wing Area	980 sq. ft.
Tail Height	37 ft.
Gross Takeoff Weight	97,800 lbs.
Max Payload	29,000 lbs.
Cruising Speed	575 mph
Range	2140 statute miles
Service Ceiling	35,000 ft.

NASA 737 TSRV Flights

(through FY 1993)

Flight #	Date	Total Flight Time	Research Flight Time	Test Site	Flight Test Objectives
1	6/7/74	3:30	3:30	WFF	Handling Qualities
2	6/11/74	3:07	3:07	WFF	Handling Qualities
3	6/18/74	2:06	2:06	WFF	Handling Qualities
4	6/20/74	2:42	2:42	WFF	RNAV Documentation
5	6/25/74	2:29	2:29	WFF	Handling Qualities
6	6/27/74	2:30	2:30	WFF	Handling Qualities
0	7/2/74	4:26	0:00		Maintenance
0	7/8/74	0:50	0:00		Maintenance
0	7/16/74	0:56	0:00		Maintenance
7	7/31/74	2:11	0:00		Auto FLTCTL Sys Dev
8A	8/2/74	1:59	1:59	WFF	RNAV Documentation
8B	8/2/74	1:22	0:00		Auto FLTCTL Sys Dev
9A	8/8/74	2:15	2:15	WFF	RNAV Documentation
9B	8/8/74	0:47	0:00		Auto FLTCTL Sys Dev
10	8/13/74	3:53	3:53	WFF	RNAV Documentation
11A	8/16/74	2:47	2:47	WFF	RNAV Documentation
11B	8/16/74	0:19	0:00		Auto FLTCTL Sys Dev
12A	8/20/74	2:28	2:28	WFF	RNAV Documentation
12B	8/20/74	0:48	0:48	WFF	RNAV Documentation
13A	8/23/74	0:42	0:42	WFF	Baseline Noise Meas
13B	8/23/74	0:27	0:27		RNAV Documentation
13C	8/23/74	0:35	0:00		Auto FLTCTL Sys Dev
14	8/30/74	2:50	0:00		Auto FLTCTL Sys Dev
15	9/20/74	2:28	2:28	NAFEC	FAA Baseline
16A	9/26/74	2:39	2:39	WFF	Baseline Noise Meas
16B	9/26/74	0:53	0:00		Auto FLTCTL Sys Dev
17A	9/27/74	0:34	0:34	WFF	Baseline Noise Meas
17B	9/27/74	1:51	0:00		Auto FLTCTL Sys Dev
18	10/2/74	2:39	2:39	WFF	RNAV Documentation
19A	10/4/74	6:40	6:40	WFF	Baseline Noise Meas

Flight #	Date	Total Flight Time	Research Flight Time	Test Site	Flight Test Objectives
19B	10/4/74	0:52	0:00		Auto FLTCTL Sys Dev
20	10/7/74	3:34	3:34	WFF	Baseline Noise Meas
21A	10/11/74	3:51	0:00	WFF	Autoland Development
21B	10/11/74	0:21	0:00		Auto FLTCTL Sys Dev
22	10/29/74	1:35	1:35	NAFEC	FAA Baseline
23A	10/31/74	1:39	1:39	NAFEC	FAA Baseline
23B	10/31/74	2:17	0:00	WFF	Autoland Development
23C	10/31/74	2:08	0:00	WFF	Flt Director Dev
24A	11/5/74	1:32	0:00	WFF	Autoland Development
24B	11/5/74	3:11	3:11	WFF	Flt Director Dev
25	11/6/74	3:42	3:42	NAFEC	FAA Baseline
26A	11/8/74	1:04	1:04	NAFEC	FAA Baseline
26B	11/8/74	0:14	0:00	WFF	Autoland Development
26C	11/8/74	1:30	1:30	WFF	Flt Director Dev
27	11/12/74	0:45	0:45	NAFEC	FAA Baseline
28	11/13/74	4:04	4:04	NAFEC	FAA Baseline
29	11/14/74	1:03	1:03	NAFEC	FAA Baseline
30	11/18/74	4:00	4:00	NAFEC	FAA Baseline
31	11/19/74	3:37	3:37	NAFEC	FAA Baseline
32	11/21/74	1:40	1:40	NAFEC	FAA Baseline
33	11/22/74	4:54	4:54	NAFEC	FAA Baseline
34	11/23/74	5:06	5:06	NAFEC	FAA Baseline
35A	12/3/74	0:52	0:52	WFF	RNAV Documentation
35B	12/3/74	1:40	0:00		Auto FLTCTL Sys Dev
36A	12/4/74	0:08	0:08	WFF	RNAV Documentation
36B	12/4/74	3:02	3:02	WFF	RNAV Documentation
36C	12/4/74	2:50	2:50	WFF	RNAV Documentation
37	2/3/75	1:32	0:00		Maintenance
38	5/2/75	1:51	0:00		Maintenance
39	5/6/75	2:29	0:00	NAFEC	VCWS-Autoflt Ctl
40	6/9/75	2:00	0:00	NAFEC	VCWS-Autoflt Ctl
41	6/16/75	1:55	0:00	NAFEC	VCWS-Autoflt Ctl
42	6/17/75	3:39	0:00		Pilot Proficiency
43	6/18/75	3:05	0:00		Pilot Proficiency
44A	6/19/75	1:50	0:00	NAFEC	VCWS-Autoflt Ctl
44B	6/19/75	1:30	0:00	WFF	CWS-ILS Nav Dev
45	6/20/75	2:04	2:04	WFF	5 Deg Appr Noise
46	6/24/75	1:30	0:00	NAFEC	VCWS-Autoflt Ctl
47	6/25/75	1:30	0:00		Pilot Proficiency
48	7/1/75	3:25	0:00	NAFEC	VCWS-Autoflt Ctl
49	7/2/75	2:35	0:00	NAFEC	VCWS-Autoflt Ctl
50	7/3/75	2:30	2:30	WFF	5 Deg Appr Noise
51	7/8/75	3:05	0:00		Pilot Proficiency
52	7/9/75	3:18	0:00		Pilot Proficiency
53	7/16/75	2:29	0:00	NAFEC	VCWS-Autoflt Ctl
54	7/17/75	2:27	0:00		Pilot Proficiency

Flight #	Date	Total Flight Time	Research Flight Time	Test Site	Flight Test Objectives
55	7/18/75	1:57	0:00	WFF	CWS-ILS Nav Dev
56	7/22/75	1:00	1:00	WFF	Baseline Noise Meas
57	7/24/75	2:12	0:00	NAFEC	VCWS-Autoflt Ctl
58	7/25/75	2:42	2:42	WFF	RNAV Documentation
59A	7/30/75	1:35	0:00	WFF	Laser Antenna C/O
59B	7/30/75	2:15	0:00	WFF	C-Band Beacon Check
60	7/31/75	2:22	2:22	WFF	Baseline Noise Meas
61	8/1/75	3:19	3:19	WFF	Baseline Noise Meas
62A	8/5/75	1:55	0:00		Pilot Proficiency
62B	8/5/75	2:26	0:00		Pilot Proficiency
63	8/25/75	2:23	0:00		Pilot Proficiency
64	8/29/75	4:01	0:00		Pilot Proficiency
65	9/2/75	2:00	2:00	WFF	RNAV Documentation
66	9/3/75	2:05	2:05	WFF	4-D Nav Guidance Doc
67A	9/4/75	1:01	0:00	WFF	Handling Qualities
67B	9/4/75	2:09	2:09	NAFEC	ICAO-MLS Dev FAA
68	9/8/75	0:50	0:00		Maintenance
69	9/15/75	1:00	0:00		Maintenance
70	9/22/75	1:15	0:00		Maintenance
71	9/24/75	0:47	0:00		Maintenance
72	9/26/75	1:00	0:00		Maintenance
73	9/30/75	1:55	1:55	WFF	RNAV Documentation
74	10/1/75	0:20	0:20	WFF	4-D Nav Guidance Doc
75	10/3/75	0:30	0:00		Maintenance
76	10/8/75	0:40	0:00		Maintenance
77	10/10/75	0:50	0:00		Maintenance
78	10/14/75	3:05	3:05	WFF	4-D Nav Guidance Doc
79	10/20/75	0:25	0:00		Maintenance
80	12/9/75	0:55	0:00		Maintenance
81	12/11/75	0:55	0:00		Maintenance
82A	12/17/75	0:35	0:04	WFF	Handling Qualities
82B	12/17/75	1:05	0:00	NAFEC	MLS Antenna Meas
83	12/18/75	2:15	0:00	NAFEC	MLS Antenna Meas
84	12/18/75	1:00	0:10	WFF	Handling Qualities
85	1/23/76	2:25	0:00		Maintenance
86	1/30/76	1:20	0:00		Angle of Attack C/O
87A	2/13/76	0:48	0:48		Thrust Pitch
87B	2/13/76	1:42	0:00		Pilot Proficiency
88	2/27/76	2:40	0:00	WFF	RSFS Exp Sys C/O
89	3/3/76	1:00	0:00		Maintenance
90	3/5/93	0:10	0:00	WFF	RSFS Exp Sys C/O
91	3/7/76	3:35	0:00		Maintenance
92	3/11/76	2:30	0:00	WFF	RSFS Exp Sys C/O
93	3/17/76	2:19	2:19	WFF	4-D Nav Guidance Doc
94	3/22/76	0:55	0:00	NAFEC	ICAO-MLS Dev FAA
95	3/23/76	2:05	2:05	NAFEC	ICAO-MLS Dev FAA

Flight #	Date	Total Flight Time	Research Flight Time	Test Site	Flight Test Objectives
96	3/24/76	2:40	2:40	NAFEC	ICAO-MLS Dev FAA
97	3/25/76	2:53	2:08	NAFEC	ICAO-MLS Dev FAA
98	3/29/76	1:45	0:00		Maintenance
99A	3/30/76	0:50	0:00	NAFEC	ICAO-MLS Dev FAA
99B	3/30/76	1:25	1:25	NAFEC	ICAO-MLS Dev FAA
100	3/31/76	2:45	2:45	NAFEC	ICAO-MLS Dev FAA
101A	4/1/76	1:30	1:30	NAFEC	ICAO-MLS Dev FAA
101B	4/1/76	1:25	1:25	NAFEC	ICAO-MLS Dev FAA
102A	4/2/76	1:30	1:30	NAFEC	ICAO-MLS Dev FAA
102B	4/2/76	0:40	0:00	NAFEC	ICAO-MLS Dev FAA
103A	4/13/76	0:40	0:00	NAFEC	MLS-ICAO Autoland Dev
103B	4/13/76	2:00	2:00	NAFEC	MLS-ICAO Autoland Development
103C	4/13/76	0:54	0:54	NAFEC	MLS-ICAO Autoland Dev
104A	4/14/76	2:00	2:00	NAFEC	MLS-ICAO Autoland Development
104B	4/14/76	1:15	1:15	NAFEC	MLS Curved Path Dev
105	4/22/76	1:20	1:20	NAFEC	MLS Curved Path Dev
106A	4/23/76	0:15	0:15	NAFEC	MLS Curved Path Dev
106B	4/23/76	1:44	1:44	NAFEC	MLS Curved Path Dev
107A	4/24/76	0:35	0:00	NAFEC	MLS-ICAO Autoland Development
107B	4/24/76	1:05	1:05	NAFEC	MLS-ICAO Autoland Development
107C	4/24/76	0:55	0:55	NAFEC	MLS Curved Path Dev
108A	4/29/76	1:40	0:00	NAFEC	VCWS-Autoflt Ctl
108B	4/29/76	0:30	0:30	NAFEC	MLS Curved Path Dev
108C	4/29/76	0:30	0:30	NAFEC	MLS-ICAO Autoland Development
109A	4/30/76	0:38	0:38	NAFEC	MLS Curved Path Dev
109B	4/30/76	0:39	0:39	NAFEC	MLS-ICAO Autoland Development
110A	5/1/76	0:23	0:23	NAFEC	MLS Curved Path Dev
110B	5/1/76	0:22	0:22	NAFEC	MLS-ICAO Autoland Development
111A	5/2/76	0:42	0:00	NAFEC	MLS-ICAO Autoland Development
111B	5/2/76	0:37	0:37	NAFEC	MLS Curved Path Dev
111C	5/2/76	0:15	0:15	NAFEC	MLS-ICAO Autoland Development
111D	5/2/76	0:40	0:00	NAFEC	MLS-ICAO Autoland Development
112	5/3/76	1:22	0:00		Maintenance
113A	5/6/76	0:40	0:00		Maintenance
113B	5/6/76	0:38	0:00		Maintenance
113C	5/6/76	1:00	0:00	NAFEC	MLS-ICAO Autoland Development
114A	5/7/76	0:20	0:20	NAFEC	MLS Curved Path Dev
114B	5/7/76	0:20	0:20	NAFEC	MLS-ICAO Autoland Development
114C	5/7/76	0:37	0:37	NAFEC	MLS Curved Path Dev
114D	5/7/76	0:40	0:40	NAFEC	MLS Curved Path Dev
114E	5/7/76	0:36	0:36	NAFEC	MLS-ICAO Autoland Development
114F	5/7/76	0:40	0:40	NAFEC	MLS-ICAO Autoland Development
115	5/8/76	0:50	0:00	NAFEC	MLS-ICAO Autoland Development
116A	5/11/76	0:50	0:00	NAFEC	MLS Demo to ICAO
116B	5/11/76	0:52	0:52	NAFEC	MLS Demo to ICAO
117A	5/12/76	1:20	1:20	NAFEC	MLS Demo to ICAO

Flight #	Date	Total Flight Time	Research Flight Time	Test Site	Flight Test Objectives
117B	5/12/76	0:33	0:33	NAFEC	MLS Demo to ICAO
117C	5/12/76	1:15	1:15	NAFEC	MLS Demo to ICAO
118A	5/13/76	0:35	0:35	NAFEC	MLS Demo to ICAO
118B	5/13/76	1:11	1:11	NAFEC	MLS Demo to ICAO
118C	5/13/76	1:10	1:10	NAFEC	MLS Demo to ICAO
119A	5/14/76	0:45	0:00	NAFEC	MLS Demo to ICAO
119B	5/14/76	0:45	0:00	NAFEC	MLS Demo to ICAO
119C	5/14/76	0:45	0:00	NAFEC	MLS Demo to ICAO
120	5/17/76	1:00	0:00	NAFEC	MLS Demo to ICAO
121A	5/18/76	0:40	0:40	NAFEC	MLS Demo to ICAO
121B	5/18/76	0:50	0:50	NAFEC	MLS Demo to ICAO
122A	5/19/76	1:20	1:20	NAFEC	MLS Demo to ICAO
122B	5/19/76	1:10	1:10	NAFEC	MLS Demo to ICAO
123A	5/20/76	0:45	0:45	NAFEC	MLS Demo to ICAO
123B	5/20/76	1:00	1:00	NAFEC	MLS Demo to ICAO
123C	5/20/76	1:20	1:20	NAFEC	MLS Demo to ICAO
124	5/21/76	1:50	0:00	NAFEC	MLS Demo to ICAO
125A	6/8/76	0:50	0:00		Maintenance
125B	6/8/76	0:40	0:00		Maintenance
126A	6/11/76	2:30	0:00	NAC	VCWS-Autoflt Ctl
126B	6/11/76	1:35	1:35	WFF	Handling Qualities
127A	6/16/76	1:45	1:45	WFF	Handling Qualities
127B	6/16/76	1:20	1:20	WFF	Handling Qualities
128	6/22/76	2:05	0:00	NAFEC	CWS-ILS Nav Dev
129A	6/24/76	2:00	0:00		Angle of Attack C/O
129B	6/24/76	1:15	0:00	WFF	Aerodynamic Noise
130A	6/29/76	0:25	0:00	WFF	4-D Nav Guidance Doc
130B	6/29/76	1:20	1:20	WFF	4-D Nav Guidance Doc
130C	6/29/76	1:00	0:00	WFF	Laser Antenna C/O
131A	7/7/76	0:45	0:00	NAFEC	MLS Driven Displays
131B	7/7/76	2:30	2:30	NAFEC	MLS Driven Displays
131C	7/7/76	0:45	0:00	NAFEC	MLS Driven Displays
132A	7/9/76	1:00	0:00	NAFEC	Antenna Test
132B	7/9/76	0:30	0:30	NAFEC	Antenna Test
132C	7/9/76	1:04	1:04	NAFEC	EL-2 Flare
132D	7/9/76	1:11	1:11	NAFEC	MLS Driven Displays
132E	7/9/76	1:00	0:00		Antenna Test
133A	7/13/76	0:52	0:00	NAFEC	MLS Driven Displays
133B	7/13/76	2:00	2:00	NAFEC	MLS Driven Displays
133C	7/13/76	1:25	1:00	NAFEC	MLS Driven Displays
134A	7/15/76	0:55	0:00	NAFEC	VCWS-Autoflt Ctl
134B	7/15/76	1:00	1:00	NAFEC	Body Mounted Accel
134C	7/15/76	2:15	2:15	NAFEC	Body Mounted Accel
134D	7/15/76	0:45	0:00	NAFEC	Body Mounted Accel
135A	7/20/76	0:50	0:00	NAFEC	Body Mounted Accel
135B	7/20/76	1:25	1:25	NAFEC	Body Mounted Accel

Flight #	Date	Total Flight Time	Research Flight Time	Test Site	Flight Test Objectives
135C	7/20/76	1:20	1:20	NAFEC	Body Mounted Accel
135D	7/20/76	0:40	0:00	NAFEC	Body Mounted Accel
135E	7/20/76	1:00	0:00	NAFEC	Body Mounted Accel
136A	7/26/76	1:00	0:00	NAFEC	MLS Demo TRSB
136B	7/26/76	0:50	0:50	NAFEC	MLS Demo TRSB
136C	7/26/76	1:00	0:00	NAFEC	MLS Demo TRSB
137A	7/29/76	0:50	0:00	NAFEC	MLS Demo TRSB
137B	7/29/76	1:30	1:30	NAFEC	MLS Demo TRSB
137C	7/29/76	0:50	0:00	NAFEC	MLS Demo TRSB
138A	8/2/76	0:45	0:00	NAFEC	MLS Demo TRSB
138B	8/2/76	1:10	1:10	NAFEC	MLS Demo TRSB
138C	8/2/76	0:35	0:35	NAFEC	MLS Demo TRSB
139A	8/3/76	1:15	1:15	NAFEC	MLS Demo TRSB
139B	8/3/76	1:20	1:20	NAFEC	MLS Demo TRSB
139C	8/3/76	1:10	1:10	NAFEC	MLS Demo TRSB
139D	8/3/76	0:55	0:55	NAFEC	MLS Demo TRSB
140A	8/5/76	1:00	0:00	NAFEC	MLS Driven Displays
140B	8/5/76	2:29	2:29	NAFEC	MLS Driven Displays
140C	8/5/76	0:45	0:00	NAFEC	MLS Driven Displays
141A	8/31/76	2:30	2:30	NAFEC	Functional C/O WWCS
141B	8/31/76	0:30	0:30	NAFEC	Functional C/O WWCS
141C	8/31/76	0:30	0:30	NAFEC	Functional C/O WWCS
142A	9/8/76	3:20	3:20	NAFEC	Functional C/O WWCS
142B	9/8/76	0:20	0:20	NAFEC	Functional C/O WWCS
143	9/14/76	1:30	1:30	NAFEC	Functional C/O WWCS
144	9/22/76	1:25	1:25	NAFEC	Functional C/O WWCS
145	9/29/76	2:30	2:30	WFF	RNAV Documentation
146A	10/1/76	0:30	0:00	WFF	4-D Nav Guidance Doc
146B	10/1/76	1:20	1:20	WFF	4-D Nav Guidance Doc
146C	10/1/76	0:30	0:00	WFF	4-D Nav Guidance Doc
147	10/4/76	0:50	0:00		Maintenance
148	10/13/76	0:40	0:00		Maintenance
149A	10/19/76	0:21	0:00	WFF	4-D Nav Guidance Doc
149B	10/19/76	1:11	1:11	WFF	4-D Nav Guidance Doc
149C	10/19/76	1:11	1:11	WFF	4-D Nav Guidance Doc
149D	10/19/76	0:36	0:00	WFF	4-D Nav Guidance Doc
150A	10/21/76	0:27	0:00	WFF	Functional Flt Demo
150B	10/21/76	1:35	1:35	WFF	Functional Flt Demo
150C	10/21/76	1:00	1:00	WFF	Functional Flt Demo
150D	10/21/76	0:39	0:00	WFF	Functional Flt Demo
151A	10/28/76	1:35	1:00	WFF	Functional Flt Demo
151B	10/28/76	1:05	0:30	WFF	Functional Flt Demo
152A	11/1/76	0:57	0:36	WFF	Functional Flt Demo
152B	11/1/76	0:33	0:33	WFF	Functional Flt Demo
152C	11/1/76	1:09	0:50	WFF	Functional Flt Demo
153A	11/2/76	1:00	1:00	WFF	Functional Flt Demo

Flight #	Date	Total Flight Time	Research Flight Time	Test Site	Flight Test Objectives
153B	11/2/76	0:45	0:45	WFF	Functional Flt Demo
154	11/4/76	2:12	0:00		Angle of Attack C/O
155	11/9/76	2:09	0:00		Aerodynamic Noise
156A	11/11/76	1:30	1:30	WFF	Functional Flt Demo
156B	11/11/76	0:21	0:00		Pilot Proficiency
157	11/29/76	1:30	0:00		Maintenance
158	12/10/76	1:15	0:00		Maintenance
159A	1/19/77	1:00	0:00		Pilot Proficiency
159B	1/19/77	0:40	0:00		Pilot Proficiency
159C	1/19/77	0:45	0:00		Pilot Proficiency
160A	1/21/76	1:40	1:10	WFF	Spoiler Aileron Test
160B	1/21/76	1:00	1:00	WFF	Runway Turnoff Test
161	3/10/77	1:00	0:00		Mag Heading Compar
162	3/11/77	1:01	0:00		Maintenance
163	3/15/77	1:30	1:30	WFF	Functional Flt Demo
164	3/17/77	1:30	1:30	WFF	Functional Flt Demo
165	3/23/77	1:35	1:35	WFF	Functional Flt Demo
166	3/24/77	1:35	1:35	WFF	Functional Flt Demo
167A	3/29/77	1:36	0:00		Sideslip Calibration
167B	3/29/77	0:16	0:16	WFF	RNAV Documentation
168	4/1/77	3:05	2:04	WFF	RNAV Documentation
169	4/6/77	1:40	1:40	WFF	Functional Flt Demo
170	4/8/77	2:45	2:45	WFF	4-D Nav Guidance Doc
171	4/14/77	1:30	0:00		Maintenance
172	6/21/77	1:30	0:00		Pilot Proficiency
173	6/24/77	2:30	0:00		Pilot Proficiency
174	8/1/77	1:15	0:00		Maintenance
175	9/11/77	1:00	0:00		Maintenance
176	9/22/77	1:45	0:00		Maintenance
177	10/2/77	3:00	0:00		Maintenance
178	10/7/77	2:00	2:00	NAFEC	NAFEC MLS Dev Flts
179	10/8/77	2:50	2:50	NAFEC	NAFEC MLS Dev Flts
180	10/10/77	2:55	2:55	NAFEC	NAFEC MLS Dev Flts
181	10/11/77	2:15	2:15	NAFEC	NAFEC MLS Dev Flts
182	10/12/77	2:00	2:00	NAFEC	NAFEC MLS Dev Flts
183	10/13/77	1:10	0:50	NAFEC	NAFEC MLS Dev Flts
184	10/17/77	2:00	0:00	NAFEC	Maintenance
185	10/20/77	2:35	2:35	NAFEC	New Vel/CWS Cont Dis
186	10/21/77	4:00	4:00	Buenos Aires	Nav Experiments
187	10/22/77	8:00	8:00	Buenos Aires	Nav Experiments
188	10/23/77	3:00	3:00	Buenos Aires	Nav Experiments
189A	10/26/77	0:50	0:50	Buenos Aires	TRSB Demo, Argentina
189B	10/26/77	0:50	0:50	Buenos Aires	TRSB Demo, Argentina
190A	10/27/77	0:24	0:00	Buenos Aires	TRSB Demo, Argentina
190B	10/27/77	1:35	1:35	Buenos Aires	TRSB Demo, Argentina
190C	10/27/77	0:30	0:00	Buenos Aires	TRSB Demo, Argentina

Flight #	Date	Total Flight Time	Research Flight Time	Test Site	Flight Test Objectives
191A	10/28/77	0:25	0:00	Buenos Aires	TRSB Demo, Argentina
191B	10/28/77	3:00	3:00	Buenos Aires	TRSB Demo, Argentina
191C	10/28/77	0:15	0:00	Buenos Aires	TRSB Demo, Argentina
192A	10/29/77	0:25	0:00	Buenos Aires	TRSB Demo, Argentina
192B	10/29/77	1:15	1:15	Buenos Aires	TRSB Demo, Argentina
192C	10/29/77	0:20	0:00	Buenos Aires	TRSB Demo, Argentina
193A	10/31/77	1:25	1:25	Buenos Aires	TRSB Demo, Argentina
193B	10/31/77	1:00	1:00	Buenos Aires	TRSB Demo, Argentina
193C	10/31/77	0:20	0:00	Buenos Aires	TRSB Demo, Argentina
194A	11/1/77	0:20	0:00	Buenos Aires	TRSB Demo, Argentina
194B	11/1/77	2:50	2:50	Buenos Aires	TRSB Demo, Argentina
194C	11/1/77	0:20	0:00	Buenos Aires	TRSB Demo, Argentina
195A	11/2/77	0:20	0:00	Buenos Aires	TRSB Demo, Argentina
195B	11/2/77	1:25	1:25	Buenos Aires	TRSB Demo, Argentina
195C	11/2/77	1:03	1:03	Buenos Aires	TRSB Demo, Argentina
195D	11/2/77	0:25	0:00	Buenos Aires	TRSB Demo, Argentina
196A	11/3/77	0:21	0:00	Buenos Aires	TRSB Demo, Argentina
196B	11/3/77	2:29	2:29	Buenos Aires	TRSB Demo, Argentina
196C	11/3/77	0:24	0:00	Buenos Aires	TRSB Demo, Argentina
197A	11/4/77	0:20	0:00	Buenos Aires	TRSB Demo, Argentina
197B	11/4/77	2:10	2:10	Buenos Aires	TRSB Demo, Argentina
197C	11/4/77	0:20	0:00	Buenos Aires	TRSB Demo, Argentina
198A	11/7/77	0:40	0:00	Buenos Aires	TRSB Demo, Argentina
198B	11/7/77	0:30	0:30	Buenos Aires	TRSB Demo, Argentina
199	11/8/77	3:00	3:00	Buenos Aires	Nav Experiments
200A	11/9/77	3:40	3:40	Buenos Aires	Nav Experiments
200B	11/9/77	4:00	4:00	Buenos Aires	Nav Experiments
201	11/10/77	4:00	4:00	Buenos Aires	Nav Experiments
202	11/22/77	0:55	0:00		Maintenance
203	11/29/77	0:50	0:00	JFK	TRSB Demo at JFK, NY
204	12/2/77	2:35	2:35	JFK	TRSB Demo at JFK, NY
205	12/4/77	2:35	2:35	JFK	TRSB Demo at JFK, NY
206	12/5/77	2:00	2:00	JFK	TRSB Demo at JFK, NY
207	12/6/77	3:00	3:00	JFK	TRSB Demo at JFK, NY
208	12/7/77	2:30	2:30	JFK	TRSB Demo at JFK, NY
209	12/8/77	3:00	3:00	JFK	TRSB Demo at JFK, NY
210	12/9/77	2:45	2:45	JFK	TRSB Demo at JFK, NY
211	12/10/77	2:40	2:40	JFK	TRSB Demo at JFK, NY
212	12/12/77	3:00	3:00	JFK	TRSB Demo at JFK, NY
213	12/13/77	2:50	2:50	JFK	TRSB Demo at JFK, NY
214	12/14/77	1:00	0:00	JFK	TRSB Demo at JFK, NY
215	2/17/78	1:35	1:35		Energy Prob/Windshear
216	2/24/78	1:45	1:45		Energy Prob/Windshear
217	3/7/78	1:30	0:00		Maintenance
218A	3/15/78	1:11	1:11	NOR	New Vel/CWS Cont Dis
218B	3/15/78	0:35	0:35	NOR	TRSB/MLS Demo Canada

Flight #	Date	Total Flight Time	Research Flight Time	Test Site	Flight Test Objectives
218C	3/15/78	0:18	0:18		Energy Prob/Windsherar
218D	3/15/78	0:35	0:35	NOR	Variable Tau Flare
218E	3/15/78	0:07	0:07	NOR	Prelim CDTI Exp
218F	3/15/78	0:35	0:35	NOR	Nav. Expmts-Montreal
218G	3/15/78	0:18	0:18	NOR	ILS Auto Missed Appr
218H	3/15/78	1:11	1:11	NOR	TRSB/MLS Demo Canada
219A	3/16/78	0:46	0:46		SSFD Sys. C/O
219B	3/16/78	0:24	0:24		ILS Auto Missed Appr
219C	3/16/78	0:15	0:15		Energy Prob/Windsherar
219D	3/16/78	1:06	1:06		Variable Tau Flare
219E	3/16/78	0:54	0:54		Variable Tau Flare
220	3/20/78	1:35	1:35	NAFEC	Nav. Expmts-Montreal
221A	3/22/78	1:25	1:25	CAN	TRSB/MLS Demo Canada
221B	3/22/78	2:40	2:40	CAN	TRSB/MLS Demo Canada
221C	3/22/78	1:15	1:15	CAN	TRSB/MLS Demo Canada
222A	3/29/78	1:20	1:20	CAN	TRSB/MLS Demo Canada
222B	3/29/78	1:10	1:10	CAN	TRSB/MLS Demo Canada
223A	3/30/78	1:15	1:15	CAN	TRSB/MLS Demo Canada
223B	3/30/78	1:30	1:30	CAN	TRSB/MLS Demo Canada
224	3/31/78	1:15	1:15	CAN	TRSB/MLS Demo Canada
225	4/1/78	1:40	1:40	CAN	TRSB/MLS Demo Canada
226	4/2/78	3:00	3:00	CAN	TRSB/MLS Demo Canada
227A	4/3/78	0:45	0:45	CAN	TRSB/MLS Demo Canada
227B	4/3/78	0:45	0:45	CAN	TRSB/MLS Demo Canada
228A	4/5/78	1:20	1:20	CAN	TRSB/MLS Demo Canada
228B	4/5/78	1:30	1:30	CAN	TRSB/MLS Demo Canada
229A	4/6/78	1:00	1:00	CAN	TRSB/MLS Demo Canada
229B	4/6/78	1:15	1:15	CAN	TRSB/MLS Demo Canada
230A	4/7/78	1:00	1:00	CAN	TRSB/MLS Demo Canada
230B	4/7/78	1:10	1:10	CAN	TRSB/MLS Demo Canada
231A	4/8/78	1:15	1:15	CAN	TRSB/MLS Demo Canada
231B	4/8/78	1:00	1:00	CAN	TRSB/MLS Demo Canada
232A	4/12/78	1:00	1:00	CAN	TRSB/MLS Demo Canada
232B	4/12/78	1:00	1:00	CAN	TRSB/MLS Demo Canada
232C	4/12/78	0:40	0:40	CAN	TRSB/MLS Demo Canada
233	4/13/78	1:00	1:00	CAN	TRSB/MLS Demo Canada
234A	4/14/78	1:10	1:10	CAN	TRSB/MLS Demo Canada
234B	4/14/78	1:00	1:00	CAN	TRSB/MLS Demo Canada
235A	4/15/78	1:00	1:00	CAN	TRSB/MLS Demo Canada
235B	4/15/78	1:00	1:00	CAN	TRSB/MLS Demo Canada
236A	4/16/78	1:00	1:00	CAN	TRSB/MLS Demo Canada
236B	4/16/78	1:05	1:05	CAN	TRSB/MLS Demo Canada
237	4/17/78	1:40	1:40		Nav. Expmts-Montreal
238	5/9/78	0:55	0:00		Maintenance
239A	5/19/78	1:20	0:00		Maintenance
239B	5/19/78	2:10	0:00		Maintenance

Flight #	Date	Total Flight Time	Research Flight Time	Test Site	Flight Test Objectives
240A	6/7/78	0:45	0:00		Maintenance
240B	6/7/78	0:45	0:00		Maintenance
241	6/27/78	2:15	0:00		Maintenance
242	7/17/78	1:30	1:30	NAFEC	EL-2 TRSB Flare
243	7/19/78	3:35	3:35	NAFEC	EL-2 TRSB Flare
244A	7/21/78	0:55	0:00	NAFEC	MLS Back Azimuth
244B	7/21/78	2:15	2:15	NAFEC	EL-2 TRSB Flare
244C	7/21/78	0:50	0:00	NAFEC	EL-2 TRSB Flare
245A	7/25/78	0:50	0:00	NAFEC	EL-2 TRSB Flare
245B	7/25/78	2:00	2:00	NAFEC	EL-2 TRSB Flare
245C	7/25/78	0:45	0:00	NAFEC	EL-2 TRSB Flare
246A	7/27/78	0:50	0:00	NAFEC	EL-2 TRSB Flare
246B	7/27/78	0:07	0:07	NAFEC	Path In Space Flare
246C	7/27/78	2:23	2:23	NAFEC	EL-2 TRSB Flare
246D	7/27/78	0:45	0:00	NAFEC	EL-2 TRSB Flare
247A	8/1/78	1:10	0:00		Maintenance
247B	8/1/78	0:50	0:00		Maintenance
247C	8/1/78	0:55	0:00		Maintenance
248A	8/4/78	0:45	0:00	NAFEC	MLS Back Azimuth
248B	8/4/78	1:45	1:45	NAFEC	MLS Back Azimuth
249A	8/7/78	0:50	0:00	NAFEC	MLS Back Azimuth
249B	8/7/78	2:05	2:05	NAFEC	MLS Back Azimuth
249C	8/7/78	0:40	0:00	NAFEC	MLS Back Azimuth
250A	8/9/78	0:45	0:00	NAFEC	EL-2 TRSB Flare
250B	8/9/78	1:04	1:04	NAFEC	EL-2 TRSB Flare
250C	8/9/78	2:06	2:06	NAFEC	MLS Back Azimuth
250D	8/9/78	0:45	0:00	NAFEC	EL-2 TRSB Flare
251A	8/11/78	0:40	0:00	NAFEC	EL-2 TRSB Flare
251B	8/11/78	0:26	0:26	NAFEC	EL-2 TRSB Flare
251C	8/11/78	2:14	2:14	NAFEC	Path In Space Flare
251D	8/11/78	0:50	0:00	NAFEC	EL-2 TRSB Flare
252A	8/22/78	0:45	0:00	NAFEC	EL-2 TRSB Flare
252B	8/22/78	1:06	1:06	NAFEC	MLS Back Azimuth
252C	8/22/78	0:53	0:53	NAFEC	EL-2 TRSB Flare
252D	8/22/78	0:31	0:31	NAFEC	Path In Space Flare
252E	8/22/78	0:40	0:00	NAFEC	Functional C/O WWCS
253A	8/28/78	0:40	0:00	NAFEC	Path In Space Flare
253B	8/28/78	2:35	2:35	NAFEC	Path In Space Flare
253C	8/28/78	1:05	0:00	NAFEC	Path In Space Flare
254A	8/30/78	1:05	1:05	NAFEC	Path In Space Flare
254B	8/30/78	2:10	2:10	NAFEC	Path In Space Flare
254C	8/30/78	0:45	0:45	NAFEC	Path In Space Flare
255A	9/1/78	0:45	0:00	NAFEC	MLS Back Azimuth
255B	9/1/78	0:31	0:31	NAFEC	Path In Space Flare
255C	9/1/78	0:12	0:12	NAFEC	MLS Back Azimuth
255D	9/1/78	0:47	0:47	NAFEC	MLS Back Azimuth

Flight #	Date	Total Flight Time	Research Flight Time	Test Site	Flight Test Objectives
256A	9/6/78	0:50	0:00	NAFEC	MLS Back Azimuth
256B	9/6/78	2:10	2:10	NAFEC	MLS Back Azimuth
256C	9/6/78	1:00	1:00	NAFEC	Path In Space Flare
257A	9/8/78	0:35	0:00	NAFEC	MLS Back Azimuth
257B	9/8/78	3:00	3:00	NAFEC	MLS Back Azimuth
257C	9/8/78	0:55	0:00	NAFEC	Path In Space Flare
258A	9/12/78	1:00	0:00	NAFEC	Path In Space Flare
258B	9/12/78	2:10	2:10	NAFEC	MLS Back Azimuth
258C	9/12/78	0:45	0:00	NAFEC	Path In Space Flare
259A	9/14/78	0:55	0:55	NAFEC	MLS Back Azimuth
259B	9/14/78	2:30	2:30	NAFEC	MLS Back Azimuth
259C	9/14/78	0:55	0:00	NAFEC	Path In Space Flare
260A	9/18/78	1:00	0:00	NAFEC	Path In Space Flare
260B	9/18/78	1:10	1:10	NAFEC	Path In Space Flare
260C	9/18/78	0:50	0:50	NAFEC	Path In Space Flare
261A	9/20/78	3:00	2:10	NAFEC	Path In Space Flare
261B	9/20/78	0:45	0:00	NAFEC	Path In Space Flare
262A	9/22/78	3:00	3:00	NAFEC	Path In Space Flare
262B	9/22/78	1:00	1:00	NAFEC	Path In Space Flare
262C	9/22/78	0:50	0:00	NAFEC	Path In Space Flare
263	10/30/78	1:20	0:00	NAFEC	Maintenance
264A	11/7/78	0:40	0:00	NAFEC	EL-2 TRSB Flare
264B	11/7/78	1:21	1:21	NAFEC	EL-2 TRSB Flare
264C	11/7/78	0:29	0:29	WFF	Path In Space Flare
264D	11/7/78	1:10	1:10		VCWS-Autoflt Ctl
265A	11/9/78	0:35	0:00	WFF	Sim MLS Dev Flts
265B	11/9/78	0:25	0:25	WFF	Sim MLS Dev Flts
266A	11/20/78	0:45	0:00	NAFEC	EL-2 TRSB Flare
266B	11/20/78	2:25	2:25	NAFEC	EL-2 TRSB Flare
266C		0:55	0:00	NAFEC	EL-2 TRSB Flare
267A	11/28/78	0:30	0:00	WFF	CDTI-Phase 1 Exp
267B	11/28/78	2:00	2:00	WFF	CDTI-Phase 1 Exp
267C	11/28/78	0:25	0:00	WFF	CDTI-Phase 1 Exp
268A	11/30/78	0:35	0:00	WFF	FRF C/O for CDTI
268B	11/30/78	0:40	0:00	WFF	FRF C/O for CDTI
269	12/5/78	2:10	1:25	NAFEC	EL-2 TRSB Flare
269	12/5/78	2:10	1:25	NAFEC	Path In Space Flare
270A	12/7/78	1:16	1:16	WFF	CDTI-Phase 1 Exp
270B	12/7/78	2:07	2:07	WFF	CDTI-Phase 1 Exp
270C	12/7/78	1:32	1:32	WFF	CDTI-Phase 1 Exp
270D	12/7/78	0:20	0:00	WFF	CDTI-Phase 1 Exp
271	2/15/79	1:40	0:00		Maintenance
272	3/22/79	2:10	0:00		Pilot Proficiency
273	4/9/79	1:40	0:00		Maintenance
274	4/10/79	3:10	2:10	NAFEC	Handling Qualities
275	4/12/79	3:35	2:05	NAFEC	Handling Qualities

Flight #	Date	Total Flight Time	Research Flight Time	Test Site	Flight Test Objectives
276	4/17/79	3:45	3:45		LFM/PD C/O
277A	4/19/79	1:15	0:30	WFF	FRF C/O for CDTI
277B	4/19/79	0:25	0:10	WFF	Energy Prob/Windshear
278	4/24/79	2:30	1:45	WFF	Sim MLS Dev Flts
278	4/24/79	0:55	0:40	WFF	Energy Prob/Windshear
279	4/26/79	1:35	0:00	WFF	Maintenance
279A	5/1/79	0:35	0:00	WFF	Sim MLS Dev Flts
279B	5/1/79	2:05	2:05	WFF	Sim MLS Dev Flts
279C	5/1/79	0:35	0:00	WFF	Sim MLS Dev Flts
281	5/3/79	2:55	1:45	WFF	CDTI/Occulometer
282	5/10/79	2:45	2:00	WFF	FRF C/O for CDTI
282	5/10/79	1:00	0:45	WFF	Energy Prob/Windshear
283	5/15/79	3:15	2:15	WFF	FRF C/O for CDTI
284	5/17/79	1:00	0:15	NAFEC	CDTI/Occulometer
285	6/1/79	3:10	3:10	ATL	LFM/PD C/O
286	6/5/79	3:00	3:00	ATL	LFM/PD C/O
287	6/8/79	3:10	3:10	ATL	LFM/PD C/O
288	6/12/79	2:50	2:50	ATL	LFM/PD C/O
289	6/18/79	4:00	0:00		LFM/PD C/O
290	6/19/79	1:20	1:20	Denver	LFM/PD C/O
291	6/20/79	3:15	3:15	Denver	LFM/PD C/O
292	6/21/79	3:30	3:30	Denver	LFM/PD C/O
293	6/22/79	3:30	3:30	Denver	LFM/PD C/O
294	6/25/79	3:20	3:20	Denver	LFM/PD C/O
295	6/26/79	3:30	3:30	Denver	LFM/PD C/O
296	6/27/79	3:15	3:15	Denver	LFM/PD C/O
297	6/28/79	3:10	3:10	Denver	LFM/PD C/O
298	6/29/79	3:05	0:00		TBM/LFM in ATC
299	7/10/79	3:50	2:50	WFF	FRF C/O for CDTI
300	7/17/79	3:50	2:20	NAFEC	CDTI/Occulometer
301	7/19/79	4:10	2:40	NAFEC	CDTI/Occulometer
302	7/24/79	1:50	0:55	WFF	Sim MLS Dev Flts
303	8/7/79	3:15	2:45	WFF	Sim MLS Dev Flts
304	8/13/79	0:40	0:00		Maintenance
305	8/29/79	0:45	0:00		Maintenance
306A	9/20/79	1:00	1:00	NAFEC	Handling Qualities
306B	9/20/79	1:10	1:10	NAFEC	Path in Space Flare
306C	9/20/79	0:50	0:50	NAFEC	Handling Qualities
307	10/2/79	0:55	0:00	WFF	Sim MLS Dev Flts
308	10/4/79	1:05	0:55	WFF	Sim MLS Dev Flts
309	10/10/79	4:05	3:10	WFF	Sim MLS Dev Flts
310	10/18/79	2:10	1:15	WFF	CDTI/Occulometer
311	10/23/79	5:20	4:30	WFF	CDTI/Occulometer
312	10/26/79	2:20	1:15	WFF	CDTI/Occulometer
313A	10/30/79	0:40	0:00	WFF	Prelim CDTI Exp
313B	10/30/79	0:25	0:25	WFF	Prelim CDTI Exp

Flight #	Date	Total Flight Time	Research Flight Time	Test Site	Flight Test Objectives
313C	10/30/79	0:15	0:15	WFF	Prelim CDTI Exp
313D	10/30/79	0:30	0:00	WFF	CDTI/Occulometer
313E	10/30/79	1:30	1:30	WFF	CDTI/Occulometer
313F	10/30/79	0:30	0:00	WFF	CDTI/Occulometer
314	11/6/79	2:15	1:25	WFF	CDTI Gen Display
315	11/8/79	5:30	4:50	WFF	CDTI Gen Display
316	11/15/79	4:55	3:55	WFF	CDTI Gen Display
317	11/20/79	0:55	0:00	WFF	CDTI/Occulometer
318	11/21/79	3:50	2:50	WFF	CDTI/Occulometer
319A	11/27/79	0:32	0:00		TBM/LFM in ATC
319B	11/27/79	2:24	2:24		TBM/LFM in ATC
319C	11/27/79	0:44	0:44	WFF	TBM/LFM in ATC
319D	11/27/79	0:30	0:00		TBM/LFM in ATC
320	11/29/79	4:40	3:50	WFF	CDTI/Occulometer
321	12/4/79	1:00	1:00	WFF	Total Energy Probe Test
321	12/4/79	0:20	0:20	WFF	CDTI/Occulometer
321	12/4/79	0:40	0:15	WFF	CDTI Gen Display
322A	12/5/79	0:20	0:00	WFF	Total Energy Probe Test
322B	12/5/79	0:50	0:50	WFF	Total Energy Probe Test
322C	12/5/79	1:30	1:30	WFF	CDTI/Occulometer
322D	12/5/79	0:50	0:50	WFF	CDTI Gen Display
322E	12/5/79	0:20	0:00	WFF	CDTI Gen Display
323	12/17/79	1:35	0:35		Total Energy Probe Test
324	4/8/80	1:30	0:00	WFF	Maintenance
325	4/11/80	2:45	2:45	WFF	Open Loop Upgrade
326A	4/15/80	0:45	0:45	NAFEC	Open Loop Upgrade
326B	4/15/80	0:20	0:20	NAFEC	Open Loop Upgrade
326B	4/15/80	0:45	0:45	NAFEC	Autothrottle C/O
326C	4/15/80	0:30	0:30	NAFEC	Autothrottle C/O
326D	4/15/80	0:10	0:10	NAFEC	Open Loop Upgrade
326D	4/15/80	1:55	1:55	NAFEC	Autothrottle C/O
327	4/17/80	3:30	3:30	ATL	TBM/LFM in ATC
328	4/22/80	2:30	2:30	LOCAL	Autothrottle C/O
329A	5/6/80	0:50	0:50	WFF	Autothrottle C/O
329B	5/6/80	0:30	0:15	WFF	High Speed Turnoff
330	5/9/80	2:50	2:50	NAFEC	Autothrottle C/O
331	7/14/80	0:40	0:00		Maintenance
332	7/24/80	0:45	0:00		Maintenance
333A	12/9/80	0:35	0:00	LOCAL	Maintenance
333B	12/9/80	1:25	1:25	WFF	Open Loop Upgrade
333C	12/9/80	1:00	1:00	WFF	Dials Flight Test
334A	12/11/80	0:10	0:00	WFF	Open Loop Upgrade
334A	12/11/80	0:20	0:20	WFF	Open Loop Upgrade
334A	12/11/80	1:30	1:30	WFF	Open Loop Upgrade
334B	12/11/80	0:30	0:00	ATR	A/C Surf Coat Drag
334B	12/11/80	2:10	2:10	ATR	A/C Surf Coat Drag

Flight #	Date	Total Flight Time	Research Flight Time	Test Site	Flight Test Objectives
334B	12/11/80	0:40	0:40		A/C Surf Coat Drag
335	1/20/81	2:45	2:45	ATL	A/C Surf Coat Drag
336A	1/23/81	1:15	1:15	ATL	Dials Flight Test
336A	1/23/81	0:50	0:50	ATL	A/C Surf Coat Drag
336B	1/23/81	2:10	2:10	ATL	A/C Surf Coat Drag
337A	1/27/81	2:00	2:00	ATL	A/C Surf Coat Drag
337A	1/27/81	0:30	0:00	WFF	A/C Surf Coat Drag
337B	1/27/81	2:15	2:15	W&PH	Open Loop Upgrade
338A	2/3/81	2:15	2:15	GVE	A/C Surf Coat Drag
338A	2/3/81	0:30	0:00	WFF	A/C Surf Coat Drag
338B	2/3/81	0:50	0:50	WFF	Dials Flight Test
338B	2/3/81	0:20	0:00	LRC	Dials Flight Test
339A	2/5/81	0:25	0:00	WFF	C/O High Spd Turnoff
339B	2/5/81	0:25	0:00	LRC	C/O High Spd Turnoff
340	3/13/81	3:35	0:00		Pilot Proficiency
341	3/26/81	2:00	0:00	LOCAL	Pilot Proficiency
342	4/6/81	1:15	0:00	LOCAL	Maintenance
343	4/9/81	1:00	0:00	LOCAL	Maintenance
344	4/28/81	1:25	1:25	LOCAL	Open Loop Upgrade
344A	4/28/81	0:25	0:25	WFF	Open Loop Upgrade
344B	4/28/81	0:45	0:45	WFF	Open Loop Upgrade
344C	4/28/81	0:30	0:30	WFF	Open Loop Upgrade
345	4/30/81	0:55	0:00	LOCAL	Maintenance
346	5/12/81	0:15	0:00	WFF	Open Loop Upgrade
346A	5/12/81	0:15	0:15	WFF	Open Loop Upgrade
346B	5/12/81	0:30	0:30	WFF	Open Loop Upgrade
346B	5/12/81	0:30	0:00	WFF	Open Loop Upgrade
347A	6/16/81	1:30	1:30	WFF	Open Loop Upgrade
347B	6/16/81	1:00	1:00	WFF	Dials Flight Test
347C	6/16/81	1:20	0:40	WFF	Open Loop Upgrade
348A	6/23/81	1:20	1:20	LOCAL	Total Energy Probe Test
348B	6/23/81	1:20	0:50	WFF	Open Loop Upgrade
348C	6/23/81	0:15	0:15	WFF	Dials Flight Test
349A	6/30/81	0:22	0:00	WFF	Dials Flight Test
349B	6/30/81	1:13	1:13	WFF	Dials Flight Test
349C	6/30/81	0:21	0:21	WFF	NewILS Update
349D	6/30/81	0:24	0:00	WFF	NewILS Update
350A	7/23/81	0:20	0:00	WFF	Dials Flight Test
350B	7/23/81	1:50	1:50	WFF	Dials Flight Test
350C	7/23/81	1:55	1:55	WFF	NewILS Update
350D	7/23/81	0:20	0:00	WFF	NewILS Update
351A	7/30/81	0:25	0:00	WFF	NewILS Update
351B	7/30/81	2:25	2:25	WFF	NewILS Update
351C	7/30/81	0:25	0:00	WFF	NewILS Update
352A	8/25/81	0:20	0:00	WFF	Dials Flight Test
352B	8/25/81	0:35	0:35	WFF	Dials Flight Test

Flight #	Date	Total Flight Time	Research Flight Time	Test Site	Flight Test Objectives
352C	8/25/81	0:20	0:00	WFF	Dials Flight Test
353A	9/29/81	0:20	0:00	WFF	Dials Flight Test
353B	9/29/81	2:40	2:40	WFF	Dials Flight Test
353C	9/29/81	0:20	0:00	WFF	Dials Flight Test
354A	10/8/81	0:30	0:00	WFF	Flight Path Angle
354B	10/8/81	0:40	0:40	WFF	Flight Path Angle
354C	10/8/81	0:20	0:00	WFF	Flight Path Angle
355A	10/20/81	0:20	0:00	WFF	Maintenance
355A	10/20/81	0:30	0:30	WFF	Flight Path Angle
355A	10/20/81	0:50	0:50	WFF	RNAV/MLS Trans
355B	10/20/81	1:40	1:40	WFF	Dials Flight Test
355C	10/20/81	0:20	0:00	WFF	Dials Flight Test
356A	11/3/81	0:50	0:00	WFF	Flight Path Angle
356B	11/3/81	1:00	1:00	WFF	Flight Path Angle
356C	11/3/81	0:40	0:40	WFF	Flight Path Angle
356C	11/3/81	1:20	1:20	WFF	Prelim. LCWS
356C	11/3/81	0:25	0:00	WFF	Flight Path Angle
357A	11/18/81	0:40	0:00	WFF	Maintenance
357A	11/18/81	0:20	0:00	WFF	Dials Flight Test
357B	11/18/81	0:50	0:50	WFF	RNAV/MLS Trans
357C	11/18/81	2:00	2:00	WFF	Dials Flight Test
357D	11/18/81	0:15	0:00	WFF	Dials Flight Test
358A	11/25/81	0:20	0:00	WFF	Dials Flight Test
358B	11/25/81	1:00	1:00	WFF	Total Energy Probe Test
358C	11/25/81	0:20	0:00	WFF	Dials Flight Test
359A	12/1/81	0:40	0:00	WFF	Dials Flight Test
359B	12/1/81	0:40	0:40	WFF	Dials Flight Test
359C	12/1/81	0:40	0:00	WFF	Dials Flight Test
360A	12/3/81	0:40	0:00	ATL	Maintenance
360B	12/3/81	1:20	1:20	ATL	A/C Surf Coat Drag
360C	12/3/81	0:40	0:00	ATL	A/C Surf Coat Drag
361A	12/4/81	2:40	2:40	ATL	A/C Surf Coat Drag
361A	12/4/81	0:25	0:00	WFF	A/C Surf Coat Drag
361B	12/4/81	1:10	1:10	WFF	Dials Flight Test
361C	12/4/81	0:20	0:00	WFF	Dials Flight Test
362	12/8/81	2:40	2:40	ATL	A/C Surf Coat Drag
363	12/9/81	2:20	2:20	ATL	A/C Surf Coat Drag
364A	12/11/81	2:15	2:15	ATL	A/C Surf Coat Drag
364B	12/11/81	0:20	0:00	WFF	A/C Surf Coat Drag
364C	12/11/81	0:50	0:50	WFF	Dials Flight Test
364D	12/11/81	0:20	0:00	WFF	Dials Flight Test
365A	12/16/81	0:40	0:00	FAATC	NewILS Update
365B	12/16/81	2:05	2:05	FAATC	NewILS Update
365C	12/16/81	0:40	0:00	FAATC	NewILS Update
366	12/18/81	1:20	0:00	PIED.	Maintenance
367	2/1/82	0:40	0:00	LRC	Maintenance

Flight #	Date	Total Flight Time	Research Flight Time	Test Site	Flight Test Objectives
368	6/16/82	0:40	0:00	LRC	Maintenance
369	6/22/82	1:20	0:00	LRC	Pilot Proficiency
370	7/30/82	1:20	0:00	LRC	Maintenance
371	7/30/82	0:35	0:00	WFF	STEP
371	7/30/82	1:45	1:45	WFF	STEP
371C	7/30/82	0:35	0:00	WFF	STEP
372A	8/5/82	0:40	0:00	WFF	STEP
372B	8/5/82	1:00	1:00	WFF	STEP
372C	8/5/82	1:20	1:20	WFF	STEP
372D	8/5/82	0:30	0:00	WFF	STEP
373A	8/10/82	0:30	0:00	WFF	STEP
373B	8/10/82	2:15	2:15	WFF	STEP
373C	8/10/82	0:20	0:00	WFF	STEP
374A	8/17/82	0:25	0:00	WFF	STEP
374B	8/17/82	1:00	1:00	WFF	STEP
374C	8/17/82	1:30	1:30	WFF	STEP
374D	8/17/82	0:45	0:00	WFF	STEP
375A	8/24/82	0:40	0:00	WFF	STEP
375B	8/24/82	0:25	0:25	WFF	STEP
375C	8/24/82	1:50	1:50	WFF	STEP
375D	8/24/82	0:50	0:00	WFF	STEP
376	9/2/82	1:00	0:00	PIED.	Maintenance
377	9/3/82	0:40	0:00	LRC	Maintenance
378	9/7/82	0:15	0:00	LRC	Maintenance
379A	9/8/82	0:20	0:00	WFF	STEP
379B	9/8/82	0:45	0:45	WFF	STEP
379C	9/8/82	1:20	1:20	WFF	STEP
379D	9/8/82	1:00	1:00	WFF	STEP
379E	9/8/82	0:55	0:00	WFF	STEP
380A	9/14/82	0:20	0:00	WFF	STEP
380B	9/14/82	0:40	0:40	WFF	STEP
380C	9/14/82	0:10	0:10	WFF	STEP
380D	9/14/82	1:05	1:05	WFF	STEP
380E	9/14/82	1:15	1:15	WFF	STEP
380F	9/14/82	0:50	0:00	WFF	STEP
381A	9/23/82	0:30	0:10	WFF	STEP
381B	9/23/82	2:20	2:20	WFF	STEP
381C	9/23/82	1:40	1:40	WFF	STEP
381D	9/23/82	0:35	0:00	WFF	STEP
382A	9/28/82	0:20	0:00	WFF	STEP
382B	9/28/82	2:50	2:50	WFF	STEP
382C	9/28/82	2:45	2:45	WFF	STEP
382D	9/28/82	0:55	0:00	WFF	STEP
383A	10/5/82	0:50	0:30	WFF	STEP
383B	10/5/82	2:05	2:05	WFF	STEP
383C	10/5/82	1:05	1:05	WFF	STEP

Flight #	Date	Total Flight Time	Research Flight Time	Test Site	Flight Test Objectives
383D	10/5/82	1:10	1:10	WFF	STEP
383E	10/5/82	0:50	0:00	WFF	STEP
384A	10/15/82	0:15	0:00	WFF	STEP
384A	10/15/82	2:50	2:50	WFF	STEP
384B	10/15/82	0:30	0:30	WFF	STEP
384C	10/15/82	1:30	1:30	WFF	STEP
384C	10/15/82	0:50	0:00	WFF	STEP
385A	10/22/82	0:15	0:00	WFF	STEP
385A	10/22/82	2:40	2:40	WFF	STEP
385B	10/22/82	1:35	1:35	WFF	STEP
385B	10/22/82	0:40	0:00	WFF	STEP
386A	10/29/82	0:20	0:00	WFF	STEP
386A	10/29/82	0:45	0:45	WFF	STEP
386B	10/29/82	1:55	1:55	WFF	STEP
386C	10/29/82	2:35	2:35	WFF	STEP
386D	10/29/82	0:50	0:00	WFF	STEP
387A	11/2/82	0:15	0:00	WFF	STEP
387A	11/2/82	1:30	1:30	WFF	STEP
387B	11/2/82	0:55	0:55	WFF	STEP
387C	11/2/82	1:45	1:45	WFF	STEP
387C	11/2/82	0:45	0:00	WFF	STEP
388A	11/9/82	0:20	0:00	WFF	STEP
388B	11/9/82	0:35	0:35	WFF	STEP
388C	11/9/82	0:25	0:05	WFF	STEP
389A	11/10/82	0:25	0:00	WFF	STEP
389B	11/10/82	0:20	0:00	WFF	STEP
389C	11/10/82	0:40	0:00	WFF	STEP
390	11/23/82	1:20	0:00	LOCAL	Pilot Proficiency
391A	11/30/82	0:40	0:25	WFF	STEP
391B	11/30/82	2:00	2"00	WFF	STEP
391C	11/30/82	2:50	2:25	WFF	STEP
391C	11/30/82	0:20	0:00	WFF	STEP
392A	12/7/82	0:15	0:00	WFF	STEP
392A	12/7/82	0:45	0:45	WFF	STEP
392B	12/7/82	0:15	0:15	WFF	STEP
392C	12/7/82	2:55	2:55	WFF	STEP
392C	12/7/82	0:50	0:00	WFF	STEP
393A	12/9/82	0:15	0:00	WFF	STEP
393A	12/9/82	1:45	1:45	WFF	STEP
393B	12/9/82	3:05	3:05	WFF	STEP
393C	12/9/82	0:45	0:00	WFF	STEP
394A	12/14/82	0:15	0:00	WFF	STEP
394A	12/14/82	2:40	2:40	WFF	STEP
394B	12/14/82	2:30	2:30	WFF	STEP
394B	12/14/82	0:45	0:00	WFF	STEP
395A	1/11/83	0:20	0:00	WFF	STEP

Flight #	Date	Total Flight Time	Research Flight Time	Test Site	Flight Test Objectives
395A	1/11/83	2:30	2:30	WFF	STEP
395B	1/11/83	2:40	2:40	WFF	STEP
395C	1/11/83	0:15	0:15	WFF	STEP
395C	1/11/83	0:30	0:00	WFF	STEP
396A	1/25/83	0:20	0:00	WFF	STEP
396A	1/25/83	2:40	2:40	WFF	STEP
396B	1/25/83	2:00	2:00	WFF	STEP
396C	1/25/83	0:50	0:00	WFF	STEP
397A	1/27/83	0:20	0:00	WFF	STEP
397A	1/27/83	0:30	0:30	WFF	STEP
397B	1/27/83	0:30	0:00	WFF	STEP
398A	2/1/83	0:15	0:00	WFF	STEP
398A	2/1/83	0:55	0:55	WFF	STEP
398B	2/1/83	2:00	2:00	WFF	STEP
398C	2/1/83	1:00	1:00	WFF	STEP
398D	2/1/83	1:25	1:25	WFF	STEP
398D	2/1/83	0:40	0:00	WFF	STEP
399A	2/3/83	0:15	0:00	WFF	STEP
399A	2/3/83	3:15	3:15	WFF	STEP
399B	2/3/83	2:45	2:45	WFF	STEP
399B	2/3/83	0:15	0:00	WFF	STEP
400A	2/8/83	0:15	0:00	WFF	STEP
400A	2/8/83	0:15	0:15	WFF	GAPAN Nav Demo
400B	2/8/83	2:00	2:00	WFF	STEP
400C	2/8/83	1:20	1:20	WFC	STEP
400C	2/8/83	0:40	0:00	WFF	STEP
401A	2/10/83	0:15	0:00	WFF	STEP
401A	2/10/83	0:55	0:55	WFF	GAPAN Nav Demo
401B	2/10/83	1:20	1:20	WFF	STEP
401C	2/10/83	2:25	2:25	WFF	STEP
401C	2/10/83	0:15	0:00	WFF	STEP
402A	2/15/83	0:15	0:00	WFF	STEP
402A	2/15/83	2:55	2:55	WFF	STEP
402B	2/15/83	2:55	2:55	WFF	STEP
402B	2/15/83	0:40	0:00	WFF	STEP
403A	2/24/83	0:20	0:00	WFF	STEP
403A	2/24/83	2:05	2:05	WFF	STEP
403A	2/24/83	0:35	0:35	WFF	STEP
403B	2/24/83	1:20	1:20	WFF	GAPAN Nav Demo
403C	2/24/83	0:55	0:00	WFF	STEP
404A	3/3/83	0:40	0:40	WFF	GAPAN Nav Demo
404B	3/3/83	1:05	1:05	WFF	GAPAN Nav Demo
404C	3/3/83	1:20	1:20	WFF	STEP
404D	3/3/83	1:45	1:45	WFF	STEP
404E	3/3/83	1:10	1:10	WFF	STEP
404E	3/3/83	0:15	0:00	WFF	STEP

Flight #	Date	Total Flight Time	Research Flight Time	Test Site	Flight Test Objectives
404E	3/3/83	0:20	0:20	WFF	STEP
405A	3/22/83	0:40	0:40	WFF	GAPAN Nav Demo
405A	3/22/83	0:15	0:15	WFF	STEP
405B	3/22/83	0:15	0:15	WFF	STEP
405B	3/22/83	0:20	0:20	WFF	Open Loop Upgrade
405C	3/22/83	0:15	0:15	WFF	STEP
405C	3/22/83	0:40	0:40	WFF	STEP
406A	3/23/83	0:40	0:40	WFF	GAPAN Nav Demo
406B	3/23/83	0:20	0:20	WFF	GAPAN Nav Demo
406C	3/23/83	0:20	0:20	WFF	GAPAN Nav Demo
406C	3/23/83	0:30	0:30	WFF	GAPAN Nav Demo
406D	3/23/83	0:30	0:30	WFF	GAPAN Nav Demo
406E	3/23/83	0:20	0:20	WFF	GAPAN Nav Demo
407A	3/30/83	0:30	0:00	WASH	STEP
407B	3/30/83	0:35	0:00	LRC	STEP
408	6/13/83	1:20	0:00	WFF	A/C Grd Hdlg Tests
409A	6/15/83	0:15	0:00	WFF	A/C Grd Hdlg Tests
409A	6/15/83	0:05	0:00	WFF	A/C Grd Hdlg Tests
409B	6/15/83	0:10	0:10	WFF	A/C Grd Hdlg Tests
409C	6/15/83	0:10	0:10	WFF	A/C Grd Hdlg Tests
409D	6/15/83	0:05	0:05	WFF	A/C Grd Hdlg Tests
409D	6/15/83	0:15	0:00	LRC	A/C Grd Hdlg Tests
410A	6/17/83	0:15	0:00	WFC	A/C Grd Hdlg Tests
410A	6/17/83	0:05	0:05	WFC	A/C Grd Hdlg Tests
410B	6/17/83	0:10	0:10	WFF	A/C Grd Hdlg Tests
410C	6/17/83	0:05	0:05	WFF	A/C Grd Hdlg Tests
410D	6/17/83	0:10	0:10	WFF	A/C Grd Hdlg Tests
410E	6/17/83	0:10	0:10	WFF	A/C Grd Hdlg Tests
410F	6/17/83	0:10	0:10	WFF	A/C Grd Hdlg Tests
410G	6/17/83	0:10	0:10	WFF	A/C Grd Hdlg Tests
410H	6/17/83	0:10	0:10	WFF	A/C Grd Hdlg Tests
410I	6/17/83	0:55	0:00	PIED.	A/C Grd Hdlg Tests
411	6/21/83	0:45	0:00	LRC	A/C Grd Hdlg Tests
412A	6/21/83	0:15	0:00	WFF	A/C Grd Hdlg Tests
412A	6/21/83	0:15	0:15	LRC	A/C Grd Hdlg Tests
412B	6/21/83	0:20	0:20	WFF	A/C Grd Hdlg Tests
412C	6/21/83	0:15	0:15	WFF	A/C Grd Hdlg Tests
412D	6/21/83	0:10	0:10	WFF	A/C Grd Hdlg Tests
412E	6/21/83	0:10	0:10	WFF	A/C Grd Hdlg Tests
412F	6/21/83	0:10	0:10	WFF	A/C Grd Hdlg Tests
412G	6/21/83	0:10	0:10	WFF	A/C Grd Hdlg Tests
412H	6/21/83	0:05	0:05	WFF	A/C Grd Hdlg Tests
412I	6/21/83	0:40	0:00	LRC	A/C Grd Hdlg Tests
413A	6/23/83	0:30	0:00	FAATC	A/C Grd Hdlg Tests
413A	6/23/83	0:05	0:05	FAATC	A/C Grd Hdlg Tests
413B	6/23/83	0:30	0:30	FAATC	A/C Grd Hdlg Tests

Flight #	Date	Total Flight Time	Research Flight Time	Test Site	Flight Test Objectives
414A	6/24/83	0:50	0:50	FAATC	A/C Grd Hdlg Tests
414B	6/24/83	0:15	0:15	FAATC	A/C Grd Hdlg Tests
414C	6/24/83	0:15	0:15	FAATC	A/C Grd Hdlg Tests
414D	6/24/83	0:15	0:15	FAATC	A/C Grd Hdlg Tests
414E	6/24/83	0:05	0:05	FAATC	A/C Grd Hdlg Tests
414F	6/24/83	0:05	0:05	FAATC	A/C Grd Hdlg Tests
414G	6/24/83	0:30	0:00	LRC	A/C Grd Hdlg Tests
415A	6/28/83	0:15	0:00	WFF	A/C Grd Hdlg Tests
415A	6/28/83	0:10	0:10	WFF	A/C Grd Hdlg Tests
415B	6/28/83	0:40	0:40	WFF	A/C Grd Hdlg Tests
415C	6/28/83	0:20	0:20	WFF	A/C Grd Hdlg Tests
415D	6/28/83	0:25	0:00	WFF	A/C Grd Hdlg Tests
416	2/10/84	1:10	0:00	LOCAL	Maintenance
417	5/18/84	1:15	0:00	LOCAL	Maintenance
418	8/7/84	1:10	0:00	LOCAL	Maintenance
419A	8/7/84	0:20	0:20	WFF	Open Loop Upgrade
419B	8/7/84	0:50	0:50	WFF	Open Loop Upgrade
420A	9/12/84	2:10	2:10	WFF	TSRV Flt Verif Tests
420B	9/12/84	0:20	0:00	WFF	TSRV Flt Verif Tests
421	9/13/84	1:50	1:50	WFF	TSRV Flt Verif Tests
422A	10/18/84	2:10	2:10	WFF	TSRV Flt Verif Tests
422B	10/18/84	1:30	1:30	WFF	TSRV Flt Verif Tests
422B	10/18/84	0:20	0:00	WFF	TSRV Flt Verif Tests
423A	10/23/84	1:30	1:30	WFF	TSRV Flt Verif Tests
423A	10/23/84	0:30	0:00	WFF	TSRV Flt Verif Tests
424A	10/26/84	1:40	1:40	WFF	TSRV Flt Verif Tests
424B	10/26/84	1:00	1:00	WFF	TSRV Flt Verif Tests
424C	10/26/84	1:10	1:10	WFF	TSRV Flt Verif Tests
425A	10/29/84	0:15	0:00	WFF	TSRV Flt Verif Tests
425A	10/29/84	2:35	2:35	WFF	TSRV Flt Verif Tests
425B	10/29/84	0:30	0:30	WFF	TSRV Flt Verif Tests
425B	10/29/84	0:15	0:00	WFF	TSRV Flt Verif Tests
426A	11/20/84	0:20	0:00	WFF	A/C Grd Hdlg Tests
426B	11/20/84	0:10	0:10	WFF	A/C Grd Hdlg Tests
426C	11/20/84	0:20	0:20	WFF	A/C Grd Hdlg Tests
426D	11/20/84	0:05	0:05	WFF	A/C Grd Hdlg Tests
426E	11/20/84	0:20	0:00	WFF	A/C Grd Hdlg Tests
427A	11/28/84	0:40	0:00	FAATC	A/C Grd Hdlg Tests
427B	11/28/84	0:40	0:00	FAATC	A/C Grd Hdlg Tests
428A	12/3/84	1:00	0:00	PIED.	Maintenance
428B	12/18/84	0:55	0:00	LRC	Maintenance
429	2/5/85	0:00	0:00	LRC	A/C Grd Hdlg Tests
430	3/6/85	1:25	0:00	BHAS	Runway Friction
431	3/7/85	0:20	0:20	BHAS	Runway Friction
432	3/8/85	0:30	0:30	BHAS	Runway Friction
433A	3/9/85	0:15	0:15	BHAS	Runway Friction

Flight #	Date	Total Flight Time	Research Flight Time	Test Site	Flight Test Objectives
433B	3/9/85	1:45	0:00	LRC	Runway Friction
434A	3/22/85	0:30	0:00	WFF	A/C Grd Hdlg Tests
434B	3/22/85	0:50	0:50	WFF	A/C Grd Hdlg Tests
434C	3/22/85	0:30	0:00	LRC	A/C Grd Hdlg Tests
435	4/18/85	0:50	0:00	WFF	Runway Friction
436A	5/31/85	1:30	1:10	WFF	TSRV Flt Verif Tests
436B	5/31/85	2:40	2:20	WFF	TSRV Flt Verif Tests
437A	6/10/85	1:20	1:00	WFF	TSRV Flt Verif Tests
437A	6/10/85	1:10	1:10	WFF	Airport 85 Program
437B	6/10/85	1:25	0:40	WFF	TSRV Flt Verif Tests
437B	6/10/85	1:00	1:00	WFF	Airport 85 Program
438A	6/12/85	0:50	0:30	WFF	TSRV Flt Verif Tests
438B	6/12/85	1:25	1:25	WFF	TSRV Flt Verif Tests
439A	7/1/85	0:20	0:00	WFF	Airport 85 Program
439A	7/1/85	0:20	0:20	WFF	Airport 85 Program
439B	7/1/85	1:30	0:00	WFF	Airport 85 Program
439C	7/1/85	1:25	0:00	WFF	Airport 85 Program
440A	7/3/85	0:25	0:25	WFF	Airport 85 Program
440B	7/3/85	1:45	1:45	WFF	Airport 85 Program
440C	7/3/85	1:15	1:15	WFF	Airport 85 Program
440D	7/3/85	0:55	0:55	WFF	Airport 85 Program
441A	7/5/85	0:30	0:20	WFF	Airport 85 Program
441B	7/5/85	1:10	1:10	WFF	Airport 85 Program
441C	7/5/85	1:05	1:05	WFF	Airport 85 Program
441D	7/5/85	0:20	0:00	WFF	Airport 85 Program
442A	7/9/85	0:25	0:00	WFF	Airport 85 Program
442B	7/9/85	1:30	1:30	WFF	Airport 85 Program
442C	7/9/85	2:35	2:35	WFF	Airport 85 Program
442D	7/9/85	1:35	1:10	WFF	Airport 85 Program
443A	7/11/85	0:40	0:00		Airport 85 Program
443B	7/11/85	0:30	0:00	WFF	Airport 85 Program
443C	7/11/85	2:30	2:30	WFF	Airport 85 Program
443D	7/11/85	1:40	1:40	WFF	Airport 85 Program
443E	7/11/85	0:35	0:10	WFF	Airport 85 Program
443F	7/11/85	0:40	0:00	LRC	Airport 85 Program
444A	7/13/85	0:25	0:00	WFF	Airport 85 Program
444B	7/13/85	0:10	0:00	WFF	Airport 85 Program
444C	7/13/85	1:30	1:30	WFF	Airport 85 Program
444D	7/13/85	2:45	2:45	WFF	Airport 85 Program
444E	7/13/85	1:40	1:10	WFF	Airport 85 Program
445A	7/15/85	0:25	0:00	WFF	Airport 85 Program
445B	7/15/85	1:50	1:50	WFF	Airport 85 Program
445C	7/15/85	0:35	0:35	WFF	Airport 85 Program
445D	7/15/85	0:25	0:00	WFF	Airport 85 Program
446A	7/17/85	0:20	0:00	WFF	Airport 85 Program
446B	7/17/85	1:50	1:50	WFF	Airport 85 Program

Flight #	Date	Total Flight Time	Research Flight Time	Test Site	Flight Test Objectives
446C	7/17/85	0:20	0:00	WFF	Airport 85 Program
447A	7/28/85	1:50	0:00	DEN	Airport 85 Program
447B	7/28/85	2:00	0:00	DEN	Airport 85 Program
448A	7/31/85	2:45	2:45	DEN	Airport 85 Program
449A	8/1/85	1:40	1:40	DEN	Airport 85 Program
449B	8/1/85	1:00	1:00	DEN	Airport 85 Program
450	8/2/85	3:15	3:15	DEN	Airport 85 Program
451	8/3/85	3:00	3:00	DEN	Airport 85 Program
452A	8/5/85	1:10	1:10	DEN	Airport 85 Program
452B	8/5/85	1:10	1:10	DEN	Airport 85 Program
453A	8/6/85	2:20	2:20	DEN	Airport 85 Program
453B	8/6/85	1:35	1:35	DEN	Airport 85 Program
454A	8/10/85	1:25	0:00	FERRY	Airport 85 Program
454B	8/10/85	2:00	0:00	FERRY	Airport 85 Program
455A	9/4/85	0:20	0:20	WFF	TSRV Flt Verif Tests
455A	9/4/85	2:45	2:45	WFF	Total Energy Ctl Sys
455B	9/4/85	2:05	2:05	WFF	Total Energy Ctl Sys
456A	9/6/85	0:30	0:30	WFF	TSRV Flt Verif Tests
456B	9/6/85	0:30	0:30	WFF	TSRV Flt Verif Tests
456C	9/6/85	1:00	1:00	WFF	Total Energy Ctl Sys
456D	9/6/85	2:15	2:15	WFF	Total Energy Ctl Sys
457A	9/10/85	0:40	0:40	WFF	TSRV Flt Verif Tests
457B	9/10/85	1:55	1:55	WFF	Total Energy Ctl Sys
458A	9/12/85	0:35	0:35	WFF	TSRV Flt Verif Tests
458B	9/12/85	0:45	0:45	WFF	TSRV Flt Verif Tests
458C	9/12/85	1:00	1:00	WFF	TSRV Flt Verif Tests
459A	9/16/85	1:50	1:50	WFF	Total Energy Ctl Sys
459B	9/16/85	0:45	0:45	WFF	Total Energy Ctl Sys
460A	9/19/85	1:50	1:50	NORF	Total Energy Ctl Sys
460B	9/19/85	0:10	0:00	LRC	Total Energy Ctl Sys
461A	9/25/85	3:00	3:00	LOCAL	Total Energy Ctl Sys
461B	9/25/85	1:15	1:15	LOCAL	Total Energy Ctl Sys
461B	9/25/85	0:30	0:30	LOCAL	Engine Perf Data
461B	9/25/85	0:30	0:30	LOCAL	Hyd Samples
462A	10/1/85	0:40	0:40	WFF	TSRV Flt Verif Tests
462B	10/1/85	1:00	1:00	WFF	Total Energy Ctl Sys
462C	10/1/85	2:30	2:30	LOCAL	Total Energy Ctl Sys
462C	10/1/85	0:30	0:30	LOCAL	Hyd Samples
463	5/7/87	0:30	0:30	LOCAL	Functional Check Flt
464	5/12/87	0:20	0:20	LOCAL	Functional Check Flt
465	5/15/87	1:35	1:35	LOCAL	Functional Check Flt
466A	6/2/87	2:00	2:00	WFF	Functional & Timer
466B	6/2/87	1:50	1:50	WFF	Functional & Timer
467A	6/9/87	0:45	0:45	WFF	Baseline Validation
467B	6/9/87	2:15	2:15	WFF	Baseline Validation
468A	6/11/87	1:50	1:50	WFF	Director Demo

Flight #	Date	Total Flight Time	Research Flight Time	Test Site	Flight Test Objectives
468B	6/11/87	2:05	2:05	WFF	Director Demo
469A	6/15/87	1:10	1:10	WFF	Director Demo
469B	6/15/87	1:25	1:25	WFF	Director Demo
470A	6/23/87	2:55	2:55	WFF	Baseline
470B	6/23/87	2:45	2:45	WFF	Timer & Baseline
471A	6/30/87	2:10	2:10	WFF	Timer (am portion)
471B	6/30/87	3:45	3:45	WFF	Timer (pm portion)
472A	7/9/87	1:15	1:15	WFF	Timer Data Runs
472B	7/9/87	2:00	1:40	WFF	Timer Data Runs
473A	7/17/87	2:15	2:15	WFF	Timer Data Runs
473B	7/17/87	1:55	1:55	WFF	Timer Data Runs
474A	7/21/87	2:20	2:20	WFF	Timer Data Runs
474B	7/21/87	2:20	2:20	WFF	Timer Data Runs
474C	7/21/87	0:25	0:00	WFF	Timer Data Runs
475A	7/23/87	2:30	2:30	WFF	Baseline Validation
475B	7/23/87	1:40	1:40	WFF	Baseline Validation
476A	7/28/87	2:00	1:40	WFF	Timer Data Runs
476B	7/28/87	1:15	0:50	WFF	Timer Data Runs
477A	7/30/87	0:50	0:00	WFF	Timer Data Runs
477B	7/30/87	1:45	1:45	WFF	Timer Data Runs
477C	7/30/87	2:00	1:40	WFF	Timer Data Runs
478A	7/30/87	0:45	0:00	PIED.	Ferry to Piedmont, NC
478B	8/3/87	0:45	0:00	LRC	Ferry to LaRC
479A	8/4/87	1:00	0:15	WFF	Timer Data Runs
479B	8/4/87	1:55	1:55	WFF	Timer Data Runs
479C	8/4/87	1:10	0:40	WFF	Timer Data Runs
480A	8/11/87	2:15	1:15	WFF	Timer Data Runs
470B	8/11/87	2:25	2:05	WFF	Timer Data Runs
481A	8/13/87	2:25	2:00	WFF	Timer Data Runs
481B	8/13/87	1:40	1:05	WFF	Timer Data Runs
482A	9/3/87	2:10	1:20	WFF	RNAV/MLS Transition
482B	9/3/87	1:25	1:25	WFF	VV Flare/RNAV MLS
482C	9/3/87	0:20	0:00	LRC	Ferry to LRC fromWFF
483A	9/15/87	2:05	2:05	WFF	DFVLR
483B	9/15/87	2:30	2:10	WFF	DFVLR
484A	9/22/87	2:55	2:45	WFF	DFVLR
484B	9/22/87	2:40	2:40	WFF	DFVLR
485	9/25/87	1:05	0:00	WFF	Ferry to LRC from WFF
486A	9/29/87	2:50	2:50	WFF	DFVLR
486B	9/29/87	3:15	3:15	WFF	DFVLR
487A	10/1/87	3:30	3:30	WFF	DFVLR
487B	10/1/87	0:50	0:00	WFF	DFVLR
488	12/16/87	1:00	0:00	LOCAL	Functional Check Flt
489A	12/17/87	0:30	0:30	WFF	Ferry & LEBU Test
489B	12/17/87	1:48	1:48	WFF	Tests at 3 Rep. Tsts
489C	12/17/87	0:18	0:18	WFF	Demo

Flight #	Date	Total Flight Time	Research Flight Time	Test Site	Flight Test Objectives
489D	12/17/87	0:30	0:30	WFF	Demo
489E	12/17/87	1:18	1:18	WFF	MLS Performance
489F	12/17/87	0:18	0:00	LRC	Ferry to LRC
489O	1/19/88	2:00	2:00	WFF	LEBU Data Flight
490A	1/19/88	2:00	2:00	WFF	LEBU Data Flight
490B	1/19/88	1:30	1:12	WFF	LEBU Data Flight
491	2/5/88	2:18	2:18	WFF	LEBU Data Flight
492	2/11/88	2:48	2:36	WFF	LEBU Data Flight
493	2/22/88	2:42	2:42	WFF	LEBU Data Flight
494	2/26/88	4:00	2:54	WFF	LEBU Data Flight
495	3/7/88	0:42	0:00	LOCAL	Pilot Proficiency
496A	3/7/88	0:36	0:36	WFF	LEBU Data Flight
496B	3/7/88	1:54	1:54	WFF	LEBU Data Flight
497	3/8/88	2:54	2:54	WFF	LEBU Data Flight
498A	3/15/88	0:30	0:00	WFF	Ferry to WFF
498B	3/15/88	2:12	2:12	WFF	TOPMS Tests
498C	3/15/88	0:30	0:00	LRC	Ferry to LRC
499A	3/22/88	2:00	1:18	WFF	Ferry to WFF
499B	3/22/88	2:12	1:12	WFF	TOPMS Tests
500A	3/24/88	2:18	1:48	WFF	Ferry to WFF/RNAV
500B	3/24/88	1:30	1:18	WFF	RNAV/MLS Runs
501A	3/29/88	0:18	0:00	WFF	Ferry to WFF
501B	3/29/88	0:18	0:00	WFF	Ferry to LRC
502A	4/5/88	1:42	0:00	PAFB	Ferry to Patrick AFB
502B	4/5/88	0:54	0:12	KSC	Ferry to KSC & Ret
503A	4/6/88	2:00	2:00	KSC	TOPMS Flt Tests
503B	4/6/88	1:12	1:12	KSC	TOPMS Flt Tests
503C	4/6/88	1:30	1:30	KSC	TOPMS Flt Tests
504	4/7/88	2:18	2:18	LRC	TOPMS Rudder Engine
505	4/21/88	3:00	3:00	LOCAL	Riblet LEBU Tests
506	4/26/88	3:00	3:00	LOCAL	Riblet LEBU Tests
507	6/30/88	0:12	0:00	LOCAL	Maintenance FCF
508A	6/30/88	1:24	1:24	WFF	Baseline Verification
508B	6/30/88	2:12	2:12	WFF	Baseline Verification
509A	7/7/88	1:18	1:18	WFF	Baseline Verification
509B	7/7/88	0:36	0:36	WFF	Baseline Verification
509C	7/7/88	2:18	2:18	WFF	Baseline Verification
510A	7/14/88	1:00	1:00	WFF	Baseline Verification
510B	7/14/88	1:42	1:42	FAATC	Baseline Verification
510C	7/14/88	0:54	0:54	FAATC	Baseline Verification
511	7/25/88	0:06	0:06	LOCAL	Functional Ck Flt
512A	7/25/88	3:24	3:24	WFF	TOPMS C/O
512B	7/25/88	1:24	1:24	WFF	TOPMS C/O
519	5/2/89	0:42	0:00	LOCAL	Maintenance
520	5/2/89	2:42	2:42	WFF	Flight Verif Tests
521	5/4/89	2:00	2:00	WFF	Helmet-Mounted Display

Flight #	Date	Total Flight Time	Research Flight Time	Test Site	Flight Test Objectives
522	5/8/89	4:06	4:06	WFF	Helmet-Mounted Display
523	5/9/89	2:36	2:36	WFF	Helmet-Mounted Display
524	5/16/89	1:36	1:36	WFF	Helmet-Mounted Display
525	5/18/89	3:48	3:48	WFF	Helmet-Mounted Display
526	5/19/89	4:00	4:00	WFF	Helmet-Mounted Display
527	5/23/89	2:12	2:12	WFF	Helmet-Mounted Display
528	5/24/89	4:42	4:42	WFF	Helmet-Mounted Display
529	5/25/89	4:30	4:30	WFF	Helmet-Mounted Display
530	5/26/89	1:42	1:42	WFF	Helmet-Mounted Display
531	6/7/89	3:54	3:54	PHF/WFF	Flight Verif Tests
532	6/13/89	4:30	4:30	PHF/WFF	Flight Verif Tests
533	6/15/89	2:00	2:00	WFF	Helmet-Mounted Display
534	7/7/89	0:18	0:00	WFF	Ferry to LRC
535	7/11/89	1:30	0:00	LRC	Ferry to AL
536	9/8/89	2:24	0:00	BHM, AL	Ferry to LRC
537	10/23/89	2:12	0:00	LOCAL	Maintenance
538	10/25/89	5:36	5:36	WFF	Funct Ck Flt/IR Wndshr
539	11/13/89	5:18	5:18	WFF	IR Wndshr/TOPMS
540	11/17/89	1:00	0:00	LRC	Maintenance
541	11/20/89	2:30	2:30	WFF	Data Link/IR Wndshr
542	11/29/89	3:36	3:36	WFF	Data Link/IR Wndshr
543	12/5/89	4:24	4:24	WFF	LCWS/EMACS
544	12/14/89	2:54	2:54	WFF	Data Link/IR Wndshr
545	3/27/90	1:36	0:00	LOCAL	Maintenance
546	3/27/90	3:18	3:18	WFF	Flt Verif/Data Link
547	4/5/90	5:06	5:06	WFF	Flt Verif/IR Wndshr
548	4/12/90	3:06	3:06	WFF	Data Link
549	4/19/90	4:30	4:30	WFF	Data Link
550	4/24/90	3:30	3:30	WFF	Data Link
551	4/27/90	3:40	3:40	WFF	Data Link
552	5/1/90	3:24	3:24	WFF	Data Link
553	5/4/90	4:00	4:00	WFF	Data Link
554	5/8/90	4:12	4:12	WFF	Data Link
555	5/15/90	2:42	2:42	WFF	EMACS
556	5/31/90	0:24	0:00	LOCAL	Maintenance
557	5/31/90	3:00	3:00	WFF	EMACS/IR Wndshr
558	6/7/90	1:00	1:00	LOCAL	High Lift
559	6/11/90	1:00	1:00	LOCAL	High Lift
560	6/12/90	1:48	1:48	WFF	Data Link
561	6/15/90	2:00	2:00	WFF	Data Link
562	6/18/90	4:30	4:30	WFF	Data Link
563	6/20/90	1:30	1:30	WFF	Data Link
564	6/21/90	3:18	3:18	WFF	Data Link
565	6/27/90	3:48	3:48	WFF	Data Link
566	6/29/90	0:12	0:00	LRC	Pilot Proficiency
567	6/29/90	3:36	3:36	WFF	Data Link

Flight #	Date	Total Flight Time	Research Flight Time	Test Site	Flight Test Objectives
568	7/2/90	3:24	3:24	WFF	Data Link
569	7/6/90	5:00	5:00	WFF/D.C.	FAA/NASA ATOPS Demo
570	9/21/90	1:54	0:00	LOCAL	Maintenance
571	9/24/90	4:12	4:12	WFF	Flt Verif Tests
572	10/2/90	3:12	3:12	WFF	GPS/INS Autolnd
573	10/10/90	2:36	2:36	WFF	GPS Autolnd/In Situ Wndshr
574	10/18/90	1:42	1:42	WFF	GPS Autolnd/In Situ Wndshr
575	10/24/90	4:48	4:48	WFF	GPS Autolnd/In Situ Wndshr
576	10/30/90	4:30	4:30	WFF	GPS Autolnd/In Situ Wndshr
577	11/1/90	4:24	4:24	WFF	GPS Autolnd/In Situ Wndshr
578	11/6/90	3:56	3:56	WFF	GPS Autolnd/In Situ Wndshr
579	11/8/90	5:00	5:00	WFF	GPS Autolnd/In Situ Wndshr
580	11/14/90	3:06	3:06	WFF	GPS Autolnd/In Situ Wndshr
581	11/29/90	1:00	1:00	WFF	EMACS/Hgh Spd Turnoff
582	12/7/90	0:42	0:00	LRC	Maintenance
583	12/7/90	1:12	1:12	WFF	Hgh Spd Turnoff/IR Wndshr
584	12/14/90	0:54	0:54	WFF	Hgh Spd Turnoff
585	1/31/91	3:36	3:36	WFF	High Lift
586	2/8/91	0:30	0:30	LRC/S.E. USA	Pilot Training
587	2/8/91	2:24	2:24	LRC/S.E. USA	EMACS
588	2/5/91	3:18	3:18	WFF	Radar Windshear
589	2/22/91	3:12	3:12	LRC	Radar/IR Wndshr
590	2/28/91	4:48	4:48	LRC	Radar/IR Wndshr
591	3/15/91	3:24	3:24	WFF	Radar/IR Wndshr
592	3/20/91	4:06	4:06	LRC	Radar/IR Wndshr
593	3/26/91	4:00	4:00	LRC	Radar/IR Wndshr
594	3/28/91	2:42	2:42	LRC	Radar/IR Wndshr
595	4/3/91	3:00	3:00	WFF	EMACS
596	4/25/91	1:12	0:00	LRC	Maintenance
597	4/26/91	5:48	5:48	LRC	High Lift
598	5/7/91	0:18	0:00	LRC	Maintenance
599	5/7/91	3:48	3:48	LRC	High Lift/GPS
600	5/8/91	1:18	0:48	WFF	Hgh Spd Rollout/DGPS
601	5/17/91	3:12	3:12	WFF	Windshear/Flt Verif
602	5/23/91	2:30	2:30	WFF	Windshear/GPS
603	5/29/91	3:18	3:18	WFF	Windshear
604	6/9/91	1:48	1:48	LRC	Windshear/LORAN
605	6/10/91	2:00	2:00	Orlando	Windshear
606	6/13/91	1:00	1:00	Orlando	Windshear
607	6/15/91	2:42	2:42	Orlando	Windshear
608	6/16/91	0:42	0:42	Orlando	Windshear
609	6/17/91	1:54	1:54	Orlando	Windshear
610	6/18/91	2:18	2:18	Orlando	Windshear
611	6/19/91	3:42	3:42	Orlando	Windshear
612	6/20/91	2:30	2:30	Orlando	Windshear
613	6/21/91	1:48	0:00	Orlando	Ferry to LRC

Flight #	Date	Total Flight Time	Research Flight Time	Test Site	Flight Test Objectives
614	7/7/91	4:12	4:12	LRC	Ferry/Calibration
645	7/8/91	1:00	1:00	Denver	Exp Sys C/O
616	7/9/91	0:54	0:54	Denver	Windshear
617	7/10/91	2:06	2:06	Denver	Windshear
618	7/11/91	1:54	1:54	Denver	Windshear
619	7/13/91	2:30	2:30	Denver	Windshear
620	7/17/91	3:48	3:48	Denver	Windshear
621	7/18/91	1:06	1:06	Denver	Windshear
622	7/20/91	0:30	0:30	Denver	Windshear
623	7/26/91	4:06	4:06	Denver	Ferry/Calibration
624	8/12/91	1:42	0:00	LRC	Ferry to AL
625	9/23/91	2:24	0:00	BHM, AL	Ferry to LRC
626	1/31/92	1:30	0:00	WFF	Maintenance
627	2/3/92	0:54	0:54	LRC	Flt Verif/High Lift
628	2/7/92	3:30	3:30	LRC	Flt Verif/High Lift
629	2/10/92	3:12	3:12	WFF	High Lift
630	2/12/92	6:36	6:36	WFF	High Lift
631	2/27/92	1:00	0:00	LRC	Maintenance
632	2/27/92	2:24	2:24	FAATC	ILS Modeling/LIDAR
633	3/4/92	4:30	4:30	PHF/FAATC	ILS Modeling/MLS/DGPS
634	3/25/92	1:12	0:00	LRC	Maintenance
635	3/25/92	2:42	2:42	LRC	ILS Modeling/LIDAR
636	3/30/92	5:48	0:00	LRC	Ferry to LAX
637	3/31/92	3:12	3:12	LAX	ILS Modeling/LIDAR
638	4/1/92	4:00	4:00	LAX	ILS Modeling/LIDAR
639	4/2/92	4:00	4:00	LAX	ILS Modeling/LIDAR
640	4/4/92	5:30	0:00	LAX	Ferry to LRC
641	4/27/92	1:42	0:00	LRC	Ferry to BHM, AL
642	5/13/92	2:12	0:00	BHM, AL	Ferry to LRC
643	6/24/92	1:30	0:00	LRC	Functional Tst Flt
644	6/24/92	4:06	4:06	WFF	Flt Verif Tests
645	6/26/92	3:48	3:48	WFF	Flt Verif/Windshear
646	6/30/92	1:12	0:00	WFF	Functional Tst Flt
647	6/30/92	3:24	3:24	WFF	Flt Verif/Windshear
648	7/2/92	3:18	3:18	WFF	Flt Verif/Windshear
649	7/9/92	1:42	0:00	LRC	Functional Tst Flt
650	7/13/92	4:12	4:12	LRC	Windshr/Ferry to DEN
651	7/14/92	2:30	2:30	Denver	Windshear
652	7/15/92	1:54	1:54	Denver	Windshear
653	7/18/92	1:18	1:18	Denver	Windshear
654	7/20/92	1:36	1:36	Denver	Windshear
655	7/21/92	1:54	1:54	Denver	Windshear
656	7/22/92	1:48	1:48	Denver	Windshear
657	7/23/92	2:18	2:18	Denver	Windshear
658	7/24/92	3:48	3:48	Denver	Windshr/Ferry to LRC
659	8/10/92	1:48	1:48	LRC	Windshr/Ferry to LRC

Flight #	Date	Total Flight Time	Research Flight Time	Test Site	Flight Test Objectives
660	8/11/92	1:48	1:48	Orlando	Windshear
661	8/12/92	2:30	2:30	Orlando	Windshear
662	8/13/92	2:06	2:06	Orlando	Windshear
663	8/14/92	1:36	1:36	Orlando	Windshear
664	8/15/92	1:48	1:48	Orlando	Windshear
665	8/17/92	1:42	1:42	Orlando	Windshear
666	8/19/92	2:06	2:06	Orlando	Windshear
667	8/20/92	1:48	1:48	Orlando	Windshear
668	8/21/92	1:54	1:54	Orlando	Windshear
669	8/23/92	1:36	0:00	Orlando	Hurricane-Ferry to LRC
670	8/25/92	1:36	0:00	LRC	Ferry back to Orlando
671	8/25/92	1:00	1:00	Orlando	Windshear
672	8/27/92	1:48	1:48	Orlando	Windshear
673	9/10/92	3:30	3:30	WFF	Windshear
674	9/22/92	4:18	4:18	WFF	Windshear
675	9/24/92	2:18	2:18	WFF/DCA	Windshear
676	10/6/92	1:00	1:00	LRC	Flt Verif Tests
677	10/6/92	3:00	3:00	LRC	CTAS
678	10/21/92	5:54	5:54	LRC	CTAS/Ferry to Denver
679	10/22/92	4:18	4:18	Denver	CTAS
680	10/23/92	3:18	3:18	Denver	CTAS
681	10/26/92	5:12	5:12	Denver	CTAS
682	10/27/92	5:24	5:24	Denver	CTAS
683	10/28/92	3:12	0:00	Denver	Ferry to LRC
684	11/2/92	2:42	2:42	LRC	Flt Verif/TECS
685	11/9/92	1:30	0:00	LRC	Ferry to Dothan, AL
686	11/12/92	1:24	0:00	Dothan, AL	Ferry to LRC
687	4/30/93	2:18	0:00	LOCAL	Functional Ck Flt
688	4/30/93	2:42	2:42	WFF	Flt Verif/OPMIS-DGPS
689	5/6/93	3:18	3:18	WFF	Ohio U. DGPS/OPMIS
690	5/20/93	1:48	1:48	WFF	DGPS/OPMIS/Map
691	5/25/93	3:06	3:06	WFF	DGPS/OPMIS/Map
692	5/28/93	3:42	3:42	WFF	DGPS/OPMIS/Map
693	6/10/93	3:42	3:42	WFF	DGPS/OPMIS/Map
694	6/28/93	1:12	0:00	LRC	Maintenance
695	7/7/93	2:48	2:48	LRC/PAX	DGPS/OPMIS/Map
696	7/21/93	0:30	0:00	PAX	Maintenance Ferry to LRC
697	8/10/93	1:42	1:42	LRC	Flt Verif Tests
698	8/12/93	3:24	3:24	LRC/PAX	Ohio U. DGPS
699	8/24/93	2:12	2:12	WFF	Allied Signal DGPS
700	8/26/93	3:24	3:24	WFF	Allied Signal DGPS
701	9/15/93	4:54	4:54	WFF	Wilcox DGPS ILS
702	9/21/93	3:18	3:18	WFF	Wilcox DGPS ILS

Acknowledgements

In researching and writing this history, I had the advantage of being able to talk directly to many of the people who organized and managed the original Terminal Configured Vehicle/ Advanced Transport Operating Systems program and the researchers and engineers who conducted its many research projects. Many active and retired NASA engineers donated generous amounts of their time to educate me about their work and the airplane's history and sent me copies of their personal notes and other printed material that was invaluable in piecing together this story. In addition, I am indebted to the numerous active and retired managers, engineers, and representatives from the Federal Aviation Administration, the Lockheed Corporation, the Boeing Commercial Airplane Company, the McDonnell Douglas Corporation, Honeywell, Inc., the Collins Commercial Avionics division of Rockwell International, and ARNAV Systems, Inc., who took the time to talk with me about research projects conducted with NASA's 737 and commercial applications the research influenced. The managers, public relations staff, and historians at Boeing also donated critical notes and photographs pertaining to the airplane's pre-NASA history and the early years of the TCV program. Without the information and assistance provided by all these people, this book could not have been written.

As the project progressed, the Langley Research Center staff also cheerfully answered the dozens of follow-up questions I had and willingly reviewed drafts to ensure the technical accuracy of the information being presented. In fact, throughout the course of this project, I received an immense amount of cooperation, assistance, and information, all of which was greatly appreciated. Once the manuscript was completed, there were also many people, too numerous to mention by name, who helped with the editing, design and layout of the book, and shepherded the project through its publication. Their efforts are evident on every page, and I am grateful to all of them.

I owe a special note of thanks, however, to Sandra Mims of the Advanced Transport Operating Systems office, who spent an enormous amount of time tracking down information, people, and obscure but critical documents, and even shared her office, her desk, and some days even her lunch with me to get this project finished.

Index

Abbott, Terence S.: 83
Advanced Digital Electronic Displays: 13
Advanced Transport Operating Systems (ATOPS) Program: 7, 9-23; acquires Boeing 737, 11-14; and aircraft operations research, 89-103; and aircraft systems research, 75-87; and Airport 85 research, 114-16; and Boeing 737 research systems, 14-18; and cockpit computerization, 36-39; and cockpit displayed traffic information research, 93-94; and computerization and electronic flight displays research, 25-39; and data link research, 95-99; and digital access communication research, 75, 76-78; and electronic flight display research, 27-33; and engine monitoring and control system, 75, 83-85, 120; and global positioning system research, 50-53, 102, 120, 122; and helmet mounted display research, 112-14; and high lift research, 108-109; and instrument landing system signal modelling research, 116-17; and large eddy break-up research, 108-109; and microburst windshear research, 55-73; and magnetic cable guidance research, 101-102; and microwave landing system, 11, 15, 21, 27, 34, 41-53, 120, 121; optical propulsion management interface, 78-80; and precision flare laws research, 99-101; and profile descent research, 90-93; program organization, 18-23; and runway friction research, 109-12; and takeoff performance monitoring system, 75, 76, 85-87; and technology transfer, 1-7, 33-36; and total energy control system, 75, 81-83, 120; and wing surface coatings research, 106-107
Aeronautical and Space Sciences Committee (Senate): 9
Aeronautical Radio, Inc.: 78, 80, 95
Aeronautics: aircraft operations research, 89-103; aircraft systems research, 75-87; Airport 85 research, 114-16; Boeing 737 research systems, 14-18; cockpit computerization, 36-39; cockpit displayed traffic information research, 93-94; cockpit technology, 5; computerization and electronic flight displays research, 25-39; data link research, 95-99; digital access communication research, 75, 76-78; electronic flight display research, 27-33; engine monitoring and control system research, 75, 83-85, 120; fly-by-wire technology, 4; global positioning system research, 50-53, 102, 120, 122; helmet mounted display research, 112-14; high lift research, 108-109; instrument landing system signal modelling research, 116-17; microburst windshear research, 55-73; large eddy break-up research, 108-109; magnetic cable guidance research, 101-102; microwave landing system, 11, 15, 21, 27, 34, 41-53, 120, 121; optical propulsion management interface, 78-80; precision flare laws research, 99-101; profile descent research, 90-93; runway friction research, 109-12; takeoff performance monitoring system research, 75, 76, 85-87; technology transfer and, 1-7, 33-36; total energy control system research, 75, 81-83, 120; wing surface coatings research, 106-107
Aeronautics Steering Committee, Langley Research Center: 10
Aeroparque Jorge Newbery: 47-48
Airborne Windshear Detection and Avoidance Program: 61
Airbus A-310: 108
Airbus A-320: 14, 108
Airbus Industries: 4, 108
Air Florida Airlines: 84, 109, 110
Air Force, United States: 84, 86, 114-16, 117, 120
Airport 85, Project: 114-16
Air Route Traffic Control Centers: 90, 91
Air Transport Association: 38, 51, 98
All Weather Operations Panel: 42, 44, 49
Allied Signal Corp.: 72
Aloha Airlines: 70
American Airlines: 61
Ames Research Center: 11, 38, 92
Apollo, Project: 9, 123

Armstrong, Neil A.: 9
ARNAV Systems, Inc.: 85
Ashtech, Inc.: 52
Automatic Guidance and Control System: 13
Avionics Research: 10, 25-39, 75-87; and advanced digital electronic displays, 13; and aircraft operations research, 89-103; and aircraft systems research, 75-87; and Airport 85 research, 114-16; and automatic guidance and control systems, 13; and cockpit computerization, 36-39; and cockpit displayed traffic information research, 93-94; and computerization and electronic flight displays research, 25-39; and data link research, 95-99; and digital access communication research, 75, 76-78; and electronic flight display research, 27-33; and engine monitoring and control system research, 75, 83-85, 120; and global positioning system research, 50-53, 102, 120, 122; and helmet mounted display research, 112-14; and instrument landing system signal modelling research, 116-17; and large eddy break-up research, 108-109; and microburst windshear research, 55-73; and magnetic cable guidance research, 101-102; and microwave landing system research, 11, 15, 21, 27, 34, 41-53, 120, 121; optical propulsion management interface, 78-80; and precision flare laws research, 99-101; and profile descent research, 90-93; and runway friction research, 109-12; and takeoff performance monitoring system research, 75, 76, 85-87; and technology transfer, 1-7, 33-36; and total energy control system, 75, 81-83, 120

Basnett, Michael: 71
Bendix Corp.: 43, 72
Boeing Advanced Guidance and Control Panel: 15
Boeing Commercial Airplane Co.: 4, 6, 12, 13, 14, 18, 20, 33-35, 38, 61, 63, 75, 77, 81, 89, 90, 92, 100, 106, 107, 120, 122
Boeing Computer Services: 33
Boeing 727 Aircraft: 10, 56, 59, 106, 110
Boeing 737 Aircraft: 2, 7, 11-12, 75, 84; acquired, 11-14; research systems, 14-18; and aircraft operations research, 89-103; and aircraft systems research, 75-87; and Airport 85 research, 114-16; and cockpit computerization, 36-39; and cockpit displayed traffic information research, 93-94; and computerization and electronic flight displays research, 25-39; and data link research, 95-99; and digital access communication research, 75, 76-78; and electronic flight display research, 27-33; and engine monitoring and control system, 75, 83-85, 120; and global positioning system research, 50-53, 102, 120, 122; and helmet mounted display research, 112-14; and high lift research, 108-109; and instrument landing system signal modelling research, 116-17; and microburst windshear research, 55-73; and large eddy break-up research, 108-109; and magnetic cable guidance research, 101-102; and microwave landing system, 11, 15, 21, 27, 34, 41-53, 120, 121; optical propulsion management interface, 78-80; and precision flare laws research, 99-101; and profile descent research, 90-93; program organization, 18-23; and runway friction research, 109-12; and takeoff performance monitoring system, 75, 76, 85-87; and technology transfer, 1-7, 33-36; and total energy control system, 75, 81-83, 120; and wing surface coatings research, 106-107
Boeing 747 Aircraft: 33, 37, 101
Boeing 757 Aircraft: 21, 33, 35, 38, 39, 101, 122
Boeing 767 Aircraft: 21, 33, 35, 37, 39, 92, 101, 122
Boeing 777 Aircraft: 82, 87, 99
Bond, Langhorne M.: 47
Boston, MA: 109
Bowles, Roland L.: 60, 61, 62, 71
British Aerospace (HS) 748 Aircraft: 49
Brown, George: 59-60
Brunswick Naval Air Station, ME: 110, 111
Brussels, Belgium: 47
Buckley Air National Guard Base, CO: 114
Buenos Aires, Argentina: 47-48

C-141A Aircraft: 11
Cape Canaveral, FL: 86
Civil Aviation Research and Development Policy (CARD) Study: 9-10, 42
Clinton, William J.: 22
Collier Trophy: 73
Collins Air Transport Division: 35
Condor Aircraft: 82-83
Continental Airlines: 61, 106
Convair 990 Aircraft: 11
Control Data Corporation: 14
Creedon, Jeremiah F.: 21, 60, 73

Dallas, TX: 55-56, 59, 60, 61, 73, 89, 90, 92, 121
Dallas/Ft. Worth International Airport: 55-56, 59, 60, 61, 73, 90, 92
DC-9 Aircraft: 11
DC-10 Aircraft: 30, 109
Defense, Department of: 43, 51, 119
DeHavilland H6-C Twin Otter Aircraft: 44
Delta Airlines: 55-56, 59, 107, 121
Denver, CO: 59, 61, 67-70, 71, 89, 90, 92, 93, 114, 115
Digital Access Communications: 75, 76-78
Digital Equipment Corp.: 18

Eastern Airlines: 56, 57
Electronics Directorate, Langley Research Center: 21
Electronic Flight Displays: 27-33
Engine Monitoring and Control System: 75, 83-85, 120
Erzberger, Heinz: 92
Experimental Aircraft Association: 85
Experimental Avionics Simulation and Integration Laboratory, Langley Research Center: 77-78

Fadden, Delmar: 33, 35, 37
"Fat Albert": 12
Federal Aviation Administration: 5, 11, 13, 14, 15, 20, 35, 36, 37, 38, 42-50, 53, 55, 56, 57-61, 63, 70, 72, 86, 89, 90, 91, 93, 94, 96, 97, 98, 99, 100, 102, 103, 105, 109-10, 112, 117, 119, 123
Flight Control Systems Division: 21
Flight Experiments Working Group: 20
Flight Instrumentation Division, Langley Research Center: 9
Flight Systems Division, Langley Research Center: 21, 71

General Accounting Office: 50
General Electric Corp.: 17, 18
Global Positioning System: 50-53, 102, 120, 122
Global Navigation Satellite System: 53
Goldin, Daniel S.: 7, 22
Gramm-Rudman Amendment: 22
Graves, Barry: 9, 10

Hay, George "Cliff": 60
Hazeltine Corp.: 50
Helmet Mounted Display Research: 112-14
Herzog, Hans: 18, 77, 78
High Lift Research: 108-109
Holmes, David C.: 77
Howell, William E.: 77
Hughes, Thomas P.: 3

Instrument Landing System: 26, 41-42, 116-17
International Civil Aviation Organization: 42, 43, 44, 45, 46, 47, 48, 49, 53

Jessop, Artie D.: 70, 71
Joint Airport Weather Studies: 59

Kansas University: 85
Kennedy, John F., International Airport: 48, 56
Kennedy Space Center, John F., FL: 86
Kuhn, Thomas S.: 85

L-1011 Aircraft: 3, 32, 55-56, 92, 121
LaGuardia International Airport: 48
Langley Research Center: 4, 6, 7, 9-23, 55; acquires Boeing 737, 11-14; Aeronautics Steering Committee of, 10; and aircraft operations research, 89-103; and aircraft systems research, 75-87; and Airport 85 research, 114-16; and Boeing 737 research systems, 14-18; and Civil Aviation Research and Development Policy (CARD) Study, 9-10, 42; and cockpit computerization research, 36-39; and cockpit displayed traffic information research, 93-94; and computerization and electronic flight displays research, 25-39; and data link research, 95-99; and digital access communication research, 75, 76-78; and electronic flight display research, 27-33; Electronics Directorate of, 21; and engine monitoring and control system research, 75, 83-85, 120; Experimental Avionics Simulation and Integration Laboratory of, 77-78; Flight Control Systems Division of, 21; Flight Experiments Working Group of, 20; Flight Instrumentation Division of, 9; Flight Systems Division of, 21, 71; and global positioning system research, 50-53, 102, 120, 122; and helmet mounted display research, 112-14; and high lift research, 108-109; and instrument landing system signal modelling research, 116-17; and microburst windshear research, 55-73; and large eddy break-up research, 108-109; and magnetic cable guidance research, 101-102; and microwave landing system, 11, 15, 21, 27, 34, 41-53, 120, 121; optical propulsion management interface, 78-80; and precision flare laws research, 99-101; and profile descent research, 90-93; program organization, 18-23; and runway friction research, 109-12; and takeoff performance monitoring system, 75, 76, 85-87; and technology transfer, 1-7, 33-36, 119-24; and terminal configured vehicle/advanced transport operating systems (TCV/ATOPS) program, 7, 9-23; and total energy control system research, 75, 81-83, 120; and wing surface coatings research, 106-107
Large Eddy Break-up Research: 108-109
Lear Siegler Corp.: 28
Lexington, MA: 46
Lincoln Laboratory: 46-47, 68
Litton Corp.: 17
Lockheed Corp.: 32, 61, 65
Lockheed Electra Aircraft: 10
Logan International Airport: 109
Los Angeles, CA: 99, 116-17, 120
Los Angeles International Airport: 116-17, 120
"Low Altitude Windshear and Its Hazard to Aviation": 63
Low, George M.: 9
Lufthansa Airlines: 12

McDonnell Douglas Aircraft Corp.: 4, 30, 61, 78, 80, 84, 106, 112-14, 120
Mace, William D.: 21
Magnetic Cable Guidance Research: 101-102
Marine Corps, United States: 115, 116
Massachusetts Institute of Technology: 68, 93
Microwave Landing System: 11, 15, 21, 27, 34, 41-53, 120, 121
Mitsubishi Corp.: 35
Montreal, Canada: 49

National Academy of Sciences: 59, 63
National Advisory Committee for Aeronautics: 1, 10, 55, 72, 119, 120
National Aeronautics and Space Act of 1958: 3
National Aeronautics and Space Administration: 3, 21, 73; acquires Boeing 737, 11-14; and aircraft operations research, 89-103; and aircraft systems research, 75-87; and Airport 85 research, 114-16;

and Boeing 737 program organization, 18-23; and Boeing 737 research systems, 14-18; and Civil Aviation Research and Development Policy (CARD) Study, 9-10, 42; and cockpit computerization research, 36-39; and cockpit displayed traffic information research, 93-94; and computerization and electronic flight displays research, 25-39; and data link research, 95-99; and digital access communication research, 75, 76-78; and electronic flight display research, 27-33; and engine monitoring and control system research, 75, 83-85, 120; and global positioning system research, 50-53, 102, 120, 122; and helmet mounted display research, 112-14; and high lift research, 108-109; and instrument landing system signal modelling research, 116-17; and microburst windshear research, 55-73; and large eddy break-up research, 108-109; and magnetic cable guidance research, 101-102; and microwave landing system research, 11, 15, 21, 27, 34, 41-53, 120, 121; optical propulsion management interface research, 78-80; and precision flare laws research, 99-101; and profile descent research, 90-93; and runway friction research, 109-12; and takeoff performance monitoring system research, 75, 76, 85-87; and technology transfer, 1-7, 33-36, 119-24; and terminal configured vehicle/ advanced transport operating systems (TCV/ ATOPS) program, 7, 9-23; and total energy control system research, 75, 81-83, 120; and wing surface coatings research, 106-107
National Aerospace Plane: 106, 112, 113
National Aviation Facilities Experimental Center: 45, 48, 110
National Center for Atmospheric Research: 59, 72
National Integrated Windshear Plan: 60-61, 72-73
National Transportation Safety Board: 38, 61
Naval Appropriations Act of 1915: 1
Navy, United States: 1
Newark International Airport: 48
New York, NY: 48, 56
New Orleans, LA: 56, 59, 73
New Orleans International Airport: 56, 59, 73
Nixon, Richard M.: 10
Norden Corp.: 17, 18
Norfolk, VA: 10
Northwest Airlines: 61, 110

Ohio University: 52
Optical Propulsion Management Interface: 78-80
Organization of American States: 47, 48
Orlando, FL: 67-69, 70, 71

Paine, Thomas O.: 9
Pan American World Airways: 33, 56, 59, 61
Person, Lee H.: 68, 115, 116
Plessy Company, Ltd.: 47
Pratt and Whitney Corp.: 80
Precision Flare Laws: 99-101
Profile Descent Research: 90-93

Radio Technical Commission for Aeronautics: 42
Reagan, Ronald: 1
Reeder, John: 10, 18, 38
Renton, WA: 12
Rickenbacker, Eddie: 33
Rockwell International Corp.: 35, 65, 72
Runway Friction Research: 109-12

Saudi Arabian Airlines: 32
Science Council, White House: 1
Science and Technology Committee (House): 60, 109-10
Science and Technology Policy, Office of: 1, 10
Seattle, WA: 12, 33, 35
Singer Kerflot Corp.: 45
Smith Industries: 92
Sperry Flight Systems: 37
Sperry/Honeywell Corp.: 18, 43, 51, 52, 63
Srivatsan, Raghavachari: 85-87
Supersonic Transport (SST): 12, 13, 14, 15
Sydney, Australia: 99

Takeoff Performance Monitoring System: 75, 76, 85-87
Technology Transfer: 1-7, 33-36, 119-24
Technology Utilization, Office of: 3
Terminal Configured Vehicle (TCV) Program: 7, 9-23; acquires Boeing 737, 11-14; and aircraft operations research, 89-103; and aircraft systems research, 75-87; and Airport 85 research, 114-16; and Boeing 737 research systems, 14-18; and cockpit computerization, 36-39; and cockpit displayed traffic information research, 93-94; and computerization and electronic flight displays research, 25-39; and data link research, 95-99; and digital access communication research, 75, 76-78; and electronic flight display research, 27-33; and engine monitoring and control system, 75, 83-85, 120; and global positioning system research, 50-53, 102, 120, 122; and helmet mounted display research, 112-14; and high lift research, 108-109; and instrument landing system signal modelling research, 116-17; and microburst windshear research, 55-73; and large eddy break-up research, 108-109; and magnetic cable guidance research, 101-102; and microwave landing system, 11, 15, 21, 27, 34, 41-53, 120, 121; optical propulsion management interface, 78-80; and precision flare laws research, 99-101; and profile descent research, 90-93; program organization, 18-23; and runway friction research, 109-12; and takeoff performance monitoring system, 75, 76, 85-87; and technology transfer, 1-7, 33-36; and total energy control system, 75, 81-83, 120; and wing surface coatings research, 106-107
Texas Instruments: 43
Toshiba Corp.: 35

Total Energy Control System: 75, 81-83, 120
Traffic Alert Collision Avoidance System: 94
Transportation, Department of: 9, 13, 14, 42, 43, 47
Trippe, Juan: 33

United Nations: 42
United Technologies, Inc.: 80

Wallops Island, VA: 43, 52, 86, 93, 97, 101, 110, 113-14
Wallops Flight Facility: 43, 52, 66, 86, 93, 97, 101, 110, 113-14
Warner, John: 33
Washington, DC: 10, 84, 109
Washington National Airport: 109
Westinghouse Electric Co.: 72
Windshear, Microburst: 55-73
Windshear Training Aid: 60-62
Wing Surface Coatings: 106-107
Withington, H.W.: 6, 38-39
World Airways: 109

Yenni, Kenneth R. "Dick": 68

About the Author

Lane E. Wallace is a professional aviation writer who lives in Minneapolis, Minnesota. She has published over 200 articles on a wide variety of aviation and aerospace topics ranging from biplanes and air racing to new developments in NASA research and military aircraft technology. Her writing has appeared in a number of national and international magazines, including *AOPA Pilot*, *Flight International*, *JP-4 Aeronautica*, *Flyer*, and *Panorama Difesa*. In addition, her work has earned her an honorary membership in the United States Air Force Society of Wild Weasels, as well as a citation for "Outstanding Contributions to Preserve General Aviation" by the Torrance, California Airport Association.

Ms. Wallace graduated with honors from Brown University in 1983, with a degree in Semiotics. She owns and flies her own airplane, a 1946 Cessna 120, and is currently working with a partner on a 1943 Boeing Stearman restoration project. In addition to her own airplane projects, she has also worked as a volunteer for the Planes of Fame Air Museum in Chino, California, and both the "Tsunami" and "Pond Racer" Unlimited air racing crews.

Book design and production by
Steve Chambers and Lynn Van der Veer
Creative Services, Washington, D.C.

Type composed in Adobe Garamond

Printed on recycled paper

The NASA History Series

Reference Works, NASA SP-4000:

Grimwood, James M. *Project Mercury: A Chronology.* (NASA SP-4001, 1963).

Grimwood, James M., and Hacker, Barton C., with Vorzimmer, Peter J. *Project Gemini Technology and Operations: A Chronology.* (NASA SP-4002, 1969).

Link, Mae Mills. *Space Medicine in Project Mercury.* (NASA SP-4003, 1965).

Astronautics and Aeronautics, 1963: Chronology of Science, Technology, and Policy. (NASA SP-4004, 1964).

Astronautics and Aeronautics, 1964: Chronology of Science, Technology, and Policy. (NASA SP-4005, 1965).

Astronautics and Aeronautics, 1965: Chronology of Science, Technology, and Policy. (NASA SP-4006, 1966).

Astronautics and Aeronautics, 1966: Chronology of Science, Technology, and Policy. (NASA SP-4007, 1967).

Astronautics and Aeronautics, 1967: Chronology of Science, Technology, and Policy. (NASA SP-4008, 1968).

Ertel, Ivan D., and Morse, Mary Louise. *The Apollo Spacecraft: A Chronology, Volume I, Through November 7, 1962.* (NASA SP-4009, 1969).

Morse, Mary Louise, and Bays, Jean Kernahan. *The Apollo Spacecraft: A Chronology, Volume II, November 8, 1962-September 30, 1964.* (NASA SP-4009, 1973).

Brooks, Courtney G., and Ertel, Ivan D. *The Apollo Spacecraft: A Chronology, Volume III, October 1, 1964-January 20, 1966.* (NASA SP-4009, 1973).

Ertel, Ivan D., and Newkirk, Roland W., with Brooks, Courtney G. *The Apollo Spacecraft: A Chronology, Volume IV, January 21, 1966-July 13, 1974.* (NASA SP-4009, 1978).

Astronautics and Aeronautics, 1968: Chronology of Science, Technology, and Policy. (NASA SP-4010, 1969).

Newkirk, Roland W., and Ertel, Ivan D., with Brooks, Courtney G. *Skylab: A Chronology.* (NASA SP-4011, 1977).

Van Nimmen, Jane, and Bruno, Leonard C., with Rosholt, Robert L. *NASA Historical Data Book, Vol. I: NASA Resources, 1958-1968.* (NASA SP-4012, 1976, rep. ed. 1988).

Ezell, Linda Neuman. *NASA Historical Data Book, Vol II: Programs and Projects, 1958-1968.* (NASA SP-4012, 1988).

Ezell, Linda Neuman. *NASA Historical Data Book, Vol. III: Programs and Projects, 1969-1978.* (NASA SP-4012, 1988).

Astronautics and Aeronautics, 1969: Chronology of Science, Technology, and Policy. (NASA SP-4014, 1970).

Astronautics and Aeronautics, 1970: Chronology of Science, Technology, and Policy. (NASA SP-4015, 1972).

Astronautics and Aeronautics, 1971: Chronology of Science, Technology, and Policy. (NASA SP-4016, 1972).

Astronautics and Aeronautics, 1972: Chronology of Science, Technology, and Policy. (NASA SP-4017, 1974).

Astronautics and Aeronautics, 1973: Chronology of Science, Technology, and Policy. (NASA SP-4018, 1975).

Astronautics and Aeronautics, 1974: Chronology of Science, Technology, and Policy. (NASA SP-4019, 1977).

Astronautics and Aeronautics, 1975: Chronology of Science, Technology, and Policy. (NASA SP-4020, 1979).

Astronautics and Aeronautics, 1976: Chronology of Science, Technology, and Policy. (NASA SP-4021, 1984).

Astronautics and Aeronautics, 1977: Chronology of Science, Technology, and Policy. (NASA SP-4022, 1986).

Astronautics and Aeronautics, 1978: Chronology of Science, Technology, and Policy. (NASA SP-4023, 1986).

Astronautics and Aeronautics, 1979-1984: Chronology of Science, Technology, and Policy. (NASA SP-4024, 1988).

Astronautics and Aeronautics, 1985: Chronology of Science, Technology, and Policy. (NASA SP-4025, 1990).

Management Histories, NASA SP-4100:

Rosholt, Robert L. *An Administrative History of NASA, 1958-1963.* (NASA SP-4101, 1966).

Levine, Arnold S. *Managing NASA in the Apollo Era.* (NASA SP-4102, 1982).

Roland, Alex. *Model Research: The National Advisory Committee for Aeronautics, 1915-1958.* (NASA SP-4103, 1985).

Fries, Sylvia D. *NASA Engineers and the Age of Apollo* (NASA SP-4104, 1992).

Glennen, T. Keith. *The Birth of NASA: The Diary of T. Keith Glennan*, edited by J.D. Hunley. (NASA SP-4105, 1993).

Project Histories, NASA SP-4200:

Swenson, Loyd S., Jr., Grimwood, James M., and Alexander, Charles C. *This New Ocean: A History of Project Mercury*. (NASA SP-4201, 1966).

Green, Constance McL., and Lomask, Milton. *Vanguard: A History*. (NASA SP-4202, 1970; rep. ed. Smithsonian Institution Press, 1971).

Hacker, Barton C., and Grimwood, James M. *On Shoulders of Titans: A History of Project Gemini*. (NASA SP-4203, 1977).

Benson, Charles D. and Faherty, William Barnaby. *Moonport: A History of Apollo Launch Facilities and Operations*. (NASA SP-4204, 1978).

Brooks, Courtney G., Grimwood, James M., and Swenson, Loyd S., Jr. *Chariots for Apollo: A History of Manned Lunar Spacecraft*. (NASA SP-4205, 1979).

Bilstein, Roger E. *Stages to Saturn: A Technological History of the Apollo/Saturn Launch Vehicles*. (NASA SP-4206, 1980).

Compton, W. David, and Benson, Charles D. *Living and Working in Space: A History of Skylab*. (NASA SP-4208, 1983).

Ezell, Edward Clinton, and Ezell, Linda Neuman. *The Partnership: A History of the Apollo-Soyuz Test Project*. (NASA SP-4209, 1978).

Hall, R. Cargill. *Lunar Impact: A History of Project Ranger*. (NASA SP-4210, 1977).

Newell, Homer E. *Beyond the Atmosphere: Early Years of Space Science*. (NASA SP-4211, 1980).

Ezell, Edward Clinton, and Ezell, Linda Neuman. *On Mars: Exploration of the Red Planet, 1958-1978*. (NASA SP-4212, 1984).

Pitts, John A. *The Human Factor: Biomedicine in the Manned Space Program to 1980*. (NASA SP-4213, 1985).

Compton, W. David. *Where No Man Has Gone Before: A History of Apollo Lunar Exploration Missions*. (NASA SP-4214, 1989).

Naugle, John E. *First Among Equals: The Selection of NASA Space Science Experiments* (NASA SP-4215, 1991).

Center Histories, NASA SP-4300:

Rosenthal, Alfred. *Venture into Space: Early Years of Goddard Space Flight Center*. (NASA SP-4301, 1985).

Hartman, Edwin, P. *Adventures in Research: A History of Ames Research Center, 1940-1965*. (NASA SP-4302, 1970).

Hallion, Richard P. *On the Frontier: Flight Research at Dryden, 1946-1981*. (NASA SP-4303, 1984).

Muenger, Elizabeth A. *Searching the Horizon: A History of Ames Research Center, 1940-1976*. (NASA SP-4304, 1985).

Hansen, James R. *Engineer in Charge: A History of the Langley Aeronautical Laboratory, 1917-1958*. (NASA SP-4305, 1987).

Dawson, Virginia P. *Engines and Innovation: Lewis Laboratory and American Propulsion Technology*. (NASA SP-4306, 1991).

Dethloff, Henry C. *"Suddenly Tomorrow Came ...": A History of the Johnson Space Center, 1957-1990*. (NASA SP-4307, 1993).

General Histories, NASA SP-4400:

Corliss, William R. *NASA Sounding Rockets, 1958-1968: A Historical Summary*. (NASA SP-4401, 1971).

Wells, Helen T., Whiteley, Susan H., and Karegeannes, Carrie. *Origins of NASA Names*. (NASA SP-4402, 1976).

Anderson, Frank W., Jr., *Orders of Magnitude: A History of NACA and NASA, 1915-1980*. (NASA SP-4403, 1981).

Sloop, John L. *Liquid Hydrogen as a Propulsion Fuel, 1945-1959*. (NASA SP-4404, 1978).

Roland, Alex. *A Spacefaring People: Perspectives on Early Spaceflight*. (NASA SP-4405, 1985).

Bilstein, Roger E. *Orders of Magnitude: A History of the NACA and NASA, 1915-1990*. (NASA SP-4406, 1989).

New Series in NASA History, published by The Johns Hopkins University Press:

Cooper, Henry S. F., Jr. *Before Lift-Off: The Making of a Space Shuttle Crew*. (1987).

McCurdy, Howard E. *The Space Station Decision: Incremental Politics and Technological Choice*. (1990).

Hufbauer, Karl. *Exploring the Sun: Solar Science Since Galileo*. (1991).

McCurdy, Howard E. *Inside NASA: High Technology and Organizational Change in the U.S. Space Program*. (1993).

Langley Research Center